Texts and Monographs in
Symbolic Computation

A Series of the Research Institute for Symbolic Computation,
Johannes-Kepler-University, Linz, Austria
Edited by B. Buchberger and G. E. Collins

Jochen Pfalzgraf
and Dongming Wang (eds.)

Automated Practical Reasoning

Algebraic Approaches

With a Foreword by Jim Cunningham

Springer-Verlag Wien New York

Dr. Jochen Pfalzgraf
Research Institute for Symbolic Computation
Johannes-Kepler-University Linz, Linz, Austria

Dr. Dongming Wang
Laboratoire d'Informatique Fondamentale et d'Intelligence Artificielle
Institut National Polytechnique de Grenoble, Grenoble, France

Printed in Austria

Data conversion by H.-D. Ecker, Büro für Textverarbeitung, Bonn
Printed by Novographic, Ing. Wolfgang Schmid, A-1230 Wien
Printed on acid-free and chlorine-free bleached paper

With 23 Figures

Library of Congress Cataloging-in-Publication Data

Automated practical reasoning : algebraic approaches / Jochen Pfalzgraf and Dongming Wang, eds. ; with a foreword by Jim Cunningham.
p. cm. — (Texts and monographs in symbolic computation, ISSN 0943-853X)
Includes bibliographical references and index.
ISBN 3-211-82600-9 (Wien : acid-free paper). — ISBN 0-387-82600-9 (New York : acid-free paper)
1. Automatic theorem proving. 2. Reasoning. I. Pfalzgraf, Jochen. II. Wang, Dongming. III. Series.
QA76.9.A96A9 1995
005.13'1—dc20 95-1923
CIP

ISSN 0943-853X
ISBN 3-211-82600-9 Springer-Verlag Wien New York
ISBN 0-387-82600-9 Springer-Verlag New York Wien

Series editor's foreword

This book is a collection of selected papers written by researchers of our "RISC" institute (Research Institute for Symbolic Computation) along with the ESPRIT MEDLAR Project (Mechanizing Deduction in the Logics of Practical Reasoning). Naturally, the MEDLAR Project was and is the focal point for our institute whose main objective is the combination of foundational research in the area of symbolic computation and possible applications thereof for high-tech industrial projects.

I am grateful to the director of the MEDLAR project, Jim Cunningham, for his enthusiasm, profound expertise, and continuous effort to manage a fruitful cooperation between various European working groups in the area of the project and for giving us the opportunity to be part of this challenging endeavor. I also acknowledge and feel indebted to Jochen Pfalzgraf for managing the RISC part of the MEDLAR project and to both him and Dongming Wang for editing this volume and organizing the refereeing process.

The two main contributions made by the RISC group to the MEDLAR project are in the "algebraic approaches" to computer-aided reasoning and in several connections to practical problems in robotics, expert systems, and other high-tech industrial application areas. In fact, although the papers in this volume concentrate on original findings in the foundational aspect of the field, it should be emphasized that the problems treated here have their origin in very practical projects the RISC institute carried out with companies in Austria (Germany, and Japan) throughout the past few years. Some of the results led to considerable practical improvements, for example, in tunnel construction, CAD and CAM software. This book reports on one particular project in which RISC is involved. The entire RISC book series, which we started last year and to which we will add two or three volumes every year, will develop more and more aspects of both the mathematical and algorithmic foundations and the practical applications of our work: The books by Bernd Sturmfels (Algorithms in Invariant Theory, 1993), Wen-tsün Wu (Mechanical Theorem Proving in Geometries, 1994; translated by Xiaofan Jin and Dongming Wang), Bob Caviness and Jeremy Johnson, eds. (Quantifier Elimination and Cylindrical Algebraic Decomposition, forthcoming; proceedings of the symposium on the occasion of George Collins's 65th birthday), and Franz Winkler (Computer Algebra, forthcoming) will add to the development of the theory underlying symbolic computation. The present book and the earlier book edited by Stifter and Lenarčič (Advances in Robot Kinematics, 1991; proceedings of a conference) provide first examples of possible high-tech applications.

I hope that the present book and the entire series will add to the vigour of symbolic computation as a challenging field in the intersection of mathematics and computer science and its many potential applications in all areas of technology.

Bruno Buchberger
Director RISC-Linz

Foreword

For me the MEDLAR project was motivated by observations of the mid 80s. Various philosophical logics – temporal, epistemic, deontic, and others – were being explored for their applicability in Computer Science and Artificial Intelligence. Yet there was no uniform perception about how to provide automated support for reasoning in these logics. Worse still, in the folklore of the time there were dark suggestions that this was a hopeless route, inevitably fraught with complexities worse than those which bedevilled theorem proving in classical logic.

While several groups around the world were investigating non-standard theorem provers and symbolic execution aids for particular purposes, in my case for temporal and action logics of use in the specification and design of real time software systems, it was clearly going to be important to establish effective systematic methods. These methods must separate principle from the idiosyncratic, and facilitate the mixing of logics for cases where, for example, action and time interact, action is constrained by obligations, or is determined by beliefs and desires. Furthermore, despite our temerity in considering logics which were not truth functional to be worthy of exploration, it was also clear that to reject the classical world entirely was completely against the pragmatic spirit of the enterprise.

In October 1987 Jörg Siekmann visited Imperial College from Kaiserslautern. (We were collaborating on the Esprit Formast project on which Hans-Jürgen Ohlbach was employed.) I took the opportunity to convince both Jörg and my colleague Dov Gabbay that a project on automated reasoning in non-standard logics was a viable enterprise. Meanwhile, in Toulouse, Luis Fariñas del Cerro had similar ideas, but was already part of an embryo group with Ricardo Caferra (Grenoble) and Wolfgang Bibel (Munich, later Darmstadt) whose interests centred in more traditional automated theorem proving. We agreed to merge, and we grew. It was only after several months, and at Wolfgang's instigation, that we re-focused on my original theme, now re-named "Mechanising Deduction in the Logics of Practical Reasoning," after terminological advice from Andrew Jones, our philosopher from Oslo. At least it sounded good. I scoured the dictionaries for the required acronym and discovered the MEDLAR tree, which was close enough.

This focus of MEDLAR on exploiting the non-standard philosophical logics of practical reasoning left an internal challenge. Some of the original groups had important expertise in quite different aspects of applied reasoning, most notably the classical symbolic computation of Bruno Buchberger's RISC group, which was clearly important for geometric reasoning, but there were also interests of Robert Demolombe (Toulouse) in more metalogical aspects of databases, of Ricardo Caferra in model building and analogy, of Alberto Martelli (Turin) and Ed Babb (ICL) in extending the scope of logic programming to deal with some of the issues which were arising in the proposed case studies, as well as several other individual research pursuits. It is now with satisfaction that we find, for example, papers co-authored by Demolombe and Jones on modal reasoning about the safety of information, links between linear logic and symbolic planning with the classical resolution systems of Fronhöfer at Munich and Bibel's group at Darmstadt, indeed, enough co-operation between sites to cause me confusion on the allegiance of individuals.

By the time we had embarked on MEDLAR II the theoretical aims of MEDLAR I had been realised. We had not just one general framework for mechanising logics, but at least two, as well as five different ways of realising them. Classical multi-modal systems can be semi-automatically translated, through Ohlbach's SCAN algorithm, into an efficient first order system, while both modal and substructural logics can be realised by an implementation of Gabbay's LDS. Attention has shifted to demonstrable applications, case studies of practical reasoning in machine dialogue, more tangible goals in co-operative planning by intelligent robots, and ways of fibering real applications to reduce complexity, a special interest of Jochen Pfalzgraf.

Although MEDLAR is a Basic Research project, all ESPRIT projects are ultimately justified by their potential for industrial exploitation. We have listened to reviewers' remarks about research products which have not been successful in the market and we have pruned our initial conceptions to multi-modal systems which can fit with ICL and ECRC constraint logic implementations and potentially integrate with geometric reasoning and sub-symbolic computation by artificial neural nets. Amongst the academic partners RISC has led the way by showing that symbolic computation is commercially exploitable as software, where Dongming Wang is the main investigator in the project. I do not know the impact their approach to geometric problems will have in industry, but industrial organisations are certainly interested. The next challenge of MEDLAR II is to relate reasoning about an agent's beliefs, intents, and actions to the geometric world of robots. Already the ingredients from the logics of philosophy are being realised. The collection of papers from this volume shows some of the foundational thinking from RISC for applying methods from the large field of symbolic computation. It is our joint duty to ensure they foreshadow software prototypes of reality in the MEDLAR II final report.

Jim Cunningham
MEDLAR Manager

Contents

Introduction

Jochen Pfalzgraf and Dongming Wang

This book presents a collection of articles with topics linked to the working areas of a project named MEDLAR in which both the editors are actively involved. The authors of all the contributions are currently working or worked at the Research Institute for Symbolic Computation, Johannes Kepler University Linz (RISC-Linz).

MEDLAR is the acronym for "mechanizing deduction in the logics of practical reasoning." It started as an ESPRIT II Basic Research Action and is continuing as a basic research project called MEDLAR II. Its consortium consists of research groups from the following institutions. Full partners: Imperial College, London, UK; ICL, Bracknell, UK; IRIT, Université Paul Sabatier, Toulouse, France; LIFIA-INPG, Grenoble, France; Max Planck Institut für Informatik, Saarbrücken, Germany; ONERA-CERT, Toulouse, France; Universitet i Oslo, Norway; RISC, Johannes-Kepler-Universität Linz, Austria; Technische Hochschule Darmstadt, Germany; Technische Universität München, Germany; Università di Torino, Italy. Associate partners: Agder College, Kristiansand, Norway; University of Leeds, UK; Università di Roma "La Sapienza," Italy; Filosofiska Institutionen, Uppsala, Sweden. Finally, a group from the Australian National University, Canberra, Australia has associate status.

The working areas of MEDLAR, which are rather interdisciplinary, comprise different fields of logics like classical logic, modal logic, temporal logic, logic of knowledge and belief, dynamic logic, deontic logic, linear logic and planning, and nonmonotonic logic. Moreover, typical problems of reasoning in general deductive systems, query and answer modeling approaches, and problems in the area of geometric reasoning are investigated (cf. MEDLAR 1989/1992). A major concern of the project consortium is to have a general framework for the integration of a variety of reasoning methods, especially for the mixing of different logics. This is of basic relevance for logical modeling of complex communicating systems, like cooperating agents (e.g., in robotics scenarios). See MEDLAR (1990; 1991; 1993a, b) for further information. The main contribution towards such a unifying approach has been made by D. Gabbay (1990) in his extensive work on labelled deductive systems (LDS).

The research activities of the RISC-Linz MEDLAR group encompass three basic subjects briefly reviewed below. The articles collected in this book may be considered as representative contributions by the RISC group, including pointers to other closely related publications and technical reports previously produced by the group in the frame of the project. All of this enables the reader to obtain an overall impression about the role of the RISC group in MEDLAR.

Case studies. From the outset our group has been working on case studies in robotics, collecting and discussing typical problems concerning robotics research, where all kinds of reasoning play a role (cf. Pfalzgraf et al. 1990). In the course of this work it turned out to be very useful and even indispensable to have enough example material. We started propagating the construction of robotics scenarios in a flexible and modularized fashion and collecting information from engineering literature for doing so. See Pfalzgraf et al. (1990, 1993) and Pfalzgraf and Stokkermans (1993) and relevant work by the same authors in this direction. The general idea is to provide a certain database that is helpful to everybody in the construction of special purpose sample scenarios to test and enhance particular reasoning methods in concrete testbeds. In addition to these activities, we have always been very interested in contacts to specialists from engineering departments; some of them have been invited to MEDLAR workshops for discussions and exchange of knowledge and experiences.

Geometric and algebraic reasoning. A basic area of activities of the RISC group is geometric reasoning and constructive algebraic methods with applications to robotics and automated geometry theorem proving as well as their implementation on the basis of computer algebra systems (cf. Pfalzgraf 1993, 1995; Schicho 1992, 1994; Wang 1991, 1992a, b, c, d, 1993b, d; and relevant work of M. Kalkbrener, B. Wall, and other RISC-Linz contributors). The algorithmic approaches which are used are mainly based on the theory and methods of characteristic sets, cylindrical algebraic decomposition, and Gröbner bases. In particular, the reasoning about a set of selected geometric problems by using these methods is investigated (Wang 1991). Some new methods have also been developed (see Wang 1993a, c; and M. Kalkbrener's contribution to this book). Our contributions on this subject are considered representative as specialized techniques for practical reasoning, while attention has also been paid to their integration and cooperation with other general reasoning methods.

Mathematical foundations. Concerning the mathematical foundations the RISC group works on so-called fibered structures (Pfalzgraf 1991; Cunningham and Pfalzgraf in prep.), especially logical fiberings, and an approach for modeling general semantics for deductive systems using categorical techniques (the notion of sheaves arises naturally in these models thus opening the view to sheaf semantics). Logical fiberings and, more general, fibered structures as a "generic" modeling approach were introduced to our work (Pfalzgraf 1991) and are applied to propose a model for a logical controller of certain cooperating robots (cooperating agents) scenarios (see the corresponding contribution by Pfalzgraf and Stokkermans). D. Gabbay regards the logical fiberings as semantical models for LDS and introduced the notion of "fibered semantics." In ongoing work heading towards a general semantical modeling for general deductive systems it turns out that a categorical framework is helpful, leading in a natural way to certain sheaf semantics.

We conclude this introduction with a brief and concise résumé of the contributions collected in this book.

The article by M. Kalkbrener shows that primitive polynomial remainder sequences (pprs) are more than a tool for computing greatest common divisors; the content computations in the course of computing the pprs of two multivariate polynomials provide information on the common zeros of the polynomials. This additional property enables pprs to be applied to the problem of solving systems of algebraic equations. An algorithm for the case of three polynomial variables is developed with implementation and experiments for this purpose.

J. Pfalzgraf presents a brief summary of ongoing work and prospects on a general semantical modeling approach for deductive systems based on categorical techniques. This should reflect in concise form some of our actual work in progress on the MEDLAR general framework and the mathematical foundations. The joint paper by J. Pfalzgraf and K. Stokkermans introduces the concept of logical fiberings (putting logical spaces together in order to obtain a fibered structure) and proposes it as a rather general modeling approach for the logical control of cooperating agents. This is illustrated by a selected example of cooperating robots. In the same framework a possible notion of space and time dependent logical formulas is discussed.

The contribution by J. Schicho deals with parametrization methods in algebraic geometry. Parametrization of a set means to calculate general solutions of systems of (polynomial) equations in terms of a new indeterminate (the parameter). It can be seen as the opposite process of eliminating indeterminates in a system of equations. This turns out to be very useful for various applications. The results are embedded in the framework of the classical theory of curves and surfaces.

The work of K. Stokkermans tries to link the formalization of Buchberger's Gröbner basis algorithm (which is of great importance in geometric reasoning) with the completion of term rewriting systems (which plays an equally great role in equational reasoning). The attempt to unify these approaches is done with the linguistic means of category theory, which links the work to the research done on semantics (cf. Gabbay 1990; and Pfalzgraf's contribution).

In B. Wall's article, two examples illustrate how the program package CASA for constructive algebraic geometry developed at RISC-Linz can be used to reason about geometric objects defined by algebraic equations (in different representations). The paper also contains a review of the mathematical background of a part of CASA – the series expansion of branches of algebraic curves.

The first article by D. Wang explains the reasoning about a set of selected geometric problems such as automated theorem proving, automatic derivation of formulae and decomposition of algebraic varieties by using an elimination method he recently proposed. Approaches and illustrative examples are presented for the geometric problems with the suggested formulations. In the second article by Wang, a complete implementation of Ritt–Wu's characteristic set method in Maple is reported. The paper describes the user level functions and their variants with discussions on algorithmic modifications and implementation strategies as well as a set of test results.

In "A nonmonotonic extension to Horn-clause logic," T. Weigert discusses the relationship between the fix-point semantics of the nonmonotonic Horn-clause logic and model-theoretic semantics applied to the completion of a theory. It is shown that these semantics differ in the general case, but that they coincide under certain assumptions on the theory side.

Acknowledgements

The preparation of this book as well as the work reported herein is supported by the Austrian Ministry of Science and Research (BMWF) and the Austrian National Science Foundation (FWF) under ESPRIT Basic Research Action 3125 (MEDLAR I) and Project 6471 (MEDLAR II). We would like to thank the series editors and Springer-Verlag Wien for offering to publish this collection of articles as part of the *Texts and Monographs in Symbolic Computation* series. We also would like to express our thanks to all the authors who submitted their manuscripts for publication in this book and all the referees for their time and help.

References

MEDLAR (1989/1992): Mechanizing deduction in the logics of practical reasoning. Technical Annex of ESPRIT BRA 3125, Department of Computing, Imperial College, University of London (also as Tech. Rep. RISC Linz 89-49.0); Technical Annex of ESPRIT BRP 6471, Department of Computing, Imperial College, University of London.

MEDLAR (1990): Medlar milestone 1 deliverables (Proceedings of the 12-Month Workshop, Weinberg Castle, Austria, November 4–7, 1990). Department of Computing, Imperial College, University of London.

MEDLAR (1991): Proceedings of the 24-Month Medlar Workshop (Grenoble, France, December 8–11, 1991). Department of Computing, Imperial College, University of London.

MEDLAR (1993a): Medlar final progress report. Department of Computing, Imperial College, University of London.

MEDLAR (1993b): Medlar II report PPR1 (Proceedings of the 12-Month Workshop, Leeds, UK, July 4–7, 1993). Department of Computing, Imperial College, University of London.

Gabbay, D. (1990): Labelled deductive systems, part I. CIS, University of Munich, CIS-Bericht 90-22.

Pfalzgraf, J. (1991): Logical fiberings and polycontextural systems. In: Jorrand, P., Kelemen, J. (eds.): Fundamentals of artificial intelligence research. Springer, Berlin Heidelberg New York Tokyo, pp. 170–184 (Lecture notes in computer science, vol. 535).

Pfalzgraf, J. (1993): On mathematical modeling in robotics. In: Calmet, J., Campbell, J. A. (eds.): Artificial intelligence and symbolic mathematical computing. Springer, Berlin Heidelberg New York Tokyo, pp. 116–132 (Lecture notes in computer science, vol. 737).

Pfalzgraf, J. (1995): On geometric and topological reasoning in robotics. Ann. Math. Artif. Intell. (to appear).

Pfalzgraf, J., Stokkermans, K. (1993): Scenario construction continued and extended with a view to test and enhancement of reasoning methods. Tech. Rep. RISC Linz

92-27 [also in: MEDLAR (1993a): Medlar final progress report. Department of Computing, Imperial College, University of London].

Pfalzgraf, J., Stokkermans, K., Wang, D. M. (1990): The robotics benchmark. In: MEDLAR (1990): Medlar milestone 1 deliverables. Department of Computing, Imperial College, University of London.

Pfalzgraf, J., Sigmund, U., Stokkermans, K. (1993): Comparison of two approaches to modeling robotics scenarios. Tech. Rep. RISC Linz 93-56.

Schicho, J. (1992): On the choice of pencils in the parametrization of curves. J. Symb. Comput. 14: 557–576.

Schicho, J. (1994): An algorithm for the parametrization of rational surfaces. Ph.D. thesis, University of Linz, Linz, Austria.

Stokkermans, K. (1991): A categorical approach to critical-pair/completion procedures. Tech. Rep. RISC Linz 91-58.

Stokkermans, K. (1993): A categorical formulation for critical-pair/completion procedures. In: Rusinowitch, M., Rémy, J.-L. (eds.): Conditional term rewriting systems. Springer, Berlin Heidelberg New York Tokyo, pp. 328–342 (Lecture notes in computer science, vol. 656).

Wang, D. M. (1991): Reasoning about geometric problems using algebraic methods. Tech. Rep. RISC Linz 91-51.0 [also in MEDLAR (1991): Proceedings of the 24-Month Medlar Workshop. Department of Computing, Imperial College, University of London].

Wang, D. M. (1992a): On the parallelization of characteristic-set-based algorithms. In: Zima, H. P. (ed.): Parallel computation. Springer, Berlin Heidelberg New York Tokyo, pp. 338–349 (Lecture notes in computer science, vol. 591).

Wang, D. M. (1992b): Irreducible decomposition of algebraic varieties via characteristic sets and Gröbner bases. Comput. Aided Geom. Des. 9: 471–484.

Wang, D. M. (1992c): Some improvements on Wu's method for solving systems of algebraic equations. In: Wu, W.-T., Cheng, M.-D. (eds.): Proceedings of the International Workshop on Mathematics Mechanization, Beijing, China, July 16–18, 1992, pp. 89–100.

Wang, D. M. (1992d): A strategy for speeding-up the computation of characteristic sets. In: Havel, I. M., Koubek, V. (eds.): Mathematical foundations of computer science. Springer, Berlin Heidelberg New York Tokyo, pp. 504–510 (Lecture notes in computer sciences, vol. 629).

Wang, D. M. (1993a): An elimination method based on Seidenberg's theory and its applications. In: Eyssette, F., Galligo, A. (eds.): Computational algebraic geometry. Progr. Math. 109: 301–328.

Wang, D. M. (1993b): Geometry theorem proving with existing technology. Tech. Rep. RISC Linz 93-40 [also in: MEDLAR (1993b): Medlar II report PPR1. Department of Computing, Imperial College, University of London].

Wang, D. M. (1993c): An elimination method for polynomial systems. J. Symb. Comput. 16: 83–114.

Wang, D. M. (1993d): Solving polynomial equations: characteristic sets and triangular systems. In: Jacob, G., Oussous, N. E., Steinberg, S. (eds.): Proceedings of the International IMACS Symposium on Symbolic Computation, Lille, France, June 14–17, 1993, pp. 3–9.

An algorithm for solving systems of algebraic equations in three variables

Michael Kalkbrener

1 Introduction

The most famous algorithm for computing the greatest common divisor (gcd) of two univariate polynomials over a field is, undoubtedly, the algorithm of Euclid. In attempting to generalize it to the multivariate case one easily arrives at the concept of polynomial remainder sequences and discovers the phenomenon of explosive coefficient growth (see, e.g., Brown 1971). To overcome this problem primitive polynomial remainder sequences (pprs) have been introduced. However, the classical primitive polynomial remainder sequence algorithm for computing gcds (Brown 1971) has one rather obvious disadvantage. In order to make a polynomial primitive, its content, which is the gcd of its coefficients, has to be computed. Therefore, additional gcd computations in the coefficient domain are necessary for computing a pprs. Fortunately, the costs of these content computations can be considerably reduced by subresultant techniques (Collins 1967, Brown and Traub 1971, Brown 1978) or trial division (Hearn 1979, Stoutemyer 1985).

It is the objective of this paper to show that primitive polynomial remainder sequences are more than a tool for computing gcds; the content computations in the course of computing the pprs of two multivariate polynomials f_1 and f_2 provide information on the common zeros of f_1 and f_2. Because of this additional property, primitive polynomial remainder sequences can be applied to the central problem in elimination theory, the problem of solving systems of algebraic equations.

In Sect. 2 we introduce the notion of an elimination sequence. If f_1 and f_2 are primitive polynomials in the variable x_n over the polynomial ring $K[x_1, \ldots, x_{n-1}]$, K is a field, and $f_1, f_2, \ldots, f_k$ the primitive polynomial remainder sequence of f_1 and f_2 then the elimination sequence of f_1 and f_2 consists of $k-2$ polynomials $e_2, e_3, \ldots, e_{k-1}$ in $K[x_1, \ldots, x_{n-1}]$. For every $i \in \{2, \ldots, k-1\}$ the polynomial e_i divides the content of the pseudoremainder of f_{i-1} and f_i and can be easily obtained during the computation of the pprs. In Sect. 3 we present the basic properties of elimination sequences. The main objective of this paper is the development of an algorithm for solving systems of algebraic equations in three variables which is based on the computation of primitive polynomial remainder sequences and elimination sequences. In Sect. 4 we formally state the problem we are concerned with. As a consequence of the results in Sect. 3 we easily obtain the following theorem in the bivariate case: a point (a_1, a_2) is a common zero of f_1 and f_2 if and only if (a_1, a_2) is a zero of f_k or there exists an $i \in \{2, \ldots, k-1\}$ such that (a_1, a_2) is a common zero of e_i and f_i/f_k. In Sect. 5 we present an algorithm for solving systems of bivariate algebraic equations based on this result. Unfortunately, the same strategy applied to systems of algebraic equations in three variables generates extraneous solutions. We present a method for eliminating these solutions. The core of this method is an algorithm based on the computation of pprs that decomposes a finite set of points implicitly given by a subset of $K[x_1, x_2]$ into the set of those points that are zeros of a given polynomial $g \in K[x_1, x_2]$ and the set of those points that are not zeros of g. The whole procedure for solving systems of algebraic equations in three variables is presented in Sect. 6. It has been implemented in Maple as part of the computer algebra package CASA (Gebauer et al. 1991) and has been successfully applied to problems in geodesy, in quantum optics and in the theory of neural networks (Kalkbrener 1991). The applications in neural networks theory are presented in Sect. 7.

A comparison with different Gröbner bases implementations has shown that our algorithm is an efficient tool for solving systems of algebraic equations in three variables (Kalkbrener 1991). Of course, the restriction to three variables is a serious disadvantage of this method. Therefore, it seems to be an interesting topic for future research to investigate possible generalizations to systems in more than three variables.

2 Definitions

Let K be a field and $\bar{K}$ an algebraically closed field which has infinite transcendence degree over K. For a subset F of $K[x_1, \ldots, x_n]$ the ideal generated by F in $K[x_1, \ldots, x_n]$ is denoted by Ideal(F) and the *variety* of F, i.e., the set

$$\{a \in \bar{K}^n \mid f(a) = 0 \text{ for every } f \in F\}$$

is denoted by $\mathrm{V}(F)$. If F is finite then the cardinality of F is denoted by $|F|$.

For a non-constant $h_1 \in K[x_1, \ldots, x_n]$ and a non-zero $h_2 \in K[x_1, \ldots, x_n]$ the greatest non-negative integer m such that h_1^m divides h_2 is called the *power* of h_1 in h_2, abbreviated po(h_1, h_2). Let

$$f = \sum_{r=0}^{m} q_r(x_1, \ldots, x_{n-1}) x_n^r$$

be a polynomial in $K[x_1, \ldots, x_n]$ with $q_m \neq 0$. The polynomial q_m is called the *leading coefficient* of f, abbreviated lc(f). The degree of f in x_n is denoted by deg(f). The *content* of f, written cont(f), is the polynomial gcd$(q_0, \ldots, q_m)$, and the *primitive part* of f, written $\mathrm{pp}(f)$, is the polynomial $f/\mathrm{cont}(f)$. The polynomial f is *primitive* if $\mathrm{cont}(f) = 1$. The squarefree form of f is denoted by $\mathrm{squarefree}(f)$.

For non-zero $f, g \in K[x_1, \ldots, x_n]$ there exist polynomials $\mathrm{pquo}(f, g)$ and $\mathrm{prem}(f, g)$ in $K[x_1, \ldots, x_n]$, called *pseudo-quotient* and *pseudo-remainder* of f and g, such that

$$(\mathrm{lc}(g))^d \cdot f = \mathrm{pquo}(f, g) \cdot g + \mathrm{prem}(f, g) \quad \text{and} \quad \deg(\mathrm{prem}(f, g)) < \deg(g),$$

where

$$d := \max(\{\deg(f) - \deg(g) + 1, 0\}) \quad \text{and} \quad \deg(0) := -1.$$

Let f_1, f_2 be primitive non-zero polynomials in $K[x_1, \ldots, x_n]$ with $\deg(f_1) \geq \deg(f_2)$. The sequence $f_1, f_2, \ldots, f_k$ of non-zero polynomials in $K[x_1, \ldots, x_n]$ is called the *primitive polynomial remainder sequence* of f_1 and f_2, abbreviated $\mathrm{pprs}(f_1, f_2)$, if

$$\mathrm{pp}(\mathrm{prem}(f_{i-2}, f_{i-1})) = f_i \quad \text{for } i = 3, \ldots, k \ \text{ and } \ \mathrm{prem}(f_{k-1}, f_k) = 0.$$

Throughout this paper let $f_1, f_2, \ldots, f_k$ be an arbitrary but fixed primitive polynomial remainder sequence in $K[x_1, \ldots, x_n]$. Let

$$c_i := \mathrm{cont}(\mathrm{prem}(f_{i-1}, f_i)) \quad \text{for } i = 2, \ldots, k-1$$

and

$$l_i := \mathrm{lc}(f_i)^{\deg(f_{i-1}) - \deg(f_i) + 1} \quad \text{for } i = 2, \ldots, k.$$

Obviously,

$$\begin{aligned}
l_2 \cdot f_1 &= \mathrm{pquo}(f_1, f_2) \cdot f_2 + c_2 \cdot f_3 \\
l_3 \cdot f_2 &= \mathrm{pquo}(f_2, f_3) \cdot f_3 + c_3 \cdot f_4 \\
\cdots\cdots &\qquad \cdots\cdots \\
l_{k-1} \cdot f_{k-2} &= \mathrm{pquo}(f_{k-2}, f_{k-1}) \cdot f_{k-1} + c_{k-1} \cdot f_k \\
l_k \cdot f_{k-1} &= \mathrm{pquo}(f_{k-1}, f_k) \cdot f_k.
\end{aligned} \tag{1}$$

The *elimination sequence* of f_1 and f_2, abbreviated $\mathrm{elimseq}(f_1, f_2)$, consists of $k-2$ squarefree polynomials $e_2, \ldots, e_{k-1}$ in $K[x_1, \ldots, x_{n-1}]$ that are defined in the following way:

$$e_2 := p_2, \quad e_i := \frac{p_i}{\gcd(p_i, e_2 \ldots e_{i-1})} \quad \text{for } i = 3, \ldots, k-1,$$

where

$$p_i := \mathrm{squarefree}\Big(\frac{c_2 \ldots c_i}{\gcd(c_2 \ldots c_i, l_2 \ldots l_i)}\Big) \quad \text{for } i = 2, \ldots, k-1.$$

Another characterization of elimination sequences is given in the following lemma. Its proof can be found in Kalkbrener (1992).

Lemma 1. Let $i \in \{2, \ldots, k-1\}$ and p an irreducible polynomial in $K[x_1, \ldots, x_{n-1}]$. Then p divides e_i if and only if i is the smallest element of $\{2, \ldots, k-1\}$ such that

$$\mathrm{po}\Big(p, \prod_{r=2}^{i} c_r\Big) > \mathrm{po}\Big(p, \prod_{r=2}^{i} l_r\Big).$$

Note that e_i divides c_i for $i \in \{2, \ldots, k-1\}$.

Example 1. We write x, y, z instead of x_1, x_2, x_3 in the examples. Let

$$f_1 := xz^3 + 2y + 2,$$
$$f_2 := yz^3 - yz^2 - z^2 + y^2 + y$$

be polynomials in $\mathbb{Q}[x, y, z]$.

Computation of the primitive polynomial remainder sequence of f_1 and f_2:

$$l_2 := \mathrm{lc}(f_2)^{\deg(f_1)-\deg(f_2)+1} = y^1,$$
$$c_2 := \mathrm{cont}(\mathrm{prem}(f_1, f_2)) = y + 1,$$
$$f_3 := \mathrm{pp}(\mathrm{prem}(f_1, f_2)) = xz^2 - xy + 2y,$$
$$l_3 := \mathrm{lc}(f_3)^{\deg(f_2)-\deg(f_3)+1} = x^2,$$
$$c_3 := \mathrm{cont}(\mathrm{prem}(f_2, f_3)) = xy,$$
$$f_4 := \mathrm{pp}(\mathrm{prem}(f_2, f_3)) = xyz - 2yz + 2y + 2,$$
$$l_4 := \mathrm{lc}(f_4)^{\deg(f_3)-\deg(f_4)+1} = (xy - 2y)^2,$$
$$c_4 := \mathrm{cont}(\mathrm{prem}(f_3, f_4)) = x^3y^3 - 6x^2y^3 + 12xy^3 - 8y^3 - 4xy^2 - 8xy - 4x,$$
$$f_5 := \mathrm{pp}(\mathrm{prem}(f_3, f_4)) = -1.$$

The elimination sequence of f_1 and f_2 consists of the three polynomials

$$e_2 := c_2, \quad e_3 := 1, \quad e_4 := c_4.$$

Convention: Every product of the form $\prod_{r=i}^{j} q_r$ with $j < i$ is 1.

3 Basic properties of primitive polynomial remainder sequences and elimination sequences

Theorem 2 is well-known and can be found, e.g., in Brown (1971). The proofs of the other results presented in this section are given in Kalkbrener (1991, 1992).

Theorem 2. For every $i \in \{1, \dots, k-1\}$: f_k is the gcd of f_i and f_{i+1}.

The first important property of elimination sequences is stated in the following theorem.

Theorem 3. Let $a \in \bar{K}^n$ be a common zero of f_1 and f_2. Then $f_k(a) = 0$ or there exists an $i \in \{2, \dots, k-1\}$ with $e_i(a) = 0$ and $(f_i/f_k)(a) = 0$.

Unfortunately, it is only true in the bivariate case that every common zero of e_i and f_i – and therefore also every common zero of e_i and f_i/f_k – is a common zero of f_1 and f_2 (see Theorem 7).

Example 2. Consider the pprs

$$f_1 := z^2 + xz, \qquad f_2 := z^2 - y, \qquad f_3 := xz + y, \qquad f_4 := 1$$

in $\mathbb{Q}[x, y, z]$ with the elimination sequence

$$e_2 := 1, \qquad e_3 := y^2 - x^2 y.$$

Note that $(0, 0, 1)$ is a common zero of e_3 and f_3 but not a zero of f_1 and f_2. On the other hand, if (a_1, a_2, a_3) is a common zero of e_3 and f_3 and $(a_1, a_2) \neq (0, 0)$ then (a_1, a_2, a_3) is a common zero of f_1 and f_2.

The reason for the phenomenon in the above example is that $f_3(0, 0, z) = 0$:

Theorem 4. Let $a = (a_1, \dots, a_n)$ be an element of $\bar{K}^n$ and $i \in \{2, \dots, k-1\}$. If $e_i(a) = f_i(a) = 0$ and $f_i(a_1, \dots, a_{n-1}, x_n) \neq 0$ then $f_1(a) = f_2(a) = 0$.

Obviously, f_i can be replaced by f_i/f_k in the above theorem.

Corollary 5. Let $a = (a_1, \dots, a_n)$ be an element of $\bar{K}^n$ and $i \in \{2, \dots, k-1\}$. If $e_i(a) = (f_i/f_k)(a) = 0$ and $(f_i/f_k)(a_1, \dots, a_{n-1}, x_n) \neq 0$ then $f_1(a) = f_2(a) = 0$.

As a consequence of Theorem 4 we obtain the following relations between Sylvester resultants and elimination sequences.

Theorem 6. Let f_1 and f_2 be relatively prime.

(a) There exist polynomials h_1 and h_2 in $K[x_1, \dots, x_n]$ and a natural number d such that

$$h_1 \cdot f_1 + h_2 \cdot f_2 = \left(\prod_{j=2}^{k-1} e_j\right)^d.$$

(b) The polynomial $\prod_{j=2}^{k-1} e_j$ divides the squarefree form of the Sylvester resultant of f_1 and f_2.
(c) If $\mathrm{lc}(f_1)$ and $\mathrm{lc}(f_2)$ are relatively prime then $\prod_{j=2}^{k-1} e_j$ is the squarefree form of the Sylvester resultant of f_1 and f_2.

Example 3. Let

$$f_1 := xy^3 + y + x + 1, \qquad f_2 := xy^2 + 1$$

be polynomials in $\mathbb{Q}[x, y]$. The elimination sequence of f_1 and f_2 consists of the single polynomial $x + 1$. In this case $x + 1$ divides the resultant $x^3(x+1)^2$ of f_1 and f_2 but $x + 1$ is not the squarefree form of the resultant. (Note that $\mathrm{lc}(f_1)$ and $\mathrm{lc}(f_2)$ are not relatively prime.) But we obtain from Theorem 6 (a) that also in this case every common zero of f_1 and f_2 is a zero of $x + 1$.

4 Application of elimination sequences: solution of systems of algebraic equations

In the rest of this paper we will show that primitive polynomial remainder sequences together with elimination sequences are well applicable to the central problem in elimination theory, the problem of solving systems of equations of the form

$$h_1(x_1, \dots, x_n) = 0, \dots, h_r(x_1, \dots, x_n) = 0, \tag{2}$$

where $h_1, \dots, h_r$ are polynomials in $K[x_1, \dots, x_n]$.

Elimination theory evolved during the period of constructive methods in algebra around 1900. Important classical methods are due to Kronecker (see, e.g., van der Waerden 1940) and Hentzelt (1922). A prominent role in classical elimination theory played the resultant of n homogeneous polynomials in n variables (Macaulay 1916, Hurwitz 1913, van der Waerden 1940), a tool for deciding whether these polynomials have a non-trivial common solution.

After a non-constructive period in algebra the rapid progress in computer science during the last decades has led to a renaissance of constructive methods. In elimination theory special emphasis has been put on the development of more efficient algorithms. New methods for the computation of resultants can be found in Lazard (1981), Grigor'ev and Vorobjov (1988), and Canny (1988). In addition to the classical concepts new algorithms have been developed, for instance Gröbner bases (Buchberger 1970, 1985) and characteristic sets (Ritt 1950, Wu 1984). In recent years both methods have been analyzed and refined in a number of papers.

Nowadays elimination theory is not only of theoretical interest. In recent years elimination methods have been successfully used for solving systems of algebraic equations in several areas, although the practical applicability of the current algorithms is still rather limited. To some extent this is due to the high intrinsic difficulty of solving systems of algebraic equations. Nevertheless, there seems to be much room for improvement and therefore elimination theory is still an active research area. A particularly interesting research direction is the development of algorithms which combine algebraic and numerical techniques in order to control coefficient growths. In this paper we use another promising strategy for developing more efficient elimination algorithms: we concentrate on solving a restricted class of systems of algebraic equations. In this way we can take advantage of the special structure of these systems.

Obviously, the complexity of solving a system of algebraic equations heavily depends on the number of variables involved. Therefore, the strategy used in many algorithms in elimination theory is the "successive elimination" of variables. For instance, if system (2) is given then the Gröbner bases algorithm can be used to construct a finite subset $G = \{g_1, \ldots, g_s\}$ of $K[x_1, \ldots, x_n]$ with the following two properties:

(a) equality of ideals: $\mathrm{Ideal}(\{h_1, \ldots, h_r\}) = \mathrm{Ideal}(\{g_1, \ldots, g_s\})$.
(b) elimination property:

$$\mathrm{Ideal}(G) \cap K[x_1, \ldots, x_i] = \mathrm{Ideal}(G \cap K[x_1, \ldots, x_i]) \quad \text{for every } i \in \{1, \ldots, n\},$$

where the ideal on the right-hand side is formed in $K[x_1, \ldots, x_i]$.

Because of (a), we can solve system

$$g_1(x_1, \ldots, x_n) = 0, \ldots, g_s(x_1, \ldots, x_n) = 0$$

instead of system (2). If G has only finitely many solutions then the elimination property immediately leads to a general solution method, by "successive substitution," which is formally described in Buchberger (1985).

Obviously, the same general solution method can be applied if G does not satisfy (a) and (b) but the following weaker conditions:

(a′) equality of varieties: $\mathrm{V}(\{h_1, \ldots, h_r\}) = \mathrm{V}(\{g_1, \ldots, g_s\})$.
(b′) weak elimination property:

$$\mathrm{V}(\mathrm{Ideal}(G) \cap K[x_1, \ldots, x_i]) = \mathrm{V}(\mathrm{Ideal}(G \cap K[x_1, \ldots, x_i])) \quad \text{for every } i \in \{1, \ldots, n\},$$

where the ideal on the right-hand side is formed in $K[x_1, \ldots, x_i]$. This means that G has the weak elimination property if every common zero of the polynomials in $G \cap K[x_1, \ldots, x_i]$ is a common zero of the polynomials in $\mathrm{Ideal}(G) \cap K[x_1, \ldots, x_i]$.

In this paper we are concerned with systems of algebraic equations in at most three variables. We will present an algorithm based on the computation of primitive polynomial remainder sequences and elimination sequences which solves the following problem:

Given: F, a finite non-empty subset of $K[x_1, x_2, x_3]$.
Find: $\{E_1, \ldots, E_m\}$, where $E_1, \ldots, E_m$ are finite non-empty subsets of $K[x_1, x_2, x_3]$ that have the weak elimination property and

$$V(F) = \bigcup_{i=1}^{m} V(E_i).$$

First we will restrict ourselves to systems in two variables.

5 Systems of algebraic equations in two variables

In the bivariate case things become very simple.

Theorem 7. Let $a = (a_1, a_2)$ be an element of $\bar{K}^2$. Then

$$f_1(a) = f_2(a) = 0$$

iff

$$f_k(a) = 0 \text{ or there exists an } i \in \{2, \ldots, k-1\} \text{ with } (f_i/f_k)(a) = e_i(a) = 0.$$

Proof. ($\Rightarrow$) This direction follows from Theorem 3 immediately.

($\Leftarrow$) If $f_k(a) = 0$ then it follows from Theorem 2 that $f_1(a) = f_2(a) = 0$.

Let i be an element of $\{2, \ldots, k-1\}$ such that $(f_i/f_k)(a) = e_i(a) = 0$. As f_i/f_k is primitive, $(f_i/f_k)(a_1, x_2) \neq 0$. From Corollary 5 we obtain that a is a common zero of f_1 and f_2. □

Example 4. Let

$$f_1 := y^4 - x^2y^2 + x^2y + xy - x^3 - x^2,$$
$$f_2 := xy^3 - x^2y^2 + y^2 - xy.$$

The pprs of f_1 and f_2 consists of the 4 polynomials f_1, f_2, f_3, f_4, where

$$f_3 := -xy^2 + y^2 + x^3y + x^2y - xy - x^4 \quad \text{and} \quad f_4 := y - x.$$

Therefore, $f_2/f_4 = xy^2+y$ and $f_3/f_4 = -xy+y+x^3$. The elimination sequence of f_1 and f_2 consists of the polynomials

$$e_2 := x + 1 \quad \text{and} \quad e_3 := x^5 + x^2 - x.$$

By Theorem 7, the set of zeros of the system

$$\begin{aligned} y^4 - x^2y^2 + x^2y + xy - x^3 - x^2 &= 0 \\ xy^3 - x^2y^2 + y^2 - xy &= 0 \end{aligned}$$

is the union of the sets of zeros of the three systems

$$\begin{array}{ccc} x+1=0 & x^5+x^2-x=0 & y-x=0 \\ xy^2+y=0 & -xy+y+x^3=0. & \end{array}$$

Based on Theorem 7 we will develop an algorithm that computes for a given finite non-empty subset F of $K[x_1, x_2]$ sets $E_1, \ldots, E_m \subseteq K[x_1, x_2]$ such that

$$\mathrm{V}(F) = \bigcup_{i=1}^{m} \mathrm{V}(E_i)$$

and for every $i \in \{1, \ldots, m\}$

(a) E_i has the weak elimination property,
(b) E_i has one or two elements,
(c) if E_i has two elements then E_i consists of a non-zero polynomial in $K[x_1]$ and a primitive polynomial in $K[x_1, x_2] - K[x_1]$.

We call a subset of $K[x_1, x_2]$ an *elimination set* if it has the three properties listed above.

Before we present the algorithm we restrict the input class without loss of generality. Let $\{h_1, \ldots, h_r\}$ be a subset of $K[x_1, x_2]$ and

$$M := \{\{g_1, \ldots, g_r\} \mid g_i = \mathrm{cont}(h_i) \text{ or } g_i = \mathrm{pp}(h_i) \text{ for every } i \in \{1, \ldots, r\}\}.$$

Note that for every $A \in M$ every polynomial in $A - K[x_1]$ is primitive and that

$$\mathrm{V}(\{h_1, \ldots, h_r\}) = \bigcup_{A \in M} \mathrm{V}(A).$$

Therefore, it suffices to consider finite non-empty subsets of $K[x_1, x_2]$ which have the additional property that their elements which depend on x_2 are primitive.

Algorithm BSOLVE (in: F; out: O).
Input: F, a finite non-empty subset of $K[x_1, x_2]$ such that every $f \in F - K[x_1]$ is primitive.
Output: O, a non-empty set whose elements $E_1, \ldots, E_m$ are elimination sets and

$$\mathrm{V}(F) = \bigcup_{i=1}^{m} \mathrm{V}(E_i).$$

$F_2 := F - K[x_1]$
if $|F_2| > 1$, where $|F_2|$ denotes the number of elements of F_2
then
  $p_1, p_2 :=$ two elements of F_2 with $\deg(p_1) \geq \deg(p_2)$

$F' := F - \{p_1, p_2\}$
$p_1, \ldots, p_s := \text{pprs}(p_1, p_2)$
$d_2, \ldots, d_{s-1} := \text{elimseq}(p_1, p_2)$
$O := \bigcup_{i=2}^{s-1} \texttt{bsolve}(F' \cup \{d_i, p_i/p_s\}) \cup \texttt{bsolve}(F' \cup \{p_s\})$
else
$g :=$ gcd of the elements in $F \cap K[x_1]$, where $\gcd(\emptyset) := 0$
if $|F_2| = 0$ or $g = 0$
then
$O := \{\{p\}\}$, where p is the element in $F_2 \cup \{g\}$ which generates Ideal$(F_2 \cup \{g\})$
else
$h :=$ the only element in F_2
$g' := \text{squarefree}(g)$
$q := \gcd(q_1, \ldots, q_j)$, where $q_0, q_1, \ldots, q_j \in K[x_1]$ and $h = q_j x_2^j + \ldots + q_0$
$O := \{\{g'/\gcd(g', q)\} \cup F_2\}$

Proof of termination and correctness. Let F be a set which satisfies the input specification. We prove termination and correctness by induction on the number of elements of F_2.

Induction basis: $|F_2| \leq 1$. Termination is obvious. If $|F_2| = 0$ or $g = 0$ then correctness follows from

$$\text{V}(F) = \text{V}(F_2 \cup \{g\}) = \text{V}(\{p\})$$

and the fact that $\{p\}$ is an elimination set.

Now assume that $|F_2| = 1$ and $g \neq 0$. As h is primitive we can deduce that if $a \in \bar{K}^2$ is a zero of q then a is not a zero of h. Hence,

$$\text{V}(F) = \text{V}(F_2 \cup \{g\}) = \text{V}(F_2 \cup \{g'\}) = \text{V}(F_2 \cup \{g'/\gcd(g', q)\}).$$

It remains to show that the only element $F_2 \cup \{g'/\gcd(g', q)\}$ of the output set is an elimination set. Let $a_1 \in \bar{K}$ be a zero of $g'/\gcd(g', q)$. It follows from the fact that g' is squarefree that a_1 is not a zero of $\gcd(g', q)$ and therefore not a zero of q. Thus, there exists an $a_2 \in \bar{K}$ such that

$$(a_1, a_2) \in \text{V}(F_2 \cup \{g'/\gcd(g', q)\}).$$

Hence, a_1 is a zero of every element in Ideal$(F_2 \cup \{g'/\gcd(g', q)\}) \cap K[x_1]$. Therefore, $F_2 \cup \{g'/\gcd(g', q)\}$ has the weak elimination property. As conditions 2 and 3 in the definition of elimination sets are obviously satisfied, $F_2 \cup \{g'/\gcd(g', q)\}$ is an elimination set.

Induction step: $|F_2| > 1$. Let r be the number of elements in F_2. Algorithm `bsolve` terminates with input set F if it terminates with input $(F - \{p_1, p_2\}) \cup \{d_i, p_i/p_s\}$ for every $i \in \{2, \ldots, s-1\}$ and with input $(F - \{p_1, p_2\}) \cup \{p_s\}$. Each of these sets satisfies the input specification of `bsolve` and each of these sets has at most $r - 1$ elements which are not in $K[x_1]$. Hence, termination follows from the induction hypothesis.

By Theorem 7,

$$V(F) = V(F' \cup \{p_1, p_2\}) = \bigcup_{i=2}^{s-1} V(F' \cup \{d_i, p_i/p_s\}) \cup V(F' \cup \{p_s\}).$$

From the induction hypothesis we obtain

$$V(F' \cup \{d_i, p_i/p_s\}) = \bigcup_{E \in O_i} V(E) \quad \text{for } i = 2, \ldots, s-1,$$

where O_i is the output set of `bsolve` with input $F' \cup \{d_i, p_i/p_s\}$, and

$$V(F' \cup \{p_s\}) = \bigcup_{E \in O_s} V(E),$$

where O_s is the output set of `bsolve` with input $F' \cup \{p_s\}$. Hence,

$$V(F) = \bigcup_{i=2}^{s} \bigcup_{E \in O_i} V(E) = \bigcup_{E \in O} V(E).$$

Since for every $E \in O$ there exists an $i \in \{2, \ldots, s\}$ with $E \in O_i$ we obtain from the induction hypothesis that every $E \in O$ is an elimination set. □

In the following section we present `tsolve`, an algorithm for solving systems of algebraic equations in three variables. Algorithm `tsolve` requires a subalgorithm with the following specification:

Input: E, an elimination set with finitely many zeros; g, a polynomial in $K[x_1, x_2]$.
Output: $E_1, \ldots, E_m$, elimination sets with

$$V(E) - V(\{g\}) = \bigcup_{i=1}^{m} V(E_i).$$

In the rest of this section we are concerned with the development of an algorithm based on the computation of primitive polynomial remainder sequences that satisfies this specification. Let

$g_{1,1} := 1,$
$g_{1,2} := \mathrm{pquo}(f_1, f_2),$
$g_{1,i} := g_{1,i-1} \cdot \mathrm{pquo}(f_{i-1}, f_i) + l_i \cdot g_{1,i-2} \cdot c_{i-1} \quad \text{for } i = 3, \ldots, k-1.$

Let $i \in \{2, \ldots, k-1\}$ and let $q_{1,i}$ and $p_{1,i}$ be polynomials in $K[x_1, x_2]$ such that $q_{1,i} \cdot p_{1,i} = \prod_{r=2}^{i} l_r$ and $q_{1,i}$ is a maximal factor of $\prod_{r=2}^{i} l_r$ with the property that $q_{1,i}$ and e_i are relatively prime. We define $h_{1,i} := g_{1,i}/p_{1,i}$ and $h'_{1,i} := g_{1,i-1} \cdot c_i/p_{1,i}$. We have proved in theorem 3 in Kalkbrener (1991) that

$$h_{1,i}, h'_{1,i} \in K[x_1, x_2], \quad \deg(h_{1,i}) \geq \deg(h'_{1,i}),$$
$$q_{1,i} \cdot f_1 = h_{1,i} \cdot f_i + h'_{1,i} \cdot f_{i+1}, \quad e_i \text{ divides } h'_{1,i}.$$

The polynomials $h_{1,2}, \ldots, h_{1,k-1}$ are called the *first quotient sequence* of f_1 and f_2, written fquoseq(f_1, f_2). The second quotient sequence is defined in a similar way:

$g_{2,2} := 1,$
$g_{2,3} := \text{pquo}(f_2, f_3),$
$g_{2,i} := g_{2,i-1} \cdot \text{pquo}(f_{i-1}, f_i) + l_i \cdot g_{2,i-2} \cdot c_{i-1}$ for $i = 4, \ldots, k-1$.

Let $j \in \{3, \ldots, k-1\}$ and let $q_{2,j}$ and $p_{2,j}$ be polynomials in $K[x_1, x_2]$ such that $q_{2,j} \cdot p_{2,j} = \prod_{r=3}^{j} l_r$ and $q_{2,j}$ is a maximal factor of $\prod_{r=3}^{j} l_r$ with the property that $q_{2,j}$ and e_j are relatively prime. We define $h_{2,j} := g_{2,j}/p_{2,j}$ and $h'_{2,j} := g_{2,j-1} \cdot c_j/p_{2,j}$. Again, in theorem 3 in Kalkbrener (1991) we have shown that

$$h_{2,j}, h'_{2,j} \in K[x_1, x_2], \quad \deg(h_{2,j}) \geq \deg(h'_{2,j}),$$
$$q_{2,j} \cdot f_2 = h_{2,j} \cdot f_j + h'_{2,j} \cdot f_{j+1}, \quad e_j \text{ divides } h'_{2,j}.$$

The polynomials $h_{2,3}, \ldots, h_{2,k-1}$ are called the *second quotient sequence* of f_1 and f_2, written squoseq(f_1, f_2).

Lemma 8. Let $i \in \{2, \ldots, k-1\}$, $j \in \{3, \ldots, k-1\}$ and $a \in \bar{K}^2$. Then

(a) $\gcd(e_i, h_{1,i}) = 1$,
(b) $\gcd(e_j, h_{2,j}) = 1$,
(c) if $f_1(a) = e_i(a) = 0$ and $f_i(a) \neq 0$ then $h_{1,i}(a) = 0$,
(d) if $f_2(a) = e_j(a) = 0$ and $f_j(a) \neq 0$ then $h_{2,j}(a) = 0$,
(e) if $h_{1,i}(a) = e_i(a) = 0$ then $f_1(a) = 0$,
(f) if $h_{2,j}(a) = e_j(a) = 0$ then $f_2(a) = 0$.

Proof. (a) Assume that $\gcd(e_i, h_{1,i}) \neq 1$. Since e_i divides $h'_{1,i}$ we know that $\gcd(e_i, h_{1,i})$ divides $h'_{1,i}$ and therefore $\gcd(e_i, h_{1,i})$ divides $q_{1,i} \cdot f_1$. As f_1 is primitive, $\gcd(e_i, h_{1,i})$ divides $q_{1,i}$. This is a contradiction to the fact that e_i and $q_{1,i}$ are relatively prime.

(b) By the same arguments it can be shown that $\gcd(e_j, h_{2,j}) = 1$.

The proofs of (c), (d), (e), and (f) follow from the definition of quotient sequences immediately. □

Theorem 9. Let g be a non-zero squarefree polynomial in $K[x_1]$. Denote the polynomial $g/\gcd(g, \prod_{i=2}^{k-1} e_i)$ by h. Then the following two equalities hold:

$$\begin{aligned} &\mathrm{V}(\{g, f_2\}) - \mathrm{V}(\{f_1\}) = \\ &\quad = \Big(\bigcup_{j=3}^{k-1} \mathrm{V}(\{\gcd(g, e_j), h_{2,j}\}) - \mathrm{V}(\{f_j\})\Big) \cup (\mathrm{V}(\{h, f_2/f_k\}) - \mathrm{V}(\{f_k\})\Big), \end{aligned}$$

$$\begin{aligned} &\mathrm{V}(\{g, f_1\}) - \mathrm{V}(\{f_2\}) = \\ &\quad = \Big(\bigcup_{i=2}^{k-1} \mathrm{V}(\{\gcd(g, e_i), h_{1,i}\}) - \mathrm{V}(\{f_i\})\Big) \cup (\mathrm{V}(\{h, f_1/f_k\}) - \mathrm{V}(\{f_k\})\Big). \end{aligned}$$

Proof. Let $a \in \mathrm{V}(\{g, f_2\}) - \mathrm{V}(\{f_1\})$. If $e_i(a) \neq 0$ for every $i \in \{2, \ldots, k-1\}$ then $h(a) = 0$. As f_k divides f_1 and $f_1(a) \neq 0$ we know that $f_k(a) \neq 0$. Hence,

$$a \in \mathrm{V}(\{h, f_2/f_k\}) - \mathrm{V}(\{f_k\}). \tag{3}$$

Now assume that there exists a $j \in \{2, \ldots, k-1\}$ with $e_j(a) = 0$. From $f_1(a) \neq 0$ and Theorem 7 we can deduce that $f_j(a) \neq 0$. Hence, $j \in \{3, \ldots, k-1\}$. From Lemma 8 (d) it follows that $h_{2,j}(a) = 0$. Hence,

$$a \in \mathrm{V}(\{\gcd(g, e_j), h_{2,j}\}) - \mathrm{V}(\{f_j\}).$$

Thus, together with (3), we have proved that

$$\begin{aligned} &\mathrm{V}(\{g, f_2\}) - \mathrm{V}(\{f_1\}) \subseteq \\ &\quad \subseteq \Big(\bigcup_{j=3}^{k-1} \mathrm{V}(\{\gcd(g, e_j), h_{2,j}\}) - \mathrm{V}(\{f_j\})\Big) \cup (\mathrm{V}(\{h, f_2/f_k\}) - \mathrm{V}(\{f_k\})\Big). \end{aligned}$$

Let $a \in \mathrm{V}(\{h, f_2/f_k\}) - \mathrm{V}(\{f_k\})$. Obviously,

$$g(a) = 0. \tag{4}$$

It follows from the fact that g is a non-zero squarefree polynomial in $K[x_1]$ and from the definition of h that $e_i(a) \neq 0$ for every $i \in \{2, \ldots, k-1\}$. Together with

$$f_2(a) = 0 \quad \text{and} \quad f_k(a) \neq 0 \tag{5}$$

we obtain by using Theorem 7 that $f_1(a) \neq 0$. Together with (4) and (5),

$$a \in \mathrm{V}(\{g, f_2\}) - \mathrm{V}(\{f_1\}).$$

Let $j \in \{3, \ldots, k-1\}$ and $a \in \mathrm{V}(\{\gcd(g, e_j), h_{2,j}\}) - \mathrm{V}(\{f_j\})$. Obviously,

$$g(a) = 0. \tag{6}$$

By Lemma 8 (f),

$$f_2(a) = 0. \tag{7}$$

From $e_j(a) = 0$ and Lemma 1 we deduce that $e_i(a) \neq 0$ for every $i \in \{2, \ldots, k-1\}$ with $i \neq j$. Using $f_j(a) \neq 0$ we obtain for every $i \in \{2, \ldots, k-1\}$

$$e_i(a) \neq 0 \quad \text{or} \quad f_i(a) \neq 0. \tag{8}$$

As $f_j(a) \neq 0$,

$$f_k(a) \neq 0. \tag{9}$$

By Theorem 7, (7), (8) and (9),

$$f_1(a) \neq 0. \tag{10}$$

By (6), (7) and (10),

$$a \in \mathrm{V}(\{g, f_2\}) - \mathrm{V}(\{f_1\}).$$

This completes the proof of the first equality. The proof of the second equality can be done in a similar way. □

Now it is easy to construct the desired algorithm.

Algorithm COMPLEMENT (in: P, f; out: O).
Input: P, a pair with $P = (g_1, g_2)$, where g_1 is a non-zero polynomial in $K[x_1]$, g_2 is a non-zero polynomial in $K[x_1, x_2]$, and $\gcd(g_1, g_2) = 1$; f, a non-zero polynomial in $K[x_1, x_2]$.
Output: O, a set whose elements $E_1, \ldots, E_m$ are elimination sets with

$$\mathrm{V}(\{g_1, g_2\}) - \mathrm{V}(\{f\}) = \bigcup_{i=1}^{m} \mathrm{V}(E_i).$$

$g_1' :=$ squarefree(g_1)
$g_1'' := g_1' / \gcd(g_1', \mathrm{cont}(f))$
if $\deg(f) > 0$
then
  $f' := \mathrm{pp}(f)$
  $g_2' := \mathrm{pp}(g_2)$
  if $\deg(f') \geq \deg(g_2')$
  then
    $p_1, \ldots, p_s := \mathrm{pprs}(f', g_2')$
    $d_2, \ldots, d_{s-1} := \mathrm{elimseq}(f', g_2')$
    $q_3, \ldots, q_{s-1} := \mathrm{squoseq}(f', g_2')$
    $h := g_1'' / \gcd(g_1'', \prod_{i=2}^{s-1} d_i)$
    $O := \bigcup_{j=3}^{s-1}$ `complement`$((\gcd(g_1'', d_j), q_j), p_j) \cup$
        $\cup$ `complement`$((h, g_2'/p_s), p_s)$

```
  else
    p_1, ..., p_s := pprs(g'_2, f')
    d_2, ..., d_{s-1} := elimseq(g'_2, f')
    q_2, ..., q_{s-1} := fquoseq(g'_2, f')
    h := g''_1 / gcd(g''_1, ∏_{i=2}^{s-1} d_i)
    O := ⋃_{i=2}^{s-1} complement((gcd(g''_1, d_i), q_i), p_i) ∪
              ∪ complement((h, g'_2/p_s), p_s)
else
  O := bsolve({g''_1, g_2})
```

Proof of termination and correctness. Let (g_1, g_2) and f satisfy the input specification and define

$$\text{sumdeg}((g_1, g_2), f) := \deg(g_2) + \deg(f).$$

We prove termination and correctness by induction on the function sumdeg.

Induction basis: $\text{sumdeg}((g_1, g_2), f) = 0$. Then the termination of `complement` follows from the termination of `bsolve`. From $f \in K[x_1]$ and the fact that g'_1 is squarefree it follows that for every $a \in \bar{K}$

$$\begin{aligned} g''_1(a) = 0 \quad &\text{iff} \quad g'_1(a) = 0 \text{ and } \text{cont}(f)(a) \neq 0 \\ &\text{iff} \quad g_1(a) = 0 \text{ and } f(a) \neq 0. \end{aligned}$$

Therefore, we obtain from the specification of `bsolve` that

$$\text{V}(\{g_1, g_2\}) - \text{V}(\{f\}) = \text{V}(\{g''_1, g_2\}) = \bigcup_{E \in O} \text{V}(E)$$

and that every $E \in O$ is an elimination set.

Induction step: $\text{sumdeg}((g_1, g_2), f) > 0$. If $\deg(f) = 0$ then termination and correctness follow in the same way as in the induction basis. So let us assume that

$$\deg(f) > 0. \tag{11}$$

Case: $\deg(f') \geq \deg(g'_2)$. In this case `complement` terminates with input (g_1, g_2) and f if `complement` terminates with input $(h, g'_2/p_s)$ and p_s and with input $(\gcd(g''_1, d_j), q_j)$ and p_j for every $j \in \{3, \ldots, s-1\}$. As g'_2/p_s is primitive and h is a non-zero polynomial in $K[x_1]$, $\gcd(h, g'_2/p_s) = 1$. Thus, $(h, g'_2/p_s)$ and p_s satisfy the input specification. Since

$$\begin{aligned} \text{sumdeg}((h, g'_2/p_s), p_s) &= \deg(g'_2) = \deg(g_2) < \deg(g_2) + \deg(f) \\ &= \text{sumdeg}((g_1, g_2), f), \end{aligned}$$

termination of `complement` with input $(h, g'_2/p_s)$ and p_s follows from the induction hypothesis.

Let $j \in \{3, \ldots, s-1\}$. By definition of the second quotient sequence,

$$\deg(g_2') = \deg(p_2) = \deg(q_j \cdot p_j). \tag{12}$$

Therefore,

$$q_j \neq 0. \tag{13}$$

By Lemma 8 (b), $\gcd(d_j, q_j) = 1$ and therefore $\gcd(\gcd(g_1'', d_j), q_j) = 1$. Together with (13) we obtain that $(\gcd(g_1'', d_j), q_j)$ and p_j satisfy the input specification. Combining (12) and (13),

$$\deg(g_2') = \deg(q_j) + \deg(p_j).$$

Hence, by (11),

$$\begin{aligned}\operatorname{sumdeg}((g_1, g_2), f) &> \deg(g_2) = \deg(g_2') = \\ &= \deg(q_j) + \deg(p_j) = \operatorname{sumdeg}((\gcd(g_1'', d_j), q_j), p_j).\end{aligned}$$

Therefore, termination with input $(\gcd(g_1'', d_j), q_j)$ and p_j follows from the induction hypothesis.

It remains to prove correctness. First of all, it follows from $\gcd(g_1, g_2) = 1$ that

$$\begin{aligned}\mathrm{V}(\{g_1, g_2\}) - \mathrm{V}(\{f\}) &= \mathrm{V}(\{g_1', g_2'\}) - (\mathrm{V}(\{\mathrm{cont}(f)\}) \cup \mathrm{V}(\{\mathrm{pp}(f)\})) \\ &= \mathrm{V}(\{g_1'', g_2'\}) - \mathrm{V}(\{f'\}).\end{aligned} \tag{14}$$

We obtain from Theorem 9 that

$$\begin{aligned}&\mathrm{V}(\{g_1'', g_2'\}) - \mathrm{V}(\{f'\}) = \\ &\quad = \bigcup_{j=3}^{s-1} (\mathrm{V}(\{\gcd(g_1'', d_j), q_j\}) - \mathrm{V}(\{p_j\})) \cup (\mathrm{V}(\{h, g_2'/p_s\}) - \mathrm{V}(\{p_s\})).\end{aligned}$$

By induction hypothesis,

$$\mathrm{V}(\{g_1, g_2\}) - \mathrm{V}(\{f\}) = \mathrm{V}(\{g_1'', g_2'\}) - \mathrm{V}(\{f'\}) = \bigcup_{E \in O} \mathrm{V}(E).$$

Furthermore, it follows from the induction hypothesis that every element of the output set O is an elimination set.

Case: $\deg(f') < \deg(g_2')$. Termination and correctness can be proved in the same way. □

Example 5. For the polynomials

$$g_1 := x^3 - x, \quad g_2 := y^3 - y, \quad f := y^2 + x^2 - 2x$$

in $\mathbb{Q}[x, y]$ we compute `complement`$((g_1, g_2), f)$:

$g_1' := g_1, \quad g_1'' := g_1, \quad f' := f, \quad g_2' := g_2,$
$g_2, f, -y, 1 := \text{pprs}(g_2, f),$
$x^2 - 2x + 1, x^2 - 2x := \text{elimseq}(g_2, f),$
$y, -y^2 + x^2 - 2x + 1 := \text{fquoseq}(g_2, f),$
$h := x + 1,$
$O :=$ `complement`$((x-1, y), f) \cup$ `complement`$((x, -y^2+x^2-2x+1), -y) \cup$
$\cup$ `complement`$((x+1, g_2), 1)$.

Hence, we know that

$$\begin{aligned} &\mathrm{V}(\{g_1, g_2\}) - \mathrm{V}(\{f\}) = \\ &\quad = \mathrm{V}(\{x - 1, y\}) - \mathrm{V}(\{f\}) \cup \mathrm{V}(\{x, -y^2 + x^2 - 2x + 1\}) - \mathrm{V}(\{-y\}) \cup \\ &\qquad \cup\ \mathrm{V}(\{x + 1, g_2\}) - \mathrm{V}(\{1\}). \end{aligned}$$

Furthermore, $\deg(g_2) + \deg(f)$ is greater than

$$\deg(y)+\deg(f), \quad \deg(-y^2+x^2-2x+1)+\deg(-y) \quad \text{and} \quad \deg(g_2)+\deg(1),$$

which is essential for the termination of the algorithm. In the same way we obtain

$$\begin{aligned} \texttt{complement}((x - 1, y), f) &= \{\{x - 1, y\}\}, \\ \texttt{complement}((x, -y^2 + x^2 - 2x + 1), -y) &= \{\{1\}, \{x, -y^2 + x^2 - 2x + 1\}\}, \\ \texttt{complement}((x + 1, g_2), 1) &= \{\{x + 1, g_2\}\}. \end{aligned}$$

Altogether, the output of `complement` with input (g_1, g_2) and f is

$$\{\{x - 1, y\}, \{1\}, \{x, -y^2 + x^2 - 2x + 1\}, \{x + 1, g_2\}\}.$$

Therefore,

$$\begin{aligned} &\mathrm{V}(\{x^3 - x, y^3 - y\}) - \mathrm{V}(\{y^2 + x^2 - 2x\}) = \\ &\quad = \mathrm{V}(\{x - 1, y\}) \cup \mathrm{V}(\{x, -y^2 + x^2 - 2x + 1\}) \cup \mathrm{V}(\{x + 1, y^3 - y\}). \end{aligned}$$

6 Systems of algebraic equations in three variables

In this section we assume that $n = 3$. We will develop an algorithm that solves the following problem:

Given: F, a finite non-empty subset of $K[x_1, x_2, x_3]$.

Find: $\{E_1, \ldots, E_r\}$, where $E_1, \ldots, E_r$ are finite non-empty subsets of $K[x_1, x_2, x_3]$ that have the weak elimination property and

$$V(F) = \bigcup_{i=1}^{r} V(E_i).$$

If we deal with systems of algebraic equations in three variables we encounter the problem that in general

$$V(\{f_1, f_2\}) \subseteq \bigcup_{i=2}^{k-1} V(\{e_i, f_i/f_k\}) \cup V(\{f_k\})$$

(see Theorem 3 and Example 2) holds but not

$$V(\{f_1, f_2\}) = \bigcup_{i=2}^{k-1} V(\{e_i, f_i/f_k\}) \cup V(\{f_k\})$$

(see Theorem 7) as it does in the bivariate case. Therefore, by using the same elimination strategy as in the bivariate case we obtain for a given set $F \subseteq K[x_1, x_2, x_3]$ subsets $D_1, \ldots, D_m$ of $K[x_1, x_2, x_3]$ such that

$$V(F) \subseteq \bigcup_{i=1}^{m} V(D_i).$$

In general, $V(F)$ is a proper subset of $V(D_1) \cup \ldots \cup V(D_m)$. Therefore, it is not sufficient to compute the D_i's – this is done by the subalgorithm `eliminate` – but in a second step we have to get rid of those elements of $V(D_1) \cup \ldots \cup V(D_m)$ that are not in $V(F)$. We use the following strategy:

Assume that the D_i's are ordered in such a way that there exists an $s \in \{0, \ldots, m\}$ with

$$\{1, \ldots, s\} = \{i \in \{1, \ldots, m\} \mid D_i \cap K[x_1, x_2] \text{ contains at most one element}\}.$$

It is shown in the correctness proof of `eliminate` that $D_i \cup F$ has the weak elimination property for every $i \in \{1, \ldots, s\}$. By means of a second subalgorithm, called `mod`, we compute for every $j \in \{s+1, \ldots, m\}$ subsets $E_{j,1}, \ldots, E_{j,r_j}$ of $K[x_1, x_2, x_3]$ that have the weak elimination property and

$$V((D_j \cap K[x_1, x_2]) \cup F) = \bigcup_{i=1}^{r_j} V(E_{j,i}).$$

Therefore,

$$V(F) = \bigcup_{i=1}^{s} V(D_i \cup F) \cup \bigcup_{j=s+1}^{m} \bigcup_{i=1}^{r_j} V(E_{j,i})$$

and each of the varieties on the right-hand side is given by a set that has the weak elimination property.

As in the bivariate case we restrict the input class without loss of generality.

Algorithm TSOLVE (in: F; out: O).
Input: F, a finite non-empty subset of $K[x_1, x_2, x_3]$ such that every $f \in F - K[x_1, x_2]$ is primitive.
Output: O, a set whose elements $C_1, \dots, C_m$ are finite non-empty subsets of $K[x_1, x_2, x_3]$. Each of the C_i has the weak elimination property and

$$\mathrm{V}(F) = \bigcup_{i=1}^{m} \mathrm{V}(C_i).$$

$M := \texttt{eliminate}(F)$
$M' := \{A \in M \mid |A \cap K[x_1, x_2]| \geq 2\}$
$O := \bigcup_{A \in M - M'} \{A \cup F\} \cup \bigcup_{A' \in M'} \texttt{mod}(A' \cap K[x_1, x_2], F)$

The subalgorithms `eliminate` and `mod` are defined in the following way:

Algorithm ELIMINATE (in: F; out: O).
Input: F, a finite non-empty subset of $K[x_1, x_2, x_3]$ such that every $f \in F - K[x_1, x_2]$ is primitive.
Output: O, a set whose elements $C_1, \dots, C_m$ are finite non-empty subsets of $K[x_1, x_2, x_3]$. Furthermore,

$$\mathrm{V}(F) \subseteq \bigcup_{i=1}^{m} \mathrm{V}(C_i)$$

and for every $i \in \{1, \dots, m\}$:

1. $C_i \cap K[x_1, x_2]$ is empty or an elimination set,
2. $|C_i \cap K[x_1, x_2]| \leq 1$ implies that $F \cup C_i$ has the weak elimination property.

$F_3 := F - K[x_1, x_2]$
if $|F_3| > 1$
then
  $p_1, p_2 :=$ two elements of F_3 with $\deg(p_1) \geq \deg(p_2)$
  $F' := F - \{p_1, p_2\}$
  $p_1, \dots, p_s := \mathrm{pprs}(p_1, p_2)$
  $d_2, \dots, d_{s-1} := \mathrm{elimseq}(p_1, p_2)$
  $O := \bigcup_{i=2}^{s-1} \texttt{eliminate}(F' \cup \{d_i, p_i/p_s\}) \cup \texttt{eliminate}(F' \cup \{p_s\})$
else
  $M := \texttt{bsolve}(F \cap K[x_1, x_2])$, where $\texttt{bsolve}(\emptyset) := \emptyset$
  if $|F_3| = 0$ or $|M| = 0$
  then
    $O := \{A \mid A \neq \emptyset \text{ and } (A \in M \text{ or } A = F_3)\}$

else
  $h :=$ the only element in F_3
  $q := \gcd(q_1, \ldots, q_j)$,
    where $q_0, q_1, \ldots, q_j \in K[x_1, x_2]$ and $h = q_j x_3^j + \ldots + q_0$
  $M' := \{A \in M \mid |A| = 1\}$
  $M'' := \{\text{squarefree}(f) \mid \{f\} \in M'\}$
  $O := \bigcup_{g \in M''}(\{\{g/\gcd(g, q), h\}\} \cup \texttt{bsolve}(\{\gcd(g, q), q_0\})) \cup$
    $\cup \bigcup_{A \in M - M'} \{A \cup \{h\}\}$

Algorithm MOD (in: E, F; out: O).
Input: E, an elimination set in $K[x_1, x_2]$ with two elements; F, a finite subset of $K[x_1, x_2, x_3]$.
Output: O, a set whose elements $C_1, \ldots, C_m$ are finite non-empty subsets of $K[x_1, x_2, x_3]$. Each of the C_i has the weak elimination property and

$$V(E \cup F) = \bigcup_{i=1}^{m} V(C_i).$$

if $|F - K[x_1, x_2]| \geq 2$ or there exists an $f \in F - K[x_1, x_2]$ such that $V(E \cup \{\text{lc}(f)\}) \neq \emptyset$
then
  $f :=$ an element in $F - K[x_1, x_2]$ with minimal degree in x_3
  $F' := F - \{f\}$
  $M' := \{A \mid A \in \texttt{bsolve}(E \cup \text{lc}(f))\}$
  $M'' := \{A \mid A \in \texttt{complement}(E, \text{lc}(f))\}$
  $f' := f - \text{lc}(f) \cdot x_3^{\deg(f)}$
  $F'' := \{\text{prem}(g, f) \mid g \in F'\}$
  $O := \bigcup_{A' \in M'} \texttt{mod}(A', F' \cup \{f'\}) \cup \bigcup_{A'' \in M''} \texttt{mod}(A'', F'' \cup \{f\})$
else
  $O := \{A \cup (F - K[x_1, x_2]) \mid A \in \texttt{bsolve}(E \cup (F \cap K[x_1, x_2]))\}$

Before we prove the termination and correctness of these algorithms we give the following example.

Example 6. We compute $\texttt{tsolve}(\{g_1, g_2, g_3\})$, where

$$g_1 := yz - xz + xy + 1, \quad g_2 := xz + x^2 + y^2, \quad g_3 := y^2 + x^2 - 2x.$$

First we have to compute $\texttt{eliminate}(\{g_1, g_2, g_3\})$:

$$F_3 := \{g_1, g_2\}, \quad p_1 := g_1, \quad p_2 := g_2, \quad F' := \{g_3\},$$

$$g_1, g_2, -1 = \text{pprs}(g_1, g_2),$$

$$-x - x^3 + y^3 - y^2 x = \text{elimseq}(g_1, g_2),$$

$$O := \texttt{eliminate}(\{g_3, -x - x^3 + y^3 - y^2 x, g_2\}) \cup \texttt{eliminate}(\{g_3, -1\}).$$

Using `bsolve` we obtain

$$\begin{aligned}&\texttt{eliminate}(\{g_3, -x - x^3 + y^3 - y^2x, g_2\}) = \\ &\quad = \big\{\{1, g_2\}, \quad \{1, x^2 + y^2\}, \quad \{x, g_3, g_2\}, \\ &\qquad \{x^4 - 6x^3 + 16x^2 - 4x + 1, -1 - xy + 2y - 2x, g_2\}\big\}\end{aligned}$$

and

$$\texttt{eliminate}(\{g_3, -1\}) = \{\{1, g_3\}\}.$$

Hence,

$$\begin{aligned}&\mathrm{V}(\{g_1, g_2, g_3\}) \subseteq \\ &\subseteq \mathrm{V}(\{x, g_3, g_2\}) \cup \mathrm{V}(\{x^4 - 6x^3 + 16x^2 - 4x + 1, -1 - xy + 2y - 2x, g_2\}).\end{aligned}$$

Since both varieties on the right-hand side are given by sets with two elements in $\mathbb{Q}[x, y]$ we compute $\texttt{mod}(\{x, g_3\}, \{g_1, g_2, g_3\})$ and $\texttt{mod}(\{x^4 - 6x^3 + 16x^2 - 4x + 1, -1 - xy + 2y - 2x\}, \{g_1, g_2, g_3\})$.

Computation of $\texttt{mod}(\{x, g_3\}, \{g_1, g_2, g_3\})$:

$f := g_2, \quad F' := \{g_1, g_3\}, \quad M' := \{\{x, g_3\}\}, \quad M'' := \emptyset, \quad f' := x^2 + y^2,$
$F'' := \{x + x^3 - y^3 + y^2x, g_3\}, \quad O := \texttt{mod}(\{x, g_3\}, \{g_1, g_3, x^2 + y^2\}).$

We have

$$\mathrm{V}(\{x, g_3\} \cup \{g_1, g_2, g_3\}) = \mathrm{V}(\{x, g_3\} \cup \{g_1, g_3, x^2 + y^2\}).$$

Furthermore,

$$\deg(g_1) + \deg(g_2) + \deg(g_3) > \deg(g_1) + \deg(g_3) + \deg(x^2 + y^2),$$

which is essential for the termination of the algorithm. We obtain in the same way

$$\texttt{mod}(\{x, g_3\}, \{g_1, g_3, x^2 + y^2\}) = \texttt{mod}(\{x, g_3\}, \{g_3, x^2 + y^2, xy + 1\}) = \{\{1\}\}.$$

Computation of $\texttt{mod}(\{x^4 - 6x^3 + 16x^2 - 4x + 1, -1 - xy + 2y - 2x\}, \{g_1, g_2, g_3\})$:

$f := g_2, \quad F' := \{g_1, g_3\}, \quad M' := \{\{1\}\},$
$M'' := \{\{x^4 - 6x^3 + 16x^2 - 4x + 1, -1 - xy + 2y - 2x\}\},$
$f' := x^2 + y^2, \quad F'' := \{x + x^3 - y^3 + y^2x, g_3\},$

$$\begin{aligned}O := {} & \texttt{mod}(\{1\}, \{g_1, g_3, x^2 + y^2\}) \cup \\ & \cup \texttt{mod}\big(\{x^4 - 6x^3 + 16x^2 - 4x + 1, -1 - xy + 2y - 2x\}, \\ & \qquad \{x + x^3 - y^3 + y^2x, g_3, g_2\}\big).\end{aligned}$$

By using `bsolve` we obtain

$$\mathtt{mod}(\{1\}, \{g_1, g_3, x^2 + y^2\}) = \{\{1\}\},$$

$$\begin{aligned}&\mathtt{mod}\big(\{x^4 - 6x^3 + 16x^2 - 4x + 1, -1 - xy + 2y - 2x\},\\ &\quad \{x + x^3 - y^3 + y^2x, g_3, g_2\}\big) =\\ &\quad = \{\{x^4 - 6x^3 + 16x^2 - 4x + 1, -1 - xy + 2y - 2x, g_2\}\}.\end{aligned}$$

Summarizing,

$$\mathtt{mod}(\{x, g_3\}, \{g_1, g_2, g_3\}) = \{\{1\}\}$$

and

$$\begin{aligned}&\mathtt{mod}(\{x^4 - 6x^3 + 16x^2 - 4x + 1, -1 - xy + 2y - 2x\}, \{g_1, g_2, g_3\}) =\\ &\quad = \{\{1\}, \{x^4 - 6x^3 + 16x^2 - 4x + 1, -1 - xy + 2y - 2x, g_2\}\}.\end{aligned}$$

Therefore, the only element of the output set of `tsolve` with input $\{g_1, g_2, g_3\}$ that represents a non-empty variety is

$$\{x^4 - 6x^3 + 16x^2 - 4x + 1, -1 - xy + 2y - 2x, g_2\}.$$

Hence, the systems

$$\begin{aligned} yz - xz + xy + 1 &= 0 \\ xz + x^2 + y^2 &= 0 \\ y^2 + x^2 - 2x &= 0 \end{aligned} \qquad\qquad \begin{aligned} -1 - xy + 2y - 2x &= 0 \\ xz + x^2 + y^2 &= 0 \\ x^4 - 6x^3 + 16x^2 - 4x + 1 &= 0 \end{aligned}$$

have the same solutions and

$$\{x^4 - 6x^3 + 16x^2 - 4x + 1, \quad -1 - xy + 2y - 2x, \quad xz + x^2 + y^2\}$$

has the weak elimination property.

Proof of termination and correctness of TSOLVE. Let F be a set that satisfies the input specification of `tsolve`. The termination of `tsolve` follows from the termination of `eliminate` and `mod`.

We know from the specifications of `eliminate` and `mod` that every element in O is a finite non-empty subset of $K[x_1, x_2, x_3]$.

Let a be an element of $\mathrm{V}(F)$. It follows from the specification of `eliminate` that there exists an $A \in M$ with $a \in \mathrm{V}(A)$. If $|A \cap K[x_1, x_2]| \neq 2$ then $A \cup F \in O$. Otherwise, by the specification of `mod`, there exists a $C \in \mathtt{mod}(A \cap K[x_1, x_2], F)$ with $a \in \mathrm{V}(C)$. Hence,

$$\mathrm{V}(F) \subseteq \bigcup_{C \in O} \mathrm{V}(C).$$

Furthermore,

$$V(F) \supseteq \bigcup_{C \in O} V(C)$$

follows from the definition of O and the specification of `mod`.

It follows from the specifications of `eliminate` and `mod` that every $C \in O$ has the weak elimination property. □

Proof of termination and correctness of ELIMINATE. Let F be a set which satisfies the input specification. By induction on the number of elements of F_3 we will prove that `eliminate` terminates with input F and that the output set O consists of finite non-empty subsets $C_1, \ldots, C_m$ of $K[x_1, x_2, x_3]$ with

$$V(F) \subseteq \bigcup_{i=1}^{m} V(C_i)$$

and for every $i \in \{1, \ldots, m\}$: $|C_i \cap K[x_1, x_2]| \geq 2$ implies that $C_i \cap K[x_1, x_2]$ is an elimination set.

Induction basis: $|F_3| \leq 1$. Termination follows from the termination of `bsolve`.

If $|F_3| = 0$ or $|M| = 0$ then the output set O is equal to

$$\{A \mid A \neq \emptyset \quad \text{and} \quad (A \in M \quad \text{or} \quad A = F_3)\}$$

and the results we want to prove follow from the specification of `bsolve`.

So let us assume that $|F_3| = 1$ and $|M| \neq 0$. Then,

$$O := \bigcup_{g \in M''} (\{\{g/\gcd(g,q), h\}\} \cup \texttt{bsolve}(\{\gcd(g,q), q_0\})) \cup \bigcup_{A \in M - M'} \{A \cup \{h\}\}.$$

By the specification of `bsolve`,

$$\bigcup_{A' \in M'} V(A' \cup \{h\}) = \bigcup_{g \in M''} V(\{g, h\}) =$$

$$= \bigcup_{g \in M''} (V(\{g/\gcd(g,q), h\}) \cup V(\{\gcd(g,q), q_0\})) =$$

$$= \bigcup_{g \in M''} (V(\{g/\gcd(g,q), h\}) \cup \bigcup_{A \in \texttt{bsolve}(\{\gcd(g,q), q_0\})} V(A)).$$

Therefore,

$$V(F) = V((F \cap K[x_1, x_2]) \cup \{h\}) = \bigcup_{A \in M} V(A \cup \{h\}) =$$

$$= \bigcup_{A' \in M'} V(A' \cup \{h\}) \cup \bigcup_{A \in M - M'} V(A \cup \{h\}) =$$

$$= \bigcup_{g \in M''} (\mathrm{V}(\{g/\gcd(g,q), h\}) \cup \bigcup_{A \in \mathtt{bsolve}(\{\gcd(g,q), q_0\})} \mathrm{V}(A)) \cup$$

$$\cup \bigcup_{A \in M - M'} \mathrm{V}(A \cup \{h\}) =$$

$$= \bigcup_{C \in O} \mathrm{V}(C).$$

It follows from the specification of `bsolve` that every element of the output set O is non-empty and finite.

Since every set with one element is an elimination set we obtain from the specification of `bsolve` that $C \cap K[x_1, x_2]$ is an elimination set for every $C \in O$.

Induction step: $|F_3| > 1$. Let r be the number of elements in F_3. The algorithm `eliminate` terminates with input set F if it terminates with input $(F - \{p_1, p_2\}) \cup \{d_i, p_i/p_s\}$ for every $i \in \{2, \ldots, s-1\}$ and with input $(F - \{p_1, p_2\}) \cup \{p_s\}$. Each of these sets satisfies the input specification of `eliminate` and each of these sets has at most $r-1$ elements which are not in $K[x_1, x_2]$. Hence, termination follows from the induction hypothesis.

By Theorem 3,

$$\mathrm{V}(F) = \mathrm{V}(F' \cup \{p_1, p_2\}) \subseteq \bigcup_{i=2}^{s-1} \mathrm{V}(F' \cup \{d_i, p_i/p_s\}) \cup \mathrm{V}(F' \cup \{p_s\}).$$

From the induction hypothesis we obtain

$$\mathrm{V}(F' \cup \{d_i, p_i/p_s\}) \subseteq \bigcup_{C \in O_i} \mathrm{V}(C) \quad \text{for } i = 2, \ldots, s-1,$$

where O_i is the output set of `eliminate` with input $F' \cup \{d_i, p_i/p_s\}$, and

$$\mathrm{V}(F' \cup \{p_s\}) \subseteq \bigcup_{C \in O_s} \mathrm{V}(C),$$

where O_s is the output set of `eliminate` with input $F' \cup \{p_s\}$. Hence,

$$\mathrm{V}(F) \subseteq \bigcup_{i=2}^{s} \bigcup_{C \in O_i} \mathrm{V}(C) = \bigcup_{C \in O} \mathrm{V}(C).$$

Furthermore, it follows from the induction hypothesis that every element C of the output set O is non-empty and finite and that $C \cap K[x_1, x_2]$ is an elimination set or empty.

Let $C \in O$. For proving the correctness of `eliminate` it remains to show that $|C \cap K[x_1, x_2]| \leq 1$ implies that $F \cup C$ has the weak elimination property.

Case: $C \cap K[x_1, x_2] \subseteq \{0\}$. We will prove that

$$\text{Ideal}(F \cup C) \cap K[x_1, x_2] = \{0\}$$

by induction on the number of elements of F_3.

Induction basis: $|F_3| \leq 1$. By the specification of `bsolve`, $F \cap K[x_1, x_2] \subseteq \{0\}$. Since $F \cup C$ has at most one non-zero element,

$$\text{Ideal}(F \cup C) \cap K[x_1, x_2] = \{0\}.$$

Induction step: $|F_3| > 1$. If there exists an $i \in \{2, \ldots, s-1\}$ with $C \in$ `eliminate`$(F' \cup \{d_i, p_i/p_s\})$ then in contradiction to the induction hypothesis the non-zero polynomial d_i is an element of

$$\text{Ideal}(F' \cup \{d_i, p_i/p_s\} \cup C) \cap K[x_1, x_2].$$

Therefore, $C \in$ `eliminate`$(F' \cup \{p_s\})$. From

$$\text{Ideal}(F' \cup \{p_s\} \cup C) \cap K[x_1, x_2] = \{0\} \quad \text{and} \quad \text{Ideal}(F) \subseteq \text{Ideal}(F' \cup \{p_s\})$$

we obtain $\text{Ideal}(F \cup C) \cap K[x_1, x_2] = \{0\}$. Therefore, $F \cup C$ has the weak elimination property.

Case: $C \cap K[x_1, x_2] \not\subseteq \{0\}$. Let a_1, a_2 be elements of $\bar{K}$ such that the transcendence degree of $K(a_1, a_2)$ is 1 and (a_1, a_2) is a zero of the polynomial in $C \cap K[x_1, x_2]$. By induction on the number of elements of F_3 we will prove that

$$\text{there exists an } a_3 \in \bar{K} \text{ such that } (a_1, a_2, a_3) \in \mathrm{V}(C \cup F). \tag{15}$$

Induction basis: $|F_3| \leq 1$. If $F_3 = \emptyset$ then, by the specification of `bsolve`, $(a_1, a_2, a_3) \in \mathrm{V}(C \cup F)$ for every $a_3 \in \bar{K}$. Otherwise, there exists a $g \in M''$ with $C = \{g/\gcd(g, q), h\}$. It follows from the definitions of g and q that $(g/\gcd(g, q))(a_1, a_2) = 0$ implies that there exists an $a_3 \in \bar{K}$ with $h(a_1, a_2, a_3) = 0$ and therefore, by the specification of `bsolve`,

$$(a_1, a_2, a_3) \in \mathrm{V}(C \cup F).$$

Induction step: $|F_3| > 1$. If $C \in$ `eliminate`$(F' \cup \{p_s\})$ then, by induction hypothesis, there exists an $a_3 \in \bar{K}$ with $(a_1, a_2, a_3) \in \mathrm{V}(C \cup F' \cup \{p_s\})$ and therefore

$$(a_1, a_2, a_3) \in \mathrm{V}(C \cup F).$$

Otherwise, there exists an $i \in \{2, \ldots, s-1\}$ such that $C \in$ `eliminate`$(F' \cup \{d_i, p_i/p_s\})$. Again, by induction hypothesis, there exists an $a_3 \in \bar{K}$ with

$$(a_1, a_2, a_3) \in \mathrm{V}(C \cup F' \cup \{d_i, p_i/p_s\}).$$

As p_i is primitive, $p_i(a_1, a_2, x_3) \neq 0$. By Theorem 4,

$$p_1(a_1, a_2, a_3) = p_2(a_1, a_2, a_3) = 0$$

and therefore

$$(a_1, a_2, a_3) \in V(C \cup F).$$

By (15),

$$V(C \cap K[x_1, x_2]) = V(\mathrm{Ideal}(C \cup F) \cap K[x_1, x_2]).$$

Since $|C \cap K[x_1, x_2]| = 1$, $C \cup F$ has the weak elimination property. □

Proof of termination and correctness of MOD. For a finite subset G of $K[x_1, x_2, x_3]$ define

$$\mathrm{sumdeg}(G) := \sum_{g \in G} \max(\deg(g), 0).$$

Let E and F be sets which satisfy the input specification. We will prove termination and correctness by induction on sumdeg(F).

Induction basis: sumdeg$(F) = 0$. Then $F - K[x_1, x_2] = \emptyset$ and termination and correctness follow from the termination and specification of `bsolve`.

Induction step: sumdeg$(F) > 0$.

Case: $|F - K[x_1, x_2]| = 1$ and $V(E \cup \mathrm{lc}(f)) = \emptyset$ for the only element f of $F - K[x_1, x_2]$. In this case the output set O is equal to

$$\{A \cup (F - K[x_1, x_2]) \mid A \in \mathtt{bsolve}(E \cup (F \cap K[x_1, x_2]))\}.$$

Hence, termination and correctness again follow from the termination and specification of `bsolve`.

Case: $|F - K[x_1, x_2]| \geq 2$ or there exists an $f \in F - K[x_1, x_2]$ such that

$$V(E \cup \{\mathrm{lc}(f)\}) \neq \emptyset.$$

It follows from the termination of `bsolve` and `complement` that `mod` terminates with the input sets E and F if it terminates for every $A' \in M'$ with the input sets A' and $F' \cup \{f'\}$ and for every $A'' \in M''$ with the input sets A'' and $F'' \cup \{f\}$. Let $A' \in M'$. By definition of f',

$$\begin{aligned}\mathrm{sumdeg}(F' \cup \{f'\}) &= \mathrm{sumdeg}(F') + \max(\deg(f'), 0) < \\ &< \mathrm{sumdeg}(F') + \deg(f) = \mathrm{sumdeg}(F).\end{aligned}$$

By induction hypothesis, `mod` terminates with input A', $F' \cup \{f'\}$.

Let $A'' \in M''$. By the specification of `complement`, $V(A'' \cup \{\mathrm{lc}(f)\}) = \emptyset$. Therefore, if $F'' - K[x_1, x_2]$ is empty then the termination of `mod` with input

A'', $F'' \cup \{f\}$ follows from the termination of `bsolve`. On the other hand, if $F'' - K[x_1, x_2] \neq \emptyset$ then there exists a $g \in F'$ with $\deg(g) \geq \deg(f')$. Hence, $\mathrm{sumdeg}(F'') < \mathrm{sumdeg}(F')$ and therefore

$$\mathrm{sumdeg}(F'' \cup \{f\}) < \mathrm{sumdeg}(F' \cup \{f\}) = \mathrm{sumdeg}(F).$$

By induction hypothesis, `mod` terminates with input A'', $F'' \cup \{f\}$. This completes the proof of termination.

Now we will prove that

$$\mathrm{V}(E \cup F) = \bigcup_{C \in O} \mathrm{V}(C).$$

From the specification of `bsolve` and `complement`,

$$\begin{aligned} \mathrm{V}(E \cup F) &= \mathrm{V}(E \cup \{\mathrm{lc}(f)\} \cup F) \cup (\mathrm{V}(E \cup F) - \mathrm{V}(\{\mathrm{lc}(f)\})) = \\ &= \bigcup_{A' \in M'} \mathrm{V}(A' \cup F) \cup \bigcup_{A'' \in M''} \mathrm{V}(A'' \cup F). \end{aligned} \tag{16}$$

Let $A' \in M'$. As every zero of A' is a zero of $\mathrm{lc}(f)$,

$$\begin{aligned} \mathrm{V}(A' \cup F) &= \mathrm{V}(A' \cup F' \cup \{f\}) = \\ &= \mathrm{V}(A' \cup F' \cup \{f - \mathrm{lc}(f) \cdot x_3^{\deg(f)}\}) = \mathrm{V}(A' \cup F' \cup \{f'\}). \end{aligned}$$

By induction hypothesis,

$$\mathrm{V}(A' \cup F' \cup \{f'\}) = \bigcup_{C' \in O'} \mathrm{V}(C'),$$

where O' is the output set of `mod` with input A', $F' \cup \{f'\}$. Together,

$$\mathrm{V}(A' \cup F) = \bigcup_{C' \in O'} \mathrm{V}(C'). \tag{17}$$

Let $A'' \in M''$. From $\mathrm{V}(A'' \cup \{\mathrm{lc}(f)\}) = \emptyset$ we obtain that for every $g \in K[x_1, x_2, x_3]$ and every $(a_1, a_2, a_3) \in \mathrm{V}(A'' \cup \{f\})$

$$\mathrm{prem}(g, f)(a_1, a_2, a_3) = 0 \quad \text{iff} \quad g(a_1, a_2, a_3) = 0.$$

Hence,

$$\mathrm{V}(A'' \cup F) = \mathrm{V}(A'' \cup F' \cup \{f\}) = \mathrm{V}(A'' \cup F'' \cup \{f\}).$$

Let O'' be the output set of `mod` with input A'', $F'' \cup \{f\}$. If $F'' - K[x_1, x_2] = \emptyset$ then

$$O'' := \{A \cup \{f\} \mid A \in \texttt{bsolve}(A'' \cup F'')\}$$

and therefore

$$V(A'' \cup F'' \cup \{f\}) = \bigcup_{C'' \in O''} V(C'').$$

If $F'' - K[x_1, x_2] \neq \emptyset$ then

$$\text{sumdeg}(F'' \cup \{f\}) < \text{sumdeg}(F' \cup \{f\}) = \text{sumdeg}(F).$$

Thus, by induction hypothesis,

$$V(A'' \cup F'' \cup \{f\}) = \bigcup_{C'' \in O''} V(C'').$$

Hence, in both cases,

$$V(A'' \cup F) = \bigcup_{C'' \in O''} V(C''). \tag{18}$$

By (16), (17), and (18),

$$V(E \cup F) = \bigcup_{C \in O} V(C).$$

It follows from the first case of the induction step and the induction hypothesis that every element of the output set has the weak elimination property. □

7 Applications in neural networks theory

We have implemented `tsolve` in Maple as part of a computer algebra package for constructive algebraic geometry (Gebauer et al. 1991). In this section we apply `tsolve` to systems of algebraic equations from neural networks theory. Applications of `tsolve` in geodesy, quantum optics, and geometric modeling can be found in Kalkbrener (1991).

The following three systems can be found in Noonburg (1989):

$$\begin{aligned} 1 - x + xy^2 + xz^2 &= 0 \\ 1 - y + yx^2 + yz^2 &= 0 \\ 1 - z + zx^2 + zy^2 &= 0, \end{aligned} \tag{19}$$

$$\begin{aligned} 1 - x + xy^2 - xz^2 &= 0 \\ 1 - y + yx^2 + yz^2 &= 0 \\ 1 - z - zx^2 + zy^2 &= 0, \end{aligned} \tag{20}$$

$$\begin{aligned} 1 - cx + xy^2 + xz^2 &= 0 \\ 1 - cy + yx^2 + yz^2 &= 0 \\ 1 - cz + zx^2 + zy^2 &= 0. \end{aligned} \tag{21}$$

In the last system c is a parameter.

We have solved each of these systems by using `tsolve`. The elimination was done in the following way: first variable x and then variable y was eliminated.

System (19). The set of solutions of system (19) is decomposed into the set of solutions of system

$$\begin{aligned} -1-2z+2z^2+4z^3-z^4-5z^5+2z^7&=0\\ (3z^2+z-4z^4)y^2+(3z^4+2z^5+1-2z^6-2z^3-6z^2)y-&\\ -3z^2+z^3-4z^6+7z^4-z&=0\\ (-1+y^2+z^2)x+1&=0 \end{aligned}$$

and the set of solutions of system

$$\begin{aligned} 4z^7-4z^6-4z^5-3z^3+z^2-z-1&=0\\ (16z^4+16z^5+4z^3)y+9z^3-2z^5+2z^2-6z^4+8z^6+2+3z&=0\\ (-1+y^2+z^2)x+1&=0. \end{aligned}$$

Computing time: 5.38 s (on an Apollo DN10000).

System (20). This system has the same solutions as

$$\begin{aligned} 16z^{21}-16z^{20}-32z^{19}+64z^{18}-40z^{17}-40z^{16}+64z^{15}-120z^{14}+&\\ +129z^{13}+11z^{12}-206z^{11}+262z^{10}-49z^9-171z^8+192z^7-48z^6-&\\ -58z^5+60z^4-17z^3-5z^2+5z-1&=0\\ (-19z^3+20z^5-32z^{13}+32z^{10}+60z^7-152z^9+z^2-1+79z^8-&\\ -16z^{16}+3z-90z^6+112z^{11}+27z^4+64z^{14}-104z^{12})y-&\\ -16z^{14}+36z^{12}-32z^{10}-20z^{11}-z+z^3-10z^4-31z^7+17z^6+40z^9+&\\ +5z^5+2z^2-7z^8&=0\\ (-1+y^2-z^2)x+1&=0. \end{aligned}$$

Computing time: 3.70 s (on an Apollo DN10000).

System (21). The set of solutions of system (21) is decomposed into the set of solutions of system

$$\begin{aligned} -c^2-z-c^3z+2cz^2+4z^3c^2-z^4-5z^5c+2z^7&=0\\ (3cz^2+z-4z^4)y^2+(3c^2z^4-2cz^3+2z^5-5z^2-2cz^6-c^3z^2+c)y-&\\ -3c^2z^2+z^3-4z^6+7cz^4-cz&=0\\ (-c+y^2+z^2)x+1&=0 \end{aligned}$$

and the set of solutions of system

$$z^3c^3 + c^2z^2 - 4z^5c^2 + 4z^7c - cz - 4z^6 - 4z^3 - 1 = 0$$
$$(8cz^4 + 16/cz^5 + 8/c^2z^4 + 8/c^3z^3 - 4z^3 - 2c^2z^2 + 2/cz^2 - 8z^6 + \\ + 8/c^3z^6 - 4cz - 2 + 2/c^3 + 4/c^2z)y - 2z^5c + 8/cz^6 + 3z - \\ - 6z^4 + 8/cz^3 + z^3c^2 + 2cz^2 + 2/c = 0$$
$$(-c + y^2 + z^2)x + 1 = 0.$$

Computing time: 7.20 s (on an Apollo DN10000).

K. Gatermann (1990) has solved system (21) by using an algorithm that is based on Gröbner bases computation and factorization. The computing time of this algorithm is 64 s on a SUN4 using the Gröbner bases implementation in Reduce.

References

Brown, W. S. (1971): On Euclid's algorithm and the computation of polynomial greatest common divisors. J. ACM 18: 478–504.

Brown, W. S. (1978): The subresultant PRS algorithm. ACM Trans. Math. Software 4: 237–249.

Brown, W. S., Traub, J. F. (1971): On Euclid's algorithm and the theory of subresultants. J. ACM 18: 505–514.

Buchberger, B. (1970): Ein algorithmisches Kriterium für dic Lösbarkeit eines algebraischen Gleichungssystems (in German). Aeq. Math. 4: 374–383.

Buchberger, B. (1985): Gröbner bases: an algorithmic method in polynomial ideal theory. In: Bose, N. K. (ed.): Multidimensional systems theory. D. Reidel, Dordrecht, pp. 184–232.

Canny, J. (1988): The complexity of robot motion planning. MIT Press, Cambridge, MA.

Collins, G. E. (1967): Subresultants and reduced polynomial remainder sequences. J. ACM 14: 128–142.

Gatermann, K. (1990): Symbolic solution of polynomial equation systems with symmetry. In: Proc. ISSAC '90, Tokyo, Japan, 1990, pp. 112–119.

Gebauer, R., Kalkbrener, M., Wall, B., Winkler, F. (1991): CASA: a computer algebra package for constructive algebraic geometry. In: Proc. ISSAC '91, Bonn, Germany, 1991, pp. 403–410.

Grigor'ev, D. Y., Vorobjov, N. N. (1988): Solving systems of polynomial inequalities in subexponential time. J. Symb. Comput. 5: 37–64.

Hearn, A. C. (1979): Non-modular computation of polynomial gcds using trial division. In: Proc. EUROSAM '79, Marseille, France, 1979, pp. 227–239.

Hentzelt, K. (1922): Zur Theorie der Polynomideale und Resultanten (in German). Math. Ann. 88: 53–79.

Hurwitz, A. (1913): Über die Trägheitsformen eines algebraischen Moduls (in German). Ann. Math. Pura Appl. (3a) 20: 113–151.

Kalkbrener, M. (1991): Three contributions to elimination theory. Ph.D. thesis, Research Institute for Symbolic Computation, University of Linz, Linz, Austria.

Kalkbrener, M. (1992): Primitive polynomial remainder sequences in elimination theory. Tech. Rep. MSI-Ser. 92-12, Cornell University, Ithaca, USA.

Lazard, D. (1981): Résolution des systèmes d'équationes algébriques (in French). Theor. Comput. Sci. 15: 77–110.

Macaulay, F. S. (1916): Algebraic theory of modular systems. Cambridge University Press, Cambridge.

Noonburg, V. W. (1989): A neural network modeled by an adaptive Lotka-Volterra system. SIAM J. Appl. Math. 49: 1779–1792.

Ritt, J. F. (1950): Differential algebra. American Mathematical Society, New York.

Stoutemyer, D. R. (1985): Polynomial remainder sequence greatest common divisors revisited. In: Proc. Second RIKEN Int. Symp. on Symbolic and Algebraic Computation by Computers. World Scientific Publishing, Singapore, pp. 1–12.

van der Waerden, B. L. (1940): Moderne Algebra II, 2nd edn. (in German). Springer, Berlin.

Wu, W.-t. (1984): Basic principles of mechanical theorem proving in elementary geometries. J. Syst. Sci. Math. Sci. 4: 207–235.

On a general notion of a hull

Jochen Pfalzgraf

1 Introduction

In this contribution we give a short presentation of ongoing work in the areas of the general framework and mathematical foundations in MEDLAR II. Our objective is to sketch a brief survey of the problems, the methods and existing results and we conclude with prospects of work in progress. We start with some background information and motivational remarks which form the basis of the subsequent considerations. As mentioned in the following, joint article with K. Stokkermans the logical fiberings (as introduced in Pfalzgraf 1991) provide semantical models for indexed systems of logics and they have (semantical) links to D. Gabbay's extensive theory of labelled deductive systems (LDS). He sees the logical fiberings as a (general) semantics for LDS and introduced the notion of "fibered semantics." The LDS form a general framework for the great challenge of "putting logics together" in an integrated system (cf. Gabbay 1990, 1994a, b). This indicates the central interest of fibered structures concerning a general semantics modeling approach. Compare the "sheaf semantics" arising naturally in our subsequent considerations.

Starting point of our work was a question raised by D. Gabbay about a suitable natural notion of a hull operation on deductive systems. Concretely, the problem is to find a construction which, for a given *deduction diagram* (a subset of formulas and deduction relations between them in an underlying deductive system) returns a (possibly larger) diagram which contains the original one and is "closed" under this operation. The construction we are proposing here is suggested by looking at this problem from a categorical perspective interpreting a deductive system in terms of a corresponding category. In this setting, i.e., using category theory as our linguistic basis, we are led in a natural way to the notion of a "hull" or "closure" operation in terms of a suitable co-limit with respect to the given deduction diagram in the underlying category. There is also a lattice theoretic aspect which arises naturally in terms of associated filters and ideals induced by the given relation. We are using these notions (cf. Rasiowa 1974 for details) in our approach in the sense that they provide us with local algebraic information about the system. It is a kind of "fibered algebraic semantics" as described later. Furthermore a topology on the base diagram can be introduced in a natural way. The fiber over each object ("node") of the categorical diagram as base space carries a natural structure of a Heyting algebra and therefore the fibering can become a sheaf of Heyting algebras which can thus be associated to the originally given relational structure. This finally points to a general *sheaf semantics*. Then, consequently, one can use parts of the existing material in sheaf theory and *topos* theoretic aspects as guidelines for an extended work program. These ideas are in the spirit of this article. Due to the general level on which the original problem was stated our subsequent considerations are also of general nature. But they are intended for later applications to various concrete situations.

2 Basic notions

For the convenience of the reader we start this section with the definition of a category. We do this also for pointing clearly to the close analogy between categories and reflexive, transitive relations. More precisely, it is easy to see that every such relation can be interpreted as a category having small morphism sets. This opens the door for modeling relational structures with categorical techniques and enables one to apply all the typical categorical constructions yielding *normal forms* (described by the corresponding so-called "universal property"). Of basic importance for our modeling problem will be the notion of a *(co-)limit*; we introduce it below in terms of diagrams and arrows as it is characteristic for such notions.

Definition 1. A category $\mathtt{A}$ consists of a class of *objects*, denoted by $A, B, C, \ldots \in \mathrm{Obj}(\mathtt{A})$, and for each pair of objects A, B a set of *morphisms*, $\mathrm{Mor}(A, B)$, also denoted by $\mathtt{A}(A, B)$ and a *composition relation* on morphisms such that if $f\colon A \to B$ and $g\colon B \to C$ are morphisms, then there is a morphism $g \circ f\colon A \to C$, the composition of f and g. For these notions the following two axioms are required for a category.

(i) The composition of morphisms is *associative*, that is $h \circ (g \circ f) = (h \circ g) \circ f$.
(ii) For every object A there is the *identity morphism* id_A with the properties $f \circ id_A = f$ and $id_B \circ f = f$ for all $f\colon A \to B$.

We briefly emphasize here that the arrow notation for morphisms is of basic importance. We shall use $f\colon A \to B$ as well as $A \xrightarrow{f} B$ to denote morphisms. The arrow notation is well suited to illustrate (to "visualize") a broad spectrum of modeling problems in a categorical sense. Historically it is of interest that this technical notation for functions arose only in the early 1940s in topology. It definitely had far reaching consequences (we refer to the interesting remarks in MacLane 1971: chap. I).

For further basic categorical notions like *functor, natural transformation, adjoint functors* we refer to the literature on category theory. We refer here only to a few selected publications, namely MacLane (1971), Herrlich and Strecker (1979), Goldblatt (1984), Pierce (1991), and MacLane and Moerdijk (1992).

Typical examples of categories in mathematics are, among others, the category of *groups* (objects are groups, morphisms are the group homomorphisms), the category of *monoids* (objects are monoids, morphisms are monoid homomorphisms), the category of *topological spaces* (objects are topological spaces, morphisms are the continuous functions between spaces), the category of *vector spaces* over a field (objects are the vector spaces, morphisms are the linear maps), of course the category of *sets* (sets as objects and set mappings as arrows), and so on. Summarizing, we can say that category theory extracts the basic features of "everyday's work" when dealing with spaces in a certain discipline and studying structure preserving mappings (the morphisms) between spaces.

We will now have a look at another class of categories which are naturally induced by *relations*. They form the starting point of our considerations concerning the initial question of a hull or closure operation.

Let $(X, \leq)$ denote a *partially ordered set* ("poset"). Then we can associate with this poset the following category $\mathtt{X}$. The objects of $\mathtt{X}$ are the elements of the set X and for $a, b \in X$ there is a morphism $a \to b$, if and only if a and b are in relation, i.e., $a \leq b$. It is easy to verify that this defines a category. The transitivity of $\leq$ gives the composition relation in $\mathtt{X}$ and the reflexivity guarantees the existence of the identity arrows for each object of $\mathtt{X}$. We note explicitly that there is at most one arrow between two objects (if there is one), that means for the number of elements of the morphism sets we have $|\operatorname{Mor}(a, b)| \leq 1$. Thus these examples show that there might be empty morphism sets in categories (which is not the case, for example, in the category of groups). Associativity of the composition in $\mathtt{X}$ obviously holds. Note that the antisymmetry property of the poset relation is not needed to verify that $\mathtt{X}$ becomes a category. Summarizing we can say that every reflexive, transitive relation leads to such a "small" category as introduced above.

It is exactly in this way that we intend to model the *deduction relation* in a *deductive system* $(X, \vdash)$ which is assumed to be at least reflexive and transitive. Below we indicate how we want to model relational structures in terms of (categorical) arrows, specifically the deduction relation $p \vdash q$.

Notation 2. In categorical terms we "visualize" a relation xRy by an arrow, defining the morphism $x \to y$. Accordingly, for a deductive system $(X, \vdash)$ we translate $p \vdash q$ into the arrow (morphism) $p \to q$. If we wish to emphasize the lattice theoretic aspects (which are naturally present), we may prefer to write $p \leq q$ instead of $p \vdash q$ or $p \to q$. This should show clearly enough how we establish our "translation table" in order to wander around in the different disciplines.

Now we come to the main motivation of this work namely the question posed by D. Gabbay concerning a suitable natural notion of a "hull" or "closure operation" for deductive systems. More precisely, the question can be expressed as follows. Given a deductive system $(X, \vdash)$ as above (reflexive, transitive) one wants to have an operation which can be applied to a part of $(X, \vdash)$, say S, such that a certain hull or closure $\mathbf{Cl}(S)$ of S will be produced in the sense that this hull contains "all possible" deductions and formulas which can naturally be obtained on the basis of the given subsystem S. Adding further objects and relations should not lead to another result, that is, each further deduction which is added must already be deducible from the constructed hull. This states a minimality condition typical for closure procedures. Formally we can say that a closure operator typically has the properties

$$S \subseteq \mathbf{Cl}(S) \quad \text{and} \quad \mathbf{Cl}(\mathbf{Cl}(S)) = \mathbf{Cl}(S).$$

Analyzing the previous formulation we are translating $(X, \vdash)$ into an associated category, denoted by $\mathtt{X}_{\vdash}$, as presented above for reflexive, transitive relations where the arrows $p \to q$ in $\mathtt{X}_{\vdash}$ represent the relation $p \vdash q$. Doing this we come intuitively to a proposal of a hull or closure procedure based on the categorical notion of a *co-limit*. As already mentioned we are going to "visualize" the given deductive system $(X, \vdash)$ by a suitable small category which we illustrate by an underlying diagram (we just think of the diagram of all the deduction arrows which visualize graphically the whole deduction relation). Then a part S of the deductive system is represented by a smaller diagram and the closure operation is defined for such a subdiagram.

Below we will define one of the basic notions which we need for our categorical modeling approach. It is the notion of a *diagram* which is essential in the definition of a limit and co-limit. Actually, in the general framework of (co-) limits it is possible to get back other notions like product, coproduct, terminal and initial objects, etc. by applying the (co-)limit definition to a corresponding specified base diagram. We will briefly indicate this later.

Definition 3. A *diagram* $\mathbb{D}$ in a category $\mathtt{A}$ is defined by a family of objects $\{X_i\}_{i \in I}$ and a family of morphism sets $F_{ij} \subseteq \mathrm{Mor}(X_i, X_j)$, for $i, j \in I$. We shall write $f_{ij} : X_i \to X_j$ for $f_{ij} \in F_{ij}$. It is explicitly mentioned that F_{ij} can be empty, i.e., there is not necessarily an arrow between the "nodes" X_i and X_j in the diagram.

A *cocone* $\mathcal{C}$ of the diagram $\mathbb{D}$ consists of an object X in $\mathtt{A}$ and morphisms f_i: $X_i \to X$, for $i \in I$, such that $f_i = f_j \circ f_{ij}$ for all $i, j \in I$. This can be illustrated by the following commutative triangle:

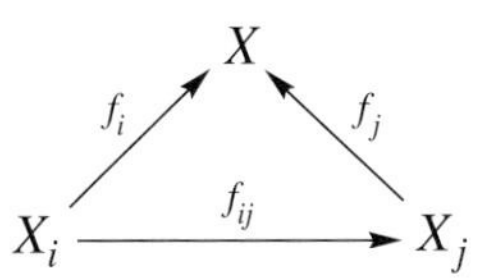

A *co-limit* of the given diagram is a cocone $\mathcal{C}$ with the following universal property (defining $\mathcal{C}$ in terms of a "normal form"):
For every other cocone $\mathcal{C}'$, given by morphisms f_i': $X_i \to X'$, $i \in I$, there exists exactly one morphism f: $X \to X'$, such that $f_i' = f \circ f_i$, for all $i \in I$.

In these terms $\mathcal{C}$ can be called a *universal cocone* of the diagram which is the co-limit, denoted by: $\varinjlim(\mathbb{D})$. (In the literature, several other notations may be found, such as $\varinjlim_{i \in I} X_i$ or $\varinjlim_{\mathbb{D}} X_i$ or $\varinjlim X_i$.) For our purposes here we find it suggestive to write $\varinjlim(\mathbb{D})$ since the co-limit as a limiting cocone depends on the given base diagram $\mathbb{D}$ and makes it "complete."

Reversing the arrows in the definition of a co-limit of a diagram $\mathbb{D}$ results in the dual notion called *limit* of $\mathbb{D}$, denoted by $\varprojlim(\mathbb{D})$.

Remark 4. Starting with a diagram $\mathbb{D}$ which consists only of the objects X_i, $i \in I$, as "nodes" but without arrows, i.e., all $F_{ij} = \emptyset$, we obtain the notion of the categorical *coproduct*, $\coprod_{i\in I} X_i$ (as a special co-limit) and *product*, $\prod_{i\in I} X_i$, respectively. The morphisms f_i in the corresponding definition of $\varinjlim$ and $\varprojlim$ are called "injections" of the coproduct and "projections" of the product, respectively. With this remark we wish to indicate that, corresponding to the shape of the base diagram $\mathbb{D}$, we can derive special notions of limits and co-limits having their specific universal properties.

We will give another motivation how far-reaching and unifying these limit notions and the categorical framework can be. Let us assume that in the previous "discrete" diagram $\mathbb{D} = \{X_i\}_{i\in I}$ the arrows $f_i\colon X_i \to \varinjlim X_i = \coprod_{i\in I} X_i$ represent the $\leq$-relation in a lattice $(X, \leq)$. If we then interpret the universal property of $\varinjlim X_i = \coprod_{i\in I} X_i$, we obtain exactly the information that this $\varinjlim X_i$ is $\sup\{X_i\}$, the *supremum* of the X_i for $i \in I$. More precisely, the universal property in that case specifies $\varinjlim X_i$ not only as an upper bound for the $\{X_i\}$, but exactly as the *least upper bound*.

Dually we see that the limit over $\mathbb{D}$ yields the *infimum*: $\varprojlim X_i = \prod X_i = \inf\{X_i\}$ in the lattice theoretic sense. Thus we get back well-known classical lattice notions as categorical limits and co-limits in a specific category (as "semantical environment") dependent on the meaning of the arrows.

Based on the previous remarks about deductive systems (before we gave the definition of a (co-)limit in categories) we propose now the following definition of a hull or closure operation for deductive systems. We use the same notations as above.

Definition 5. Let $(X, \vdash)$ be a deductive system as previously considered and $\mathbb{X}_\vdash$ the associated category – the categorical "visualization" of $(X, \vdash)$ – and let S denote a subsystem (of the given deductive system $(X, \vdash)$) which we interpret as a corresponding diagram (also denoted by S) in the category $\mathbb{X}_\vdash$. The *hull* or *closure* of S, denoted by $\mathbf{Cl}(S)$, is then defined by the co-limit of this diagram S in $\mathbb{X}_\vdash$:

$$\mathbf{Cl}(S) := \varinjlim(S).$$

Remark 6. As an additional motivational remark that it is natural to propose a closure operation as done in the previous definition we look once again at the general categorical definition of a $\varinjlim$. Let us for the moment interpret every arrow in the diagram $\mathbb{D}$ (see definition of $\varinjlim$) given by the morphisms $X_i \xrightarrow{f_{ij}} X_j$ as (general) deductions and the X_i as elements (formulas) of a deductive system and the given category as a semantical model ("visualization") of the deductive system. We assume that we are dealing with sets, in general.

Then the co-limit as universal cocone of the diagram $\mathbb{D}$ has typical properties of a closure operation. In this context, it reads as follows. An object (formula, element) X is added to the base diagram $\mathbb{D}$ together with arrows (deductions) $X_i \stackrel{f_i}{\rightarrow} X$ such that the commutativity ("compatibility of deductions") $f_i = f_j \circ f_{ij}$ holds. Moreover, for every other "new" object (formula, element) X' of the deductive system with arrows (deductions) $X_i \stackrel{f_i'}{\rightarrow} X'$ that can be added in a similar way, there is a unique arrow (deduction) $X \stackrel{f}{\rightarrow} X'$, such that all the "new" arrows (deductions) can be expressed by means of this $X \stackrel{f}{\rightarrow} X'$ and the "old" arrows (deductions): $f_i' = f \circ f_i$, $i \in I$. In this sense, forming the $\varinjlim\{X_i\}$ over $\mathbb{D}$ yields a hull and closes the diagram by the limiting cocone. That is, it cannot be extended by other formulas and deductions which cannot be expressed by already available ones.

Actually, from a more formal point of view, repeating the co-limit operation for the diagram $\varinjlim(\mathbb{D})$ itself yields "nothing new". The result is a diagram which is equivalent to the limiting cocone $\varinjlim(\mathbb{D})$ (see Pfalzgraf in prep., for technical details).

3 General relational structures

Aiming at a general framework for semantics of logics and deductive systems D. Gabbay suggested to extend the discussion of a hull operation to more general deduction relations not necessarily being transitive, but still reflexive. We start to consider this here and we keep the discussion even more general extending it to arbitrary relational structures, that means we do not even require reflexivity, for the most general approach.

In such cases we are not able to associate directly a category to the relation as we did it before since transitivity, reflexivity do not hold, in general. But from the categorical perspective again we interpret a relational structure as a certain diagram of arrows "visualizing" the given relations between the objects which form the "nodes" of the diagram. It turns out that we can always "embed" such a diagram in an associated `PATH` category having comparable behavior as the category associated to a reflexive, transitive relation, although being a little "bigger" concerning the morphism structure. Having this environment we can proceed in a natural way and again introduce the proposed hull operation via co-limits. The introduction of the associated category `PATH` allows to use and apply again the same modeling principles as previously discussed.

Actually, looking at general relational structures is quite natural since transitivity and even reflexivity are not always apparent in applications. As a practical example let us look at a road map where the nodes (objects) are towns and the arcs (arrows) are road connections, then not every pair of towns has a direct connection, in general. Therefore, in general, from a starting point we have to follow a path of direct road connections passing several nodes (towns) before we can reach a goal. Similarly, in deductive systems transitivity can be missing.

For the technical definitions, let $R \subset X \times X$ denote a (general) relation. We associate to it the following category denoted by PATH(X, R) or just PATH for short, if no confusion can arise. The *objects* are the elements $x \in X$ and *arrows (morphisms)* are defined by sequences (paths) of adjacent arrows. That means there is always a morphism $x \to y$, if $(x, y) \in R$ (or xRy), but if we have arrows (morphisms) $x \to y$ and $y \to z$, then, in general we do not have a "direct arrow" $x \to z$, since the relation need not be transitive. But what we can always do is forming a sequence (path) of consecutive arrows, like $x \to y \to z$ in the previous case. This is then a morphism of a more general type between x and z. More generally we can have (finite) sequences denoted for example by $x_0 \to x_1 \to \ldots \to x_n$ which is a morphism in $\mathrm{Mor}(x_0, x_n)$ in the new sense of our definition, but can also be interpreted as the composition of other morphisms which will be represented by adjacent parts of that whole path. In a category normally we need the identity arrow id_x for each object x. We can add this as a requirement if there is really a necessity from a theoretical viewpoint; in practice this may be irrelevant. In PATH it can be the case that there exists more than one path between two nodes a and b, therefore in PATH we can have for the sets of morphisms $|\mathrm{Mor}(a, b)| > 1$, in general, in contrast to the category which is associated to a reflexive, transitive relation as considered before. Based on these considerations we can see that PATH becomes a category.

The definition of a *closure operation* or *hull* is then defined analogously as above in terms of the *co-limit* of a corresponding subdiagram in PATH. And in principle we are again in a similar situation as previously discussed, but in a more general category. We should not forget to mention that the question of the existence of (co-)limits in a given category is not our subject in this exposition here; we are concerned with proposing a suitable notion as previously discussed. In the examples below we will see that such (co-)limit constructions are possible leading to normal forms.

We want to mention explicitly that associating the category PATH to a relation is somehow in contrast to forming the *transitive hull*. We deliberately emphasize this different point of view. Namely, concerning the modeling of relational structures an additional aspect is attracting our interest: what is the "minimal" necessary information describing a given structure? Is it necessary to embed it in the (complete) transitive closure? Or can we come along with less information (partial diagrams or so)?

We will illustrate what we mean by having a look at *combinatorial group theory*. There we describe a group without giving the complete group table (this would correspond to a complete diagram). We only give some generators and suitable relations among them and this already contains the whole information for describing the group. We can depict it as a so-called *Cayley diagram*. The nodes (objects) are group elements and on the arc (arrow) connecting two elements, say a and b, we write the corresponding generator, denoted by g here, such that $b = g \cdot a$, in arrow notation $a \xrightarrow{g} b$. Therefore such a Cayley diagram is an arrow diagram with additional information (labels, colors) on the arrows. And this nicely fits our categorical pictures. In particular, we want to point out that all the categorical diagrams involved in forming limits, co-limits are of course examples of general relational structures as we are considering them here. Other examples can be found in reduction systems as considered in rewriting or computing Gröbner bases, generally in critical-pair/completion algorithms and their associated diagrams. There the nodes (objects) are, e.g., polynomials and the labels on the directed arcs (arrows) are again polynomials (cf. Stokkermans 1992, and in this volume, where the categorical language is extensively used as a formal modeling basis in a unified comparison of different algorithmic procedures).

In this sense we think of a *generator and relations* point of view for encoding our diagram (representing the given relational structure). That means we look for a certain *skeleton* containing all the essential information about the original system (relation). Another aspect of interest is to think of a possible *spanning tree* of PATH as a certain "irredundant" representation of the original structure.

Summarizing, we have sketched the basic categorical notions of our proposed modeling approach for relational structures. Below we give an example and we argue that this semantical modeling principle can be applied in a unifying way to a rich variety of concrete problems.

4 Some examples

For illustration we consider the following example from arithmetics with which we would like to demonstrate how we can apply our general approach to obtain a concrete "visualization" of notions always using the same concept which we established previously.

Let us consider the *Euclidean algorithm* for constructing the *greatest common divisor* (gcd) of two natural numbers a and b, $\gcd(a, b)$, where we assume that $b < a$. In the Euclidean algorithm two basic arithmetical relations are used on natural numbers $a, b, \ldots, u, v, \ldots$, namely the *division*, $a|b$, and the *less relation*, $u < v$. We are going to visualize these relations by the following two types of arrows $a \mapsto b$ (for $a|b$) and $u \to v$ (for $u < v$).

Now, let $r_0, r_1, \ldots, r_n$ denote the sequence of remainders produced by the algorithm, where we start with the initial division $a = q_0 \cdot b + r_0$ with remainder $r_0 < b$, and repeat this procedure until we reach the last nontrivial remainder, denoted by r_n, which divides all the other remainders and a and b. Actually, we have $\gcd(a, b) = r_n$. Applying our categorical modeling principle we can reinterpret the gcd in terms of a limiting cone with r_n as its "top." To this end we "visualize" all the relations which are the result of the algorithm leading to the following base diagram $\mathbb{D}$

$$0 \to r_{n-1} \to r_{n-2} \to \ldots \to r_0 \to b \to a$$

(note that this corresponds to the $<$-relation). Then we take this as the base diagram and form the limit with r_n as its top object. We obtain the same result when we use the completed base diagram including the smallest remainder r_n

itself

$$0 \to r_n \to r_{n-1} \to r_{n-2} \to \ldots \to r_0 \to b \to a.$$

Having a look at the categorical definition of a limit we use the arrows $r_n \mapsto r_i$ $(i = 0, \ldots, n-1)$ and $r_n \mapsto b$, $r_n \mapsto a$, as the "projection arrows." These correspond to the arrows $\{f_i\colon X \to X_i\}_{i \in I}$ in the general definition of a limit (cf. the definition above). Thus we have $\gcd(a, b) = \overset{\lim}{\to}\{r_i, b, a\}$ as the limit of the given base diagram. We can observe that by dropping the arrows $r_i \to r_{i-1}$ in $\mathbb{D}$ and just taking the "discrete" set of objects $\{r_{n-1}, \ldots, r_0, b, a\}$ as a new base diagram (without arrows), we can write the gcd as the product of the objects $\{r_{n-1}, \ldots, r_0, b, a\}$ with the same projections as in the previous limit descriptions. Our final step in the application here is to extract in words the "universal property" of that limit (product). That means, knowing the general formulation of the universal property of a limit in category theory, we read this property in terms of our concrete arrows, that means we write down this property in our concrete semantical modeling context. This gives us back (as universal property) the well-known definition of $\gcd(a, b)$ as we learned it at school. To repeat it: "The $\gcd(a, b)$ divides all $r_{n-1}, \ldots, r_0, b, a$" (this is modeled by the projection arrows as mentioned above) and universality corresponds to the words "and every other number (object) g' dividing $r_{n-1}, \ldots, r_0, b, a$ (i.e., with projection arrows to these objects) must divide $\gcd(a, b)$, i.e., $g' \mapsto \gcd(a, b)$." This is the common schoolbook definition obtained back as universal property.

If we concentrate only on the relation $\gcd(a, b) \mapsto a$ and $\gcd(a, b) \mapsto b$ (and forget about the other remainders), then $\gcd(a, b)$ together with these two arrows again can be interpreted as a product in the categorical sense and its typical universal property yields the definition of the gcd in a similar way as we mentioned it in the previous considerations.

Now we apply another typical categorical principle, namely *duality* which, briefly spoken, means that we reverse all the arrows in the definition of the notion of a product. The result is the categorical *coproduct* of the two objects a and b. To be more precise we have an object which we denote by $\operatorname{lcm}(a, b)$ and two arrows (reversing the arrows of the $\gcd(a, b)$) $a \mapsto \operatorname{lcm}(a, b)$ and $b \mapsto \operatorname{lcm}(a, b)$. Then again interpreting the universal property of the coproduct in this specific context gives us the well-known definition of the *least common multiple* of a and b ($\operatorname{lcm}(a, b)$). If we interpret the arrow relation in terms of lattice theory then we can say that $\gcd(a, b) = \inf(a, b)$ and $\operatorname{lcm}(a, b) = \sup(a, b)$.

We recall that the categorical product (coproduct) is formed as a limiting cone (cocone) of the underlying "discrete" diagram $\{a, b\}$ given by the objects a and b. And thus $\operatorname{lcm}(a, b)$ can be considered to be the hull or closure of that diagram in the general meaning of this article.

We confined the previous considerations to natural numbers and make the remark here that, qualitatively, a similar "visualization" by a categorical diagram can be given for other (Euclidean) domains.

This example also shows that there is a natural motivation to speak about *morphisms of different type* in the underlying categorical model. This extends naturally the notion of a category but it is compatible with the categorical concepts.

In another example we show with our general modeling approach that the *prime decomposition* of natural numbers (and other domains where prime decomposition is possible) also can be formulated as a co-limit of a diagram formed by corresponding prime power chains which can be introduced in a natural categorical way (cf. Pfalzgraf in prep.).

Another little application considers a definition taken from Ohlbach (1994). We do not go into details, but only concentrate on the following definition without mentioning the context in which it was established. It deals with a system which has a relation described by an arrow "$\rightarrow$", like $w \rightarrow x$. The definition below defines a rule for the introduction of a "new arrow $\Rightarrow$" in the system.

Definition 7. For all $x, y \in X$: [$\forall w$: $w \rightarrow x$ implies $w \rightarrow y$] then [define the arrow $x \Rightarrow y$].

Interpreting this definition in terms of our categorical modeling approach we will see that it is closely related to the co-limit notion, or more specifically to a corresponding coproduct. To justify this statement we have to say what is the underlying diagram $\mathbb{D}$ for the co-limit (coproduct) and what is the "universal arrow". Anticipating, the new arrow "$\Rightarrow$" in Definition 7 corresponds to the universal arrow in the coproduct. Let us consider arbitrary $x, y \in X$ and let $W := \{w | w \rightarrow x\}$ denote the set of all elements with an arrow to x. Now we take W as base diagram $\mathbb{D}$. Since for each $w \in W$ there is an arrow $w \rightarrow x$ we then interpret $\mathbb{D}$ and all the arrows $w \rightarrow x$ as a limiting cocone representing the coproduct $\coprod_{w \in W} w = \varinjlim(\mathbb{D})$. In this sense the definition of the new arrow in Definition 7 can be interpreted as the (unique) arrow in the universal property of the coproduct. This is because in terms of the co-limit Definition 7 corresponds to the statement: if for the cocone $\{w \rightarrow x\}_{w \in W}$ there is also a $\{w \rightarrow y\}_{w \in W}$ then there is an arrow $x \Rightarrow y$. In the definition of the coproduct this arrow $x \Rightarrow y$ is provided by the universal property. Since Definition 7 defines the addition of a new arrow to the original system, we can say that, categorically, this corresponds to adding all coproducts to the given system. More generally, in terms of co-limits, this can be expressed by saying that a certain *closure operation* is performed or that we make the associated category *cocomplete*, i.e., we extend it accordingly. On the other hand, if we know that in the associated category all coproducts can be formed, then we can assume that all the new arrows already exist in form of universal arrows in the corresponding coproducts, respectively. Again remark that we do not discuss the general problem of existence of (co-)limits, though this is of basic relevance for concrete applications.

These considerations should fix the basic notions which we need for later work. We conclude this exposition with a brief discussion of prospects of work which is in progress and which is intended to be subject of a more detailed publication. In this sense we omit all the technical details here including the definition of the notions used below and refer to Pfalzgraf (in prep.) and other relevant references.

5 Prospects

Let a be a node of a given deduction diagram $\mathbb{D}$, i.e., an element/formula of the corresponding deductive system $(X, \vdash)$, for which we first assume again that it is a reflexive, transitive system. As previously done we visualize the $\vdash$ again by the arrow $\rightarrow$, then we put as a "*fiber* over a" the *principal filter* F_a (or *principal ideal* I_a) generated by a (cf. Rasiowa 1974, Goldblatt 1984, Pfalzgraf in prep.). Noting here that $F_a := \{x \in X \mid a \rightarrow x\}$ and $I_a := \{x \in X \mid x \rightarrow a\}$ it is suggestive to interpret F_a as a "source(a)" (all arrows and paths of arrows starting in a) and accordingly we can say that I_a is a "sink(a)." These notions provide us with (local) algebraic (lattice theoretic) information about the system under consideration. The collection of all the fibers indexed by the elements of the given deductive system is called total space of the resulting *fibering*. The underlying diagram, more precisely the associated category, is called base space. Each particular fiber provides us locally with certain algebraic information centered around the node a. Moreover, in these fibers we can obtain a natural *Heyting algebra* structure. Then we use the filtering sets and ideals to introduce an induced topology on the base space (i.e., the underlying diagram). This finally gives us the possibility to define an associated (pre-)sheaf of Heyting algebras and thus opens the view to a general *sheaf semantics* and *topos* theoretic aspects for deductive systems.

Obviously analogous considerations can be done for more general relational structures for which we can introduce the associated category `PATH` in which we then can perform all the analogous categorical constructions. Moreover, this associated category is then the base space of the associated fibering.

Once we have established this general semantical modeling basis it will be natural to use it for working on *classification* results of relational structures interpreting the associated (local) algebraic structures, the base diagram which is involved and the associated fiberings and sheaves in the sense of *mathematical invariants* to classify given systems.

6 Concluding remarks

Concluding we would like to point out once more that an advantage of the categorical modeling approach as we consider it, lies, among others, in the "reusability" of the concept which – once generally established – can be applied to many concrete practical situations. We can resort to it whenever it is possible to translate a problem into arrow diagrams in which the types of the arrows reflect the relations involved. What we are doing is in a certain sense a "qualitative visualization" of concrete relational structures where we always apply the same modeling principle (forming limits, co-limits). Thus we can extract "normal forms" by interpreting the corresponding universal property in the particular context (as indicated in the examples above). Indeed we are observing that many notions can be obtained as specific (co-)limits. It should be underlined that we cannot expect that this general modeling approach also delivers a "universal construction" for forming "all" limits and colimits (and hulls) – this would be too general in view of the huge variety of all kinds of relational structures. In some cases the universal property of a (co-)limit contains "hints" how to construct it concretely. In general, the information how to construct such a "candidate" (normal form) must be extracted from the given structure which is under consideration, respectively. Thus for instance, in Euclidean domains, it is exactly the Euclidean algorithm which concretely constructs the limit as previously mentioned. In a similar way we want to consider the Gröbner basis algorithm of B. Buchberger for constructing a "normal form basis" of a given polynomial ideal.

The concluding remarks of the previous section are finally concerned with topics of work which is in progress (cf. Pfalzgraf in prep.). They can be regarded as a program of ongoing work which is partly following the existing literature like that on "sheaves in geometry and logics" and on topos theory (see, e.g., MacLane and Moerdijk 1992, Goldblatt 1984). This provides a useful guideline for major parts of our work.

Acknowledgements

This work started while the author was a guest at LIFIA-IMAG, Université de Grenoble. I am grateful to Ricardo Caferra and his group for their great hospitality and for the invitation which was sponsored by the Région Rhône-Alpes – I would like to express all my thanks here. I would further like to mention the following persons (who are directly or indirectly in contact with the MEDLAR group) and thank them for interesting discussions and helpful suggestions: Jiři Adámek, Ricardo Caferra, Jim Cunningham, Dov Gabbay, Wolfgang Gehrke, Ewa Orlowska, Victor Pollara, Jiři Rosicky, Dana Scott, Viorica Sofronie, Karel Stokkermans, Todd Wilson.

Sponsored by the Austrian Ministry of Science and Research (BMWF), ESPRIT BRA 3125: MEDLAR, and the Austrian Science Foundation (FWF), ESPRIT BRP 6471: MEDLAR II.

References

Gabbay, D. (1990): Labelled deductive systems, Part I. CIS, University of Munich, CIS-Bericht 90-22.

Gabbay, D. (1994a): Labelled deductive systems – a position paper. In: Vaananen, J., Oikkonen, J. (eds.): Logic Colloquium 90. Springer, Berlin Heidelberg New York Tokyo [Slaman, T., et al. (eds.): Lecture notes in logic, vol. 2] (to appear).

Gabbay, D. (1994b): Classical vs non-classical logic. In: Gabbay, D., Hogger, C., Robinson, J. (eds.): Handbook of logic in AI and logic programming, vol. 2. Oxford University Press, Oxford, pp. 359–500.

Goldblatt, R. (1984): Topoi. The categorial analysis of logic. North-Holland, Amsterdam (Studies in logic and the foundations of mathematics, vol. 98).

Herrlich, H., Strecker, G. E. (1979): Category theory: an introduction. Heldermann, Berlin.

MacLane, S. (1971): Categories for the working mathematician. Springer, Berlin Heidelberg New York Tokyo (Graduate texts in mathematics, vol. 5).

MacLane, S., Moerdijk, I. (1992): Sheaves in geometry and logic. Springer, Berlin Heidelberg New York Tokyo.

Ohlbach, H.-J. (1994): Synthesizing semantics for extension of propositional logic. Internal report (draft), Max Planck Institut für Informatik, Saarbrücken.

Pfalzgraf, J. (1991): Logical fiberings and polycontextural systems. In: Jorrand, P., Kelemen, J. (eds.): Fundamentals of artificial intelligence research. Springer, Berlin Heidelberg New York Tokyo, pp. 170–184 (Lecture notes in computer science, vol. 535).

Pierce, B. C. (1991): Basic category theory for computer scientists. MIT Press, Cambridge, MA.

Rasiowa, H. (1974): An algebraic approach to non-classical logics. North-Holland, Amsterdam.

Stokkermans, K. (1992): A categorical formulation for critical-pair/completion procedures. In: Rusinowitch, M., Rémy, J.-L. (eds.): Conditional term rewriting systems. Springer, Berlin Heidelberg New York Tokyo, pp. 328–342 (Lecture notes in computer science, vol. 656).

On robotics scenarios and modeling with fibered structures

Jochen Pfalzgraf and Karel Stokkermans

1 Introduction

The field of robotics has been one of the main working areas of the RISC-Linz group in the MEDLAR project. In the first project year of BRA 3125 (subsequently referred to as MEDLAR I) we started with case studies (Pfalzgraf and Stokkermans 1992) in order to get an overview of material which we considered to be relevant as support and motivation of future project work. These future aspects are especially seen with regard to the applications of methods developed by the other project partners. Therefore it became more and more clear that one of the main objectives of our work on robotics has to do with the construction of "scenarios" where various reasoning methods can be applied and tested and extended. That means that we thought of providing testbeds where each partner should be able to identify a problem suitable for application of her/his corresponding methods, respectively. This would describe the ideal case. Subsequently, in the next section, we will go into more details. Actually, the development of these ideas started in the course of MEDLAR I and they found enough interest as to be continued in the first year of MEDLAR II (BRP 6471), the project successor of MEDLAR I. The existing material is intended to serve as a basis for work on parts of a MEDLAR practical reasoner (in the third year). In our case this refers to a reasoning module for specific robotics problems which corresponds to our special fields of interest namely algebraic approaches to geometric reasoning problems with emphasis on robot kinematics and singularity problems.

Parallel to our previously mentioned work we brought the notion of fiberings (fibered structures, fiber bundles) into discussion. In particular we introduced the notion of a so-called logical fibering. With regard to modeling robotics scenarios we are aiming at the application of what we call the generic modeling principle using fiberings. This is the modified approach of a typical modeling technique of fiber bundle theory.

Besides that aspect, fiberings and sheaves are a topic of our contributions to the mathematical foundations of the general MEDLAR framework. This framework is mainly based on the labeled deductive systems (LDS) as introduced and developed by D. Gabbay (1990). Following his point of view the fibered structures then serve as general semantical models.

Parallel to the previously mentioned activities intensive work on algebraic methods in geometric reasoning was carried out (Wang 1991a, b) including applications of symbolic computation methods to specific robotics problems. Work on automated geometry theorem proving was also done in the realm of these work tasks as well as work on an interactive software system (a theorem prover), see Wang (1991a, b) for more details.

All these activities are ongoing substantial parts of work in MEDLAR II. It is the objective of this contribution to present results and further developments in the robotics scenario area and the concept of fiberings, especially logical fiberings. The intention how we want to apply these techniques in the sense of what we call logical controller for cooperating robots (or agents) is discussed on the basis of examples. Besides that we include some remarks referring to the work of other project partners and how it can be related to the robotics scenario modeling.

2 Motivational remarks and background

In order to achieve flexible and advanced automation in practical reasoning, in particular in the field of planning and control, it is desirable to have a broad spectrum of automatizable reasoning methods available. These methods comprise purely logical reasoning approaches, including the use of different logics ("mixing logics"), and reasoning expressed in other mathematically oriented metalanguages and the combination of all these different aspects. This fits the MEDLAR goal of having in the ideal case a flexible multi-purpose *practical reasoning system* available integrating a variety of automatized logical and practical reasoning modules. That concerns not only purely logical systems (implementing classical, modal, linear, non-monotonic logics, etc.), but also practical reasoners implementing "query-answer modules", reasoners implementing "safety of information handlers", database modules, and also very specialized mathematical expert systems like computer algebra systems and automated geometric theorem provers for special tasks in the area of geometric reasoning (GR) like solving inverse kinematics problems for concrete robots acting in a (factory) cell, and so on.

All this sounds very advanced and constitutes a very ambitious research and development goal. We are aware that the "ideal solution" cannot really be reached – or only in some minor parts. However, first approximations are possible and the MEDLAR outcome can be seen that way. Actually, in the discussions with our engineering partners and partners from industry we noticed that they showed real interest in what is being done in MEDLAR and they explained us that, although these goals look rather advanced, the current methods and problems in CIM-like areas have reached a point where it is reasonable and worthwhile to raise the level of methodology. This provides a further motivation for research in MEDLAR subjects.

With this confirmation from actual engineering problems in complex planning and control in mind we were strongly motivated to construct scenarios for having enough concrete experimental workbenches available. Therefore, in the end of MEDLAR I we presented a "toolkit-database" for the flexible construction of individual scenarios such that everybody can build up examples serving her/his own interest and methods. Testing, applying, extending, ...; see Pfalz-

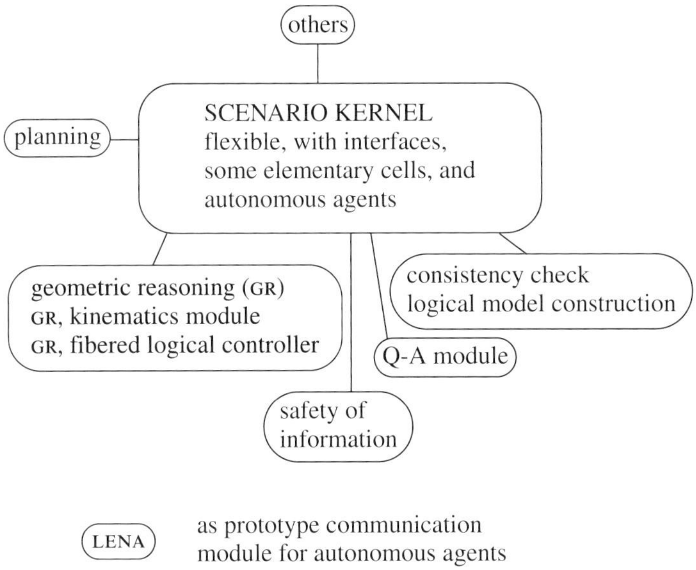

Fig. 1. Principle of scenario construction

graf and Stokkermans (1992). In this spirit we are now proposing a sample scenario with various features and suggest it as the core of a workbench. Before we go into details we would like to summarize our intentions and motivate our subsequent draft of a scenario.

What is our goal?

The construction scheme of the scenario can be illustrated as in Fig. 1.

LENA stands for "Logical Engine for Natural Agents," an initiative started by D. Gabbay aiming towards a prototypical kernel for a prospective so-called MEDLAR practical reasoner. One of its basic components is SETHEO, a theorem prover developed by the MEDLAR group of the TU Munich (cf. Letz et al. 1992).

We want an experimental environment where we can apply, test and develop. It should contain components able to deal with problems like the following.

– Concrete classical robot kinematics problems, i.e., solving diverse (inverse) kinematics tasks; path tracking, i.e., a concrete robot arm movement for a concrete working task in a cell. This incorporates having a *computer algebra module*, a *kinematics geometric reasoning module* and a *corresponding database*.
– The "logical control" of the scenario which should guarantee the correct interaction of various submodules. We wish to consider various *logical modeling approaches* to tackle this problem. This comprises among others the approach of a "fibered logical controller" applying logical fiberings as semantical tools. Syntactically, in such a context, the LDS (labeled deductive systems) are a unifying modeling framework. We also think of deployment of existing automated *model construction approaches* for first order logic to verify that the logical

model of a system under consideration is consistent (e.g., the ATINF system; Caferra and Zabel 1992). This is a very important aspect in complex technical systems where various different submodules are interacting.

– Several *planning and control* problems involving alternatives and conditions, which are to be solved by a planning module that is applied parallel to and cooperating with logical modules. This planning module will be discussed more extensively elsewhere incorporating contributions from the MEDLAR group at the TH Darmstadt.

– We look at complex scenarios involving autonomous agents and incorporating the modeling of phenomena like intelligent reaction of an agent to new, unforeseen events and taking into account that an agent or an individual subsystem of the scenario is not provided with a complete database. In such situations *query and answer procedures* may be used to resolve a lack of information of an agent by communicating with an "external expert" (having a larger database and having more specialized knowledge to resort to). Or first a communication with other "agent colleagues" could be invoked to overcome the information deficits of an individual agent.

– Closely related to the processing of information, whether coming from sensors or (databases of) other agents, is the possible need, in a scenario, to "check and control" information whether it "is reliable"; this is imaginable in dangerous situations, e.g., in a complicated control process of a complex plant. Here we think of potential applications of a *security of information module.*

– As already mentioned in all these scenario modeling problems there are extensive *database handling* and *communication between different systems* involved.

– The individual agents will need facilities for processing the information and data required for the autonomous execution of their tasks and the cooperation with other agents and subsystems of the scenario. We propose a *system state space of an agent* to model this.

The following quotation from Hörmann et al. (1993) shall serve as a further motivation coming from engineering for our later scenario construction. In particular, it contains concrete suggestions to include in a sample scenario situations and problems of (practical) reasoning which arise in *cooperating autonomous robot systems.* Such motivations can be found in many practical problems of future complex robotics applications.

"Today, there is a great range of attractive potential robot applications which cannot yet be realized. Such application areas are, for instance, hazardous working environments, nuclear power plants, the mining industry, and operations in space or in deep sea. Assembly of small lot sizes is also still not profitable. The main reason for these problems is that robots are not able to deal with uncertainties in their environment. Reasons for these uncertainties are inexact sensor readings, inaccuracies of the robot and its peripherals, and tolerances of work pieces. The current practice in industry is to avoid uncertainties by making the work cell and its components more accurate. Since this is very expensive in terms of time and cost, many applications cannot be realized in an economical way.

Another approach is to construct 'intelligent' robot systems which are able to detect deviations from the nominal world, to reason about them, and to react in a fault-tolerant way. Such a method is currently being developed within the ESPRIT Basic Research Project No. 3274 'FIRST' (Fundamentals of Intelligent Reliable Robot Systems) in cooperation with research groups in Oxford, Grenoble, Genoa, and Leuven. A prototype system for the case of convex polygons has already been developed at the Institut für Prozeßrechentechnik und Robotik (Prof. Dr.-Ing. U. Rembold, Prof. Dr.-Ing. R. Dillmann) of the University of Karlsruhe."

In the article the state of the art is discussed with respect to such methods and some detailed information is included about existing methods – in principle, these approaches might be of potential interest for an extended MEDLAR practical reasoning system in the future.

Another motivation for the application of logical fiberings came from planning, control and reasoning problems. These are of central importance in intelligent robotics systems, as they need to deal with unforeseen, uncertain, incomplete and possibly conflicting information, and to act and react to such information. We started our joint work with the Darmstadt group proposing the following kernel of a sample scenario of cooperating robots and autonomous agents. The scenario is composed of a "conservative" subscenario which is an extension of the originally simple 3-cooperating robot example (Pfalzgraf and Stokkermans 1992), where we made our first steps towards a "fibered logical controller" for cooperating robots. In that type of scenario the resource-oriented planning approaches like those investigated by the TH Darmstadt group can be nicely demonstrated. These planning approaches also enable handling uncertainty, conditional planning, and the cooperation of two robots who perform a task together that a single robot would not be able to carry out. This will be subject of a joint paper now in preparation.

This motivates further applications of these methods in other practical environments, namely the other part of the scenario where the cooperating autonomous agents are at work. Both scenarios are linked, do cooperation and consequently offer the possibility to model various communication and interaction problems.

The scenario below consists of two subscenarios. The first involves three robots solving an assembly problem. It contains several problems of practical relevance, such as uncertainty about the reason for a failure and a choice between alternative postconditions of a (part of a) plan, corresponding to nondeterminism. Several technical details, such as precise descriptions of movements, have been omitted in order to make the basic problems clearer. They can and must be incorporated in a final, realistic version of the scenario.

After describing the first subscenario (Sect. 3), an approach to modeling and solving it by the method of logical fiberings (cf. Pfalzgraf 1991, Pfalzgraf and Stokkermans 1992) is given (Sect. 4).

The description of the scenario by logical fiberings should be seen as an attempt to formulate planning problems (as considered by the TH Darmstadt group) in a uniform semantical notation which can also be used to describe

R_{26} will denote (r_2, dump-temp). The local information processing:

- Check whether `on(table, res)` is true and either `on(temp,` a`)` is true or `on(temp,` b`)` is true. Θ will map this (set of) constellation(s) of truth values to the *activation truth value* F_{26}.
- Carry out the action.
- Reset `on(temp,` a`)` (or `on(temp,` b`)`) to false and `used(dump)` to true.

R_{27} will denote (r_2, empty-dump). The local information processing:

- Check whether `used(dump)` is true and `on(table, res)` is true or all of `on(table,` a`)`, `on(table,` b`)`, `tried` and `used(dump)` are true and either one of `on(temp,` a`)` and `on(temp,` b`)` is true. Θ will map this (set of) constellation(s) of truth values to the *activation truth value* F_{27}.
- Carry out the action (removing everything on `table` and `temp` to `dump`).
- Reset all control propositions to false.

Let now $\mathrm{act}_2(y)$ be the local activation function, which is the formal description of the next action of r_2. $\mathrm{act}_2(y)$ is defined by

$$\mathrm{act}_2(y) = \begin{cases} \text{perform } R_{21} & \text{if } y = F_{21}, \\ \text{perform } R_{22} & \text{if } y = F_{22}, \\ \text{perform } R_{23} & \text{if } y = F_{23}, \\ \text{perform } R_{24} & \text{if } y = F_{24}, \\ \text{perform } R_{25} & \text{if } y = F_{25}, \\ \text{perform } R_{26} & \text{if } y = F_{26}, \\ \text{perform } R_{27} & \text{if } y = F_{27}, \\ \text{remain inactive} & \text{otherwise.} \end{cases}$$

The logical control function

The logical control function will be a heptavariate logical operation; the number of variables of course corresponds to the number of control propositions. In contrast to the bivariate transjunction obtained for the (far simpler) scenario in Pfalzgraf and Stokkermans (1992), we obtain a more complicated operation:

$$\Theta\colon\ L_0 \times L_0 \times L_0 \times L_0 \times L_2 \times L_2 \times L_2 \to \mathcal{L}\ .$$

The difference with the much simpler scenario in Pfalzgraf and Stokkermans (1992) is explicitly that we still have three logical fibers, but now they are no longer 2-valued, as they were previously. In L_0 and L_1 we use a 3-valued logic and in L_2 an 8-valued logic as fiber, respectively.

The domain of Θ is forced upon us by the fact that the first three control propositions (`on(table,` a`)`, `on(table,` b`)`, and `on(table, res)`) are checked by sensors connected to robot r_0, the fourth (`tried`) is determined by the actions of r_0 and its logical system, while the last three propositions (`on(temp,` a`)`, `on(temp,` b`)` and `used(dump)` respectively) are checked by sensors informing robot r_2. The codomain is determined by the actions to be undertaken upon a given setting of the logical propositions.

We will use the following "linguistic variables": x_{01}, x_{02}, x_{03} and x_{04} for the truth values of `on(table,` a`)`, `on(table,` b`)`, `on(table, res)` and `tried` respectively, and x_{21}, x_{22} and x_{23} for those of `on(temp,` a`)`, `on(temp,` b`)` and `used(dump)`.

The logical control function Θ is part of a more complex information processing (as formalized in the diagram of the "fibered logical controller", see below). More precisely, the input to Θ consists of tuples of logical values produced by the *sensor evaluation procedures* performed in the subsystems L_0 and L_2 and symbolized by the variables $x_{01}, x_{02}, \ldots, x_{23}$. The function Θ produces output values going to the different logical subsystems of the scenario (therefore Θ is a generalized transjunction) and these logical output values are again interpreted. This interpretation induces the appropriate action to be performed as described above.

Note that for the description of this example we do not need all particular truth values in the input, but only the classical "true" and "false" in the corresponding subsystems. A more formal treatment is now presented below.

Semantically Θ is expressed as follows:

$$\Theta\colon\ \Omega_0 \times \Omega_0 \times \Omega_0 \times \Omega_0 \times \Omega_2 \times \Omega_2 \times \Omega_2 \to \Omega\ ,$$

with $\Omega = \Omega_0 \amalg \Omega_1 \amalg \Omega_2$.

We will use the following truth values to correspond to the actions:

Table 1

Truth value	Logical subsystem	Action
T_0	L_0	r_0 remains inactive
F_{01}	L_0	r_0 performs R_{01}
F_{02}	L_0	r_0 performs R_{02}
T_1	L_1	r_1 remains inactive
F_{11}	L_1	r_1 performs R_{11}
F_{12}	L_1	r_1 performs R_{12}
T_2	L_2	r_2 remains inactive
F_{21}	L_2	r_2 performs R_{21}
F_{22}	L_2	r_2 performs R_{22}
F_{23}	L_2	r_2 performs R_{23}
F_{24}	L_2	r_2 performs R_{24}
F_{25}	L_2	r_2 performs R_{25}
F_{26}	L_2	r_2 performs R_{26}
F_{27}	L_2	r_2 performs R_{27}

Note that L_0 and L_1 are 3-valued logical systems, whereas L_2 turns out to be 8-valued

We now proceed to define the transjunction Θ by its truth table. In order to render the situation pictorially, we put the values of the first four logical propositions horizontally and the last three vertically. Impossible combinations of the

			x_{01}	0	0	0	1	1	1
			x_{02}	0	0	1	0	1	1
			x_{03}	0	1	0	0	0	0
			x_{04}	0	1	0	0	0	1
x_{21}	x_{22}	x_{23}	Θ						
0	0	0		$F_{11} \vee F_{12}$	F_{02}	F_{11}	F_{12}	F_{01}	$F_{21} \vee F_{22}$
0	0	1		F_{27}	F_{02}	F_{25}	F_{24}	F_{01}	$F_{24} \vee F_{25}$
0	1	0		F_{26}	F_{02}		F_{12}	F_{01}	F_{24}
0	1	1		F_{26}	F_{02}	F_{11}	F_{23}	F_{01}	$F_{24} \vee F_{25}$
1	0	0		F_{26}	F_{02}	F_{11}		F_{01}	F_{25}
1	0	1		F_{26}	F_{02}	F_{23}	F_{12}	F_{01}	$F_{24} \vee F_{25}$

Fig. 3

truth values of x_{01}, x_{02}, x_{03} and x_{04} have been deleted. The same has been done for impossible combinations of x_{21}, x_{22} and x_{23} (namely two pieces on `temp`). Eliminating these obviously impossible situations, there are only two more combinations of values for the control propositions left that do not occur; these are indicated by blanks in Fig. 3, which defines the transjunction controlling the working cell.

The fibered logical controller

The schema shown in Fig. 4 is called the *fibered logical controller*. $\mathcal{P}$ is the composition of the other functions in the diagram. The sensor evaluation function is supplied with the sensor information and maps it to the truth values for the "linguistic variables" $x_{01}, \ldots, x_{23}$ (where F_{01} and F_{02} are identified, just as all the F_{2i}, $1 \leq i \leq 7$).

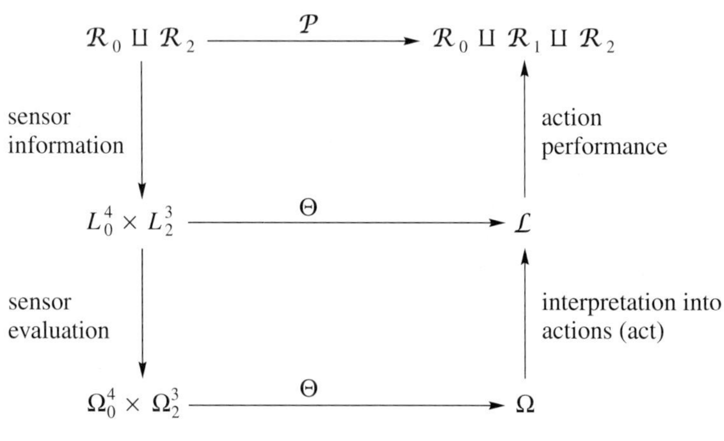

Fig. 4. The fibered logical controller. $\Omega = \Omega_0 \amalg \Omega_1 \amalg \Omega_2$; $\Omega_0 = \{T_0, F_{01}, F_{02}\}$; $\Omega_1 = \{T_1, F_{11}, F_{12}\}$; $\Omega_2 = \{T_2, F_{21}, F_{22}, F_{23}, F_{24}, F_{25}, F_{26}, F_{27}\}$; act $=$ act$_0 \amalg$ act$_1 \amalg$ act$_2$; $\mathcal{P} =$ process control function

The heptavariate function Θ: $L_0^4 \times L_2^3 \to \mathcal{L}$ is defined semantically by the bottom arrow of the diagram. The local activation functions (act_i) activate the subtasks in each robot system.

4.3 Base point dependent formulas

Considering logical modeling where local logical state spaces or deduction systems are involved which are varying over time and/or space it seems suggestive to introduce the notion of a *space-time logical fibering* for robot multi-tasking. This is the subject of ongoing work (see Pfalzgraf 1995). Here we only cast a first glance at this idea in terms of an example of logical formulas which are space dependent. A more thorough formal treatment is intended for future work.

Let ϕ, ψ, λ, etc., denote logical formulas of our language under consideration which are possible formulas in the logical state spaces, i.e., fibers, over the points $x \in X$ of our base domain, respectively.

We are going to introduce the following formalism of "formula handling" with which we are able to make formulas dependent on the points of the base space. That means that in the state space (i.e., the total space of the fibering) we can work in different ways with logical formulas which can vary from fiber to fiber in the sense that they are "switched on" (evaluable) over a certain subdomain of the base space whereas they are not "switched on" (not evaluable, not present) in the fibers over other subdomains. This allows to model logically a variety of practical situations, especially in the case of cooperating agents working in a geometrically modeled environment (base space).

For the natural numbers 0, 1 let $\phi^1 := \phi$, and $\phi^0 :=$ *empty string (empty word)*. That is to say by ϕ^1 we want to express that ϕ is "present" or "switched on," and ϕ^0 is meant to express that ϕ is "not present," "switched off."

Thus, for example, the sequent $\phi\psi^k\lambda$ is equivalent to $\phi\lambda$, iff $k = 0$. Or we look at the negation function $\neg$, then $\neg^0 =$ *identity*, i.e., $\neg^0(\phi) = \phi$. (That means we do our formula handling similar to the handling of formal words in semigroups, for example.)

With this notation we can now introduce base point dependent formulas in the following sense.

Let X denote a domain, for example a geometric domain in the plane where robots are moving around having certain subsets $U, V, W, \ldots \subset X$ as their corresponding workspace area where they are allowed to move around under certain conditions (constraints). Let furthermore χ_U: $X \to \{0, 1\}$ be the *membership function (characteristic function)* for subsets $U \subset X$ (i.e., $\chi_U(x) = 1$ iff $x \in U$ and zero otherwise). Let now $\mathtt{V}$ denote a logical evaluation function which evaluates for every $x \in X$ the local logical formulas over that base point, respectively. (Technically, we would have to define $\mathtt{V}$ on the total space of all fibers over the base space X, but we do not go into these technical details here.) Note that we apply this convention also to negation symbols alone.

Now consider expressions of formulas over X like

$$\phi^{\chi_U}, \quad \psi^{1-\chi_{U\cup V}}, \quad (\neg^{\chi_{U\cap V}})(\phi \vee \psi), \quad \phi^{\chi_U} \wedge \psi^{\chi_{U\cap V}}, \ldots$$

Then for $x \in X$, we denote by $\mathtt{V}_x$ the local evaluation of logical formulas in the state space over x. That means for example that for the formula

$$\mathtt{V}_x(\psi^{1-\chi_{U\cup V}}) := \psi^{1-\chi_{U\cup V}(x)}$$

we insert x in $\chi_{U\cup V}$ for the local evaluation at x. This yields the result that ψ appears (and is valid) whenever x is not in U and not in V. Analogously, the fourth formula means $\phi \wedge \psi$ does only appear as this conjunction iff $x \in U \cap V$. Similarly for the other examples. Many variations are possible using this principle. The same technical notations can be used for modeling time dependent formulas (we only have to extend the base space by time). We are aware that it is necessary to work out the exact mathematical details how to use this formalism technically, but we do not go into these details here. We only wanted to give a first introduction to the basic notion and to illustrate its potential use in a simple example which follows below.

We would like to close this section with a brief sketch of how we want to apply the notion of a local section (an important notion in the theory of fiber bundles) and the *generic modeling approach with fiberings.*

The idea of the latter approach is to decompose a scenario with cooperating agents into local subscenarios. Such a local part can, for example, be a local group of some cooperating robots which, in itself, forms a logically closed unit, but which is integrated in the whole process (for example, it may have to deliver parts of a working task to other agents or work cells).

The intention behind this is that the particular parts of a decomposed scenario are easier to describe locally. The complete scenario is obtained by composing the parts again. And in this composing procedure ("pasting together the patches") the interrelation (including necessary communication) between the various components must be reflected.

Since in our approach the decomposition is "controlled" by corresponding covering sets $\{U_i\}$, $i \in I$, of the geometric base space X (recall that $X = \bigcup U_i$), the interrelation between components will be modeled by suitable constraints which appear in the overlap of intersecting covering sets.

Formally, we aim at expressing such constraints by specific relations between data written in the particular fibers over the points in the corresponding overlap. For example, having $U_i \cap U_j \neq \emptyset$, for $i \neq j$, by composing the subfiberings (local state spaces) over U_i and over U_j we can consider constraint modeling problems for fibers over points $x \in U_i \cap U_j$.

If we interpret an U_i as a working area of an agent, for example, then we see $U_i \cap U_j$ as the domain where common actions, cooperations of both agents are performed. Below we give a description of a simple example that should illustrate these ideas.

The role played by a local section $\sigma\colon U_i \to E$ is to describe a current state ("snapshot") of the system over the domain U_i. In this sense we can use sequences of sections $\sigma_i^{(1)}, \sigma_i^{(2)}, \ldots$, to describe a sequence of successive (local) states of the scenario. We mention again that system constraints are modeled in the overlap $U_i \cap U_j$, but that the agent in U_i can work autonomously (i.e., independently from the agent in U_j) in the region $U_i \backslash (U_i \cap U_j)$. Roughly spoken, this is the essential idea behind our generic modeling approach. We call it generic because the previously sketched modeling principle can be applied in a "reusable way" to many different problems. The application of (local) sections will be subject of future work.

Concluding, we present an example where we apply the previously introduced notion of space dependent formulas in the case of three cooperating robots. We deliberately keep this application simple just indicating how we want to exploit the method.

We first briefly describe the selected scenario, as follows.

Three robots having workspace areas A, B, and C (we give the corresponding robots the same names A, B, C as well) are able to work independently in all those parts of their workspace where there is no overlap with the workspace of another agent.

Let us model the logical control of such (independent) work by sets of formulas $\{\alpha_A, \ldots\}$, $\{\alpha_B, \ldots\}$, and $\{\alpha_C, \ldots\}$ in the corresponding logical state space of robot A, B, and C, respectively.

In different sets of formulas we could describe the logical control of the scenario in overlaps $A \cap B$, $A \cap C$, $B \cup C$, for example. For reasons of simplicity we only deal with the common overlap of all three robots, namely the workspace area $A \cap B \cap C$.

In this overlap all the three agents should be able to cooperate in order to solve a problem which can only be done with the help of all three robots. This will correspond to certain logical constraints. Let us consider a simple case of such a situation.

Let W denote a workpiece of weight 62 kg, placed in the area $A \cap B \cap C$ of the work cell. We formulate a task T saying that the workpiece W has to be lifted and placed on a solid basis (a chassis). This chassis can be provided by robot C who can move it in the right position right below the piece W, but of course only in the case that W is lifted. Thus, task T comprises the subtasks "lift W", then "move the chassis right below W."

Now we have the situation that robot A can only lift up to 20 kg ("A can lift up to 20 kg"; this phrase is logically represented by the formula ϕ_A in the logical state space of A). Similarly, robot B can only lift up to 45 kg ("B can lift up to 45 kg" is logically expressed by a corresponding formula ϕ_B in the logical state space of B).

Accordingly, neither A alone nor B alone can lift W in their individual workspace areas, A and B, respectively. But they can do it jointly in their workspace overlap $A \cap B$. Logically, this will be expressed by the following space dependent formula:

$$(\phi_A^{\chi_A} \wedge \phi_B^{\chi_B}) \Rightarrow (\Box\, \mathrm{Lift}(W))^{\chi_{A\cap B}} \; .$$

By using the box operator $\Box$ in the previous modal formula we want to express that in the workspace overlap $A \cap B$ both robots A and B together necessarily have to fulfill the task of lifting the workpiece W ("Lift(W)"). And the exponents formally express that this formula is only "switched on" or present over $A \cap B$. This formula is contained in the logical state space of both A and B (we interpret it as a logical constraint of the system valid in overlap $A \cap B$).

Now the logical description (control) for performing the whole task T can be modeled as follows. Let $[\text{Move}_C]$ denote the logical formula corresponding to the subtask of robot C meaning "C can move the chassis right below W." With this, the logical control for the successful performance of task T of the cooperating agents can be expressed by the following space dependent formula:

$$[(\phi_A^{\chi_A} \wedge \phi_B^{\chi_B}) \Rightarrow (\Box\,\text{Lift}(W))^{\chi_{A\cap B}}] \Rightarrow [\text{Move}_C]^{\chi_{A\cap B\cap C}} \ .$$

Again, this formula is contained in the logical state space of each robot. We interpret it as a base space dependent constraint of the whole system holding exactly in the common overlap $A \cap B \cap C$. Thus expressing the situation that exactly in $A \cap B \cap C$ all the three robots can fulfill the given task by cooperation.

If we interpret the whole system as a logical fibering with continuous base space (the whole workspace area $A \cup B \cup C$) and discrete total space (the set of all local state spaces of the robots depending on the base points $x \in A \cup B \cup C$), then a fiber over x consists of all the formulas of a local state space of an agent which are "switched on" over that point (that is, which are available or applicable for the corresponding control of the system in that point). A typical feature of this modeling approach is mixing discrete and continuous structures.

Figure 5 depicts schematically what we have described.

5 A proposed model of the general state space of an agent

5.1 The state space of an agent

In the cooperating robot scenario above we concentrated on modeling the logical state spaces of individual robots and then putting all these state spaces together in a logical fibering. We then can define the whole process course by means of (local) sections.

We now want to attack more complicated scenarios, featuring agents who are able to perform more complex tasks, having a certain autonomy and cooperating capabilities.

To this end we want to extend the agent's state space (which represents the information processing and reasoning capabilities) by the following additional modules.

- An *individual* (local) *database* reflecting the current knowledge as the basis for reasoning about possible actions, environment, etc. (details will be specified in a concrete example). This local database may be *incomplete*, which can cause various communication processes with the other agents.
- An extended local *logics module* possibly incorporating different logics for reasoning (like classical, modal, temporal, linear, non-monotonic, etc.), and reasoning approaches, e.g., default reasoning, reasoning about intention, reasoning about knowledge and belief, etc.

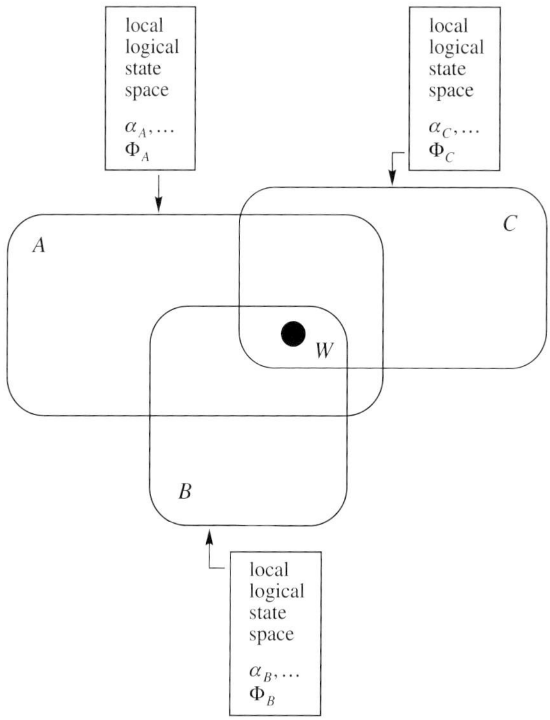

Fig. 5

– A local *planning system* which is capable of solving planning tasks of an individual agent. In addition to this, a global planning module is envisaged.
– A specific local *sensor evaluation system* processing various sensor data and supplying the logics module with the necessary data for logical reasoning (this enhances the principle already modeled in the first subscenario).
– A local *communication unit* for all necessary communications with the other agents and possibly communication with humans (HCI) involved in a complex process.
– A *kinematics module*. This is to be seen as an information processing module on the classical engineering level of robotics for the performance of concrete path finding tasks. It involves the capability to solve explicit inverse kinematics problems at the symbolic and numeric (subsymbolic) level.

We are aware that such complex scenarios involve many very hard engineering problems (e.g., sensor fusion). We are not experts in these fields. Our intention is to focus on using such scenarios to apply various kinds of reasoning, i.e., we are interested in working with methods only on the information processing level of scenarios with cooperating agents.

Figure 6 shows an extendable proposal for the state space of an autonomous agent. Again, we view it as a fibered system in itself.

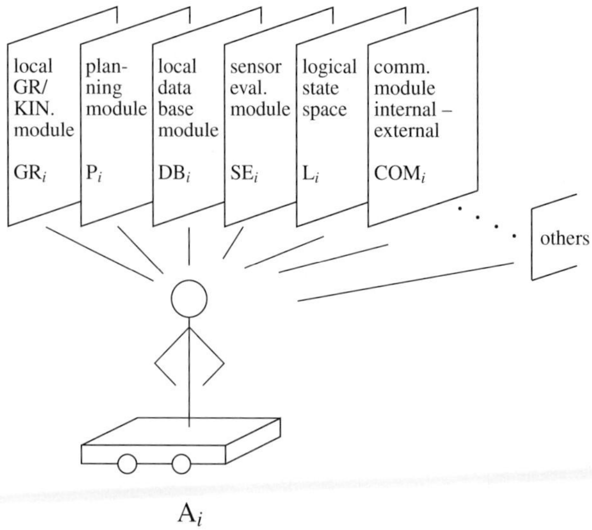

Fig. 6. Proposed reasoning state space of an agent A_i. GR_i geometric reasoner for agent i; P_i planning module for agent i; DB_i database for agent i; SE_i sensor evaluator for agent i; L_i logical state module for agent i; COM_i communication module for agent i

5.2 Further specification of the modules

Databases

The database module for each agent includes the normal, classical components of a data base, but the model must also address the problem that an individual DB_i can be incomplete for a specific task; this evokes communication, query and answer, default reasoning, etc.

In general, acquisition of further data and information to enable the agent to do the task or to conclude that he cannot do it (or at least not alone) will be one of the abilities of an intelligent autonomous agents. That is, we want to consider *non monotonous databases*.

Logics

An agent can have various local logical systems available in the sense of "mixing logics."

This module should enable the agent to do all kinds of logical reasoning; in short, it should be a "local LENA."

For more details on the logics and reasoning methods involved in this module, we refer to the relevant work of the MEDLAR partners.

Sensors and their evaluation

As already mentioned we use such a module on the information processing level (not going into technical details concerning engineering problems). Thus, sensors are assumed to provide the agent with informations about the current state of its environment and to control specific constellations arising in a task (like in the assembling of certain work pieces, path planning, etc.).

Sensor components we want to consider are among others:

- temperature sensor,
- sensors for measurement of concentrations of certain substances,
- mechanism for the recognition of dangerous fluids (chemical substances, ...),
- mechanism for visual surveillance of a plant,
- special controls of security sensitive parts: *valve* (complex security sensitive valve),
- weight sensors (default reasoning: *"too heavy"*),
- vision system for moving in an environment with obstacles,
- special tools for welding, screwing, and other assembly tasks,
- others, problem dependent.

Kinematics module
Such a module is responsible for all kinds of kinematics tasks, in particular path tracking, which arise in concrete movements of a robot. We think of the following features.

A robot agent has an own local database with the existing data how to perform a concrete path tracking (i.e., the corresponding sequence of joint parameters representing a solution of a given inverse kinematics problem). An agent is provided with a "catalogue" of all standard paths occurring normally in the working cell.

These solutions can be prepared off-line using the symbolic computation methods in GR, as frequently discussed in MEDLAR (algebraic methods for geometric reasoning and corresponding implementations, cf. the work of D. Wang).

In addition to that such a kinematics module can have still other features. For example, if an extraordinary situation arises where new unknown path tracking problems come up, then the agent can invoke either an own GR system to work on that problem "on board" or the agent can communicate with an outside system submitting the complete data and information in order to get back the right solution.

Here again we can imitate query and answer procedures with other modules in order to simulate complicated situations where a thorough communication process is necessary to collect all the data and information for accomplishing the task. This is another example of a subscenario where we can apply various reasoning methods.

As mentioned already, parts of such a kinematics module exist and are implemented in computer algebra systems (symbolic kinematic models of certain robot types).

6 Subscenario with autonomous agents

This part of the scenario involves autonomous agents working together on a hazardous task in an inaccessible environment, where they have to rely on

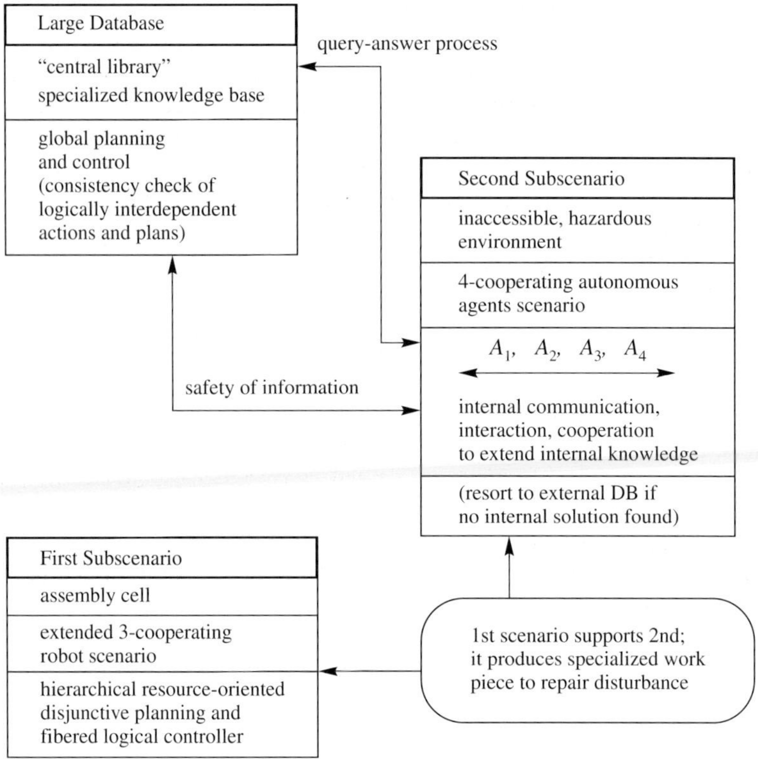

Fig. 7. Proposed extended scenario

each other for carrying out certain tasks and do reasoning about the safety of the information they exchange, acquiring it with the help of query and answer modules which work on the basis of certain databases.

Figure 7 displays schematically the principle of such an intended more complex sample scenario.

We now sketch a possible "screenplay." We imagine four autonomous agents, charged with checking a number of pipelines through which gas is flowing. The agents check the temperature, pressure and composition of the gas at certain critical points. This is done continually. If at a given time the control information is unsatisfactory, i.e., the measured values are not within safety constraints obtained from the databases, the agents can (and must) check and possibly exchange certain complicated valves at the pipeline.

Going into more detail, we think of including situations like the following as part of the sample scenario.

On checking the gas consistency, a conflict is signalized which he cannot resolve with the information stored in his own local database. He will then have to start (by means of his communication module) a query/answer procedure with the other agents (who will then have to access their own local databases) and/or the global database, in order to determine what needs to be done next.

If valves have to be exchanged, a complicated process starts. One agent is required to continue measuring temperature, pressure and gas composition, in particular near the valve that is being exchanged. Two agents are necessary to hold parts of the assembly, and one agent should do for example a welding job necessary for the replacement. This of course requires subdivision of tasks (planning) and communication.

First, when the necessity of a valve exchange is established, the autonomous agents in the second subscenario will have to ask for a new valve to be installed – this is the input of the first part of the scenario which we have discussed before. The resulting assemblies (called "res" in the description of the first subscenario) will be the valves to be installed in this second part of the scenario.

Figure 6 gives an idea of the modules to which an agent should have access.

We would like to underline here that a complete and fully automatized modeling of a complex scenario as indicated here can hardly be accomplished in the ideal sense. What we are aiming for, more realistically, in the framework of MEDLAR, is to implement parts of such a scenario, based on our work in MEDLAR I and the first year of MEDLAR II. A complete implementation in the sense of a complex, fully automatized and integrated practical reasoner comprising all the modules and features discussed above is to be seen as the ideal goal.

7 Conclusion

In this paper we have presented a method (logical fiberings) to propose a principle for a logical controller of robotics scenarios. We also indicated how to extend the modeling by logical fiberings with space/time dependent fiberings, in order to make modeling of very complex scenarios possible and natural.

The latter point will be made much more precise with the modeling of the second subscenario we have outlined. This shall be subject of future work. Thanks to the modular, fibered approach to modeling an agent's state space, it will be possible to incorporate many different reasoning modules, like modules for geometric reasoning (kinematics problems), modules for communication (both internally, i.e., within the work cell, and externally, with databases located outside), modules for local databases (for information to which the agent needs fast and direct access), modules for evaluation of sensor information and the safety thereof, modules for the logical state space description and the reasoning following from that description, etc.

Topics closely related to this article are subject of ongoing cooperations. We here refer to our joint work with U. Sigmund on relating the deductive planning approach (cf. Sigmund 1992, Große et al. 1992) to logical fiberings and thereby providing it with a semantics, and with J. Cunningham (cf. Cunningham 1993; Cunningham and Pfalzgraf in prep.), on the concept of fiberings aiming towards a logical framework for systems of rational agents. We are aware that our work is in an initial state and that we touched a broad field of challenging problems stimulating the cooperation of many disciplines.

Acknowledgments

We thank Ute Sigmund for stimulating discussions and critical comments. We would also like to express our thanks to R. Caferra, J. Cunningham, and D. Gabbay (who pointed out the relevance of fiberings as a general semantics for his theory of LDS) for interesting discussions and suggestions.

Sponsored by the Austrian Ministry of Science and Research (BMWF), ESPRIT BRA 3125: MEDLAR, and the Austrian Science Foundation (FWF), ESPRIT BRP 6471: MEDLAR II.

References

Caferra, R., Zabel, N. (1992): A method for simultaneous search for refutations and models by equational constraint solving. J. Symb. Comput. 13: 613–641.

Cunningham, J. (1993): Concurrent deduction: classical and modal. In: Working Notes of 1993 AAAI Fall Symposium on Automated Deduction in Non-Standard Logics. AAAI, Menlo Park, CA.

Gabbay, D. (1990): Labelled deductive systems, part I. CIS, University of Munich, CIS-Bericht 90-22.

Goldblatt, R. (1984): Topoi. The categorial analysis of logic. North-Holland, Amsterdam (Studies in logic and the foundations of mathematics, vol. 98).

Große, G., Hölldobler, S., Schneeberger, J., Sigmund, U., Thielscher, M. (1992): Equational logic programming, actions, and change. In: Proceedings of the Joint International Conference and Symposium on Logic Programming '92. MIT Press, Cambridge, MA, pp. 177–191.

Hörmann, K., Hübner, T., Spreng, M. (1993): Contact analysis and verification in a 2D environment with uncertainties. J. Intell. Robotic Syst. 7: 175–193.

Lambek, J., Scott, P. (1986): Introduction to higher-order categorical logic. Cambridge University Press, Cambridge (Studies in advanced mathematics, vol. 7).

Letz, R., Schumann, J., Bayerl, S., Bibel, W. (1992): SETHEO: a high-performance theorem prover. J. Autom. Reason. 8: 183–212.

MacLane, S. (1971): Categories for the working mathematician. Springer, Berlin Heidelberg New York Tokyo (Graduate texts in mathematics, vol. 5).

Pfalzgraf, J. (1991): Logical fiberings and polycontextural systems. In: Jorrand, P., Kelemen, J. (eds.): Fundamentals of artificial intelligence research. Springer, Berlin Heidelberg New York Tokyo, pp. 170–184 (Lecture notes in computer science, vol. 535).

Pfalzgraf, J. (1995): On geometric and topological reasoning in robotics. Ann. Math. Artif. Intell. (to appear).

Pfalzgraf, J., Stokkermans, K. (1992): Scenario construction continued and extended with a view to test and enhancement of reasoning methods. Tech. Rep. RISC Linz 92-27.

Sigmund, U. (1992): LLP – Lineare logische Programmierung. Master's thesis, Technische Hochschule Darmstadt, Darmstadt, Federal Republic of Germany.

Wang, D. (1991a): Reasoning about geometric problems using algebraic methods. In: Medlar Milestone II Deliverable, Grenoble, November 1991.

Wang, D. (1991b): On Wu's method for solving systems of algebraic equations. Tech. Rep. RISC Linz 91-52.

On algorithmic parametrization methods in algebraic geometry

Josef Schicho

1 Introduction

The parametrization problem can be described as the problem of finding a general closed form solution to a system of algebraic equations, where "closed form" means rational functions in one or more free parameters.

The simplest nontrivial example is the following. Consider the algebraic variety given by the equation

$$f(x, y) = x^2 + y^2 - 1 = 0.$$

We are asking for a pair (ξ, η) of rational functions in t such that $(\xi(t), \eta(t))$ is a general solution to the above equation. A possible answer is

$$\xi(t) = \frac{2t}{t^2+1}, \qquad \eta(t) = \frac{t^2-1}{t^2+1}.$$

The variety is uniquely determined by this parametric representation.

It is well known that not every variety allows a parametrization. A necessary, but not sufficient condition is irreducibility. The simplest irreducible variety that has no parametrization is an elliptic curve, for instance the one given by the equation

$$x^3 + y^3 - 1 = 0.$$

Therefore, the first step of a parametrization algorithm should be the decision whether parametrization is possible. This is a classification problem that has a long history and is still unsolved in the general case.

Automatic parametrization has many applications in computational geometry and computer aided design. A parametric representation of a variety is often much more useful than its 'implicit' representation by a system of algebraic equations. For instance, the intersection of a curve, given by a parametric representation, with a variety given by equations can be quickly computed by plugging the parametric representation into the equations. Also, parametric representation allows fast generation of points on the variety, which is needed for drawing. This is the reason why many computer algebra systems (e.g., Maple, Mathematica) request parametric representations for plotting.

The algorithms described in this paper do not only compute a parametric representation for the input variety X, but can also be extended to return rational functions that allow to compute the corresponding parameters to a point of X with given coordinates. Thus, it computes a birational correspondence of X and some affine space. In the above example,

$$t = \tau(x, y) = \frac{x}{1 - y}$$

would be such a function. This makes it easy to eliminate the parameters in a later state of the computation.

Of course, the fact that not every variety has a parametric representation limits the scope of the applications. On the other hand, the class of varieties that have such a representation (so-called unirational varieties) is large enough to model interesting things (cf. Ocken et al. 1987), and therefore having fast parametrization algorithms is a strong desire.

2 Rational and unirational varieties

In this section we give some general definitions and facts. For a broader background, we refer to any textbook in algebraic geometry, e.g., Shafarevich (1974).

Let k be an algebraically closed field. We are talking about affine varieties in some $\mathbf{A}_k^n$. Varieties of dimension 1 are called curves. Varieties of dimension 2 are called surfaces.

Definition. Let $X \in \mathbf{A}^m$ be an irreducible affine variety of dimension n. A parametrization is a rational map

$$\phi\colon\ \mathbf{A}_n \to X,$$
$$\phi((t_1, \ldots, t_n)) = (\phi_1(t_1, \ldots, t_n), \ldots, \phi_m(t_1, \ldots, t_n))$$

($\phi_1, \ldots, \phi_m$ are rational functions), such that the image $\phi(\mathbf{A}_n)$ is dense in X.

If ϕ is birational (i.e., has a rational inverse), it is called a proper parametrization.

A variety that has a parametrization is called unirational. A variety that has a proper parametrization is called rational.

Obviously, rationality and unirationality only depend on the birational equivalence class of the variety, or on the function field of the variety. A variety of dimension n is rational iff it is birational equivalent to $\mathbf{A}_n$ iff its function field is an extension of k by n transcendental variables.

An important application of this observation is that we can restrict our attention to hypersurfaces (varieties given by a single irreducible equation), by the following well known theorem.

Theorem. Every irreducible variety is birationally equivalent to a hypersurface.

Given an irreducible variety, the computation of an equivalent hypersurface and the birational isomorphism is easy, for instance with the algorithm in Kalkbrener (1991).

3 Curves

This paper contains the main results on rational curves. The idea of the common parametrization algorithm and of an improvement by the author is explained.

The birational classification of curves is quite well understood. The main notion here is the genus.

Definition. Let C be an irreducible curve in $\mathbf{A}_2$, given by an irreducible equation $C(x, y) = 0$, $\deg C = d$. The genus of C is defined as the integer

$$g(C) := \frac{(d-1)(d-2)}{2} - \sum_{P \in Sing} \frac{\mu_P(\mu_P - 1)}{2},$$

where μ_P is the multiplicity of $P \in C$, and the sum ranges over all singular points, including infinitely near ones and including those on the infinite line.

The most important fact on the genus is that it is invariant under birational isomorphisms (which is not obvious by the definition). Especially, there is the following theorem.

Theorem. A curve is unirational iff it is rational iff its genus is 0.

The main idea to parametrize a rational curve is to compute a pencil of curves, intersecting the given curve in one variable point. This intersection point can then be expressed in terms of the parameter that specifies the curve moving in the pencil (see Fig. 1).

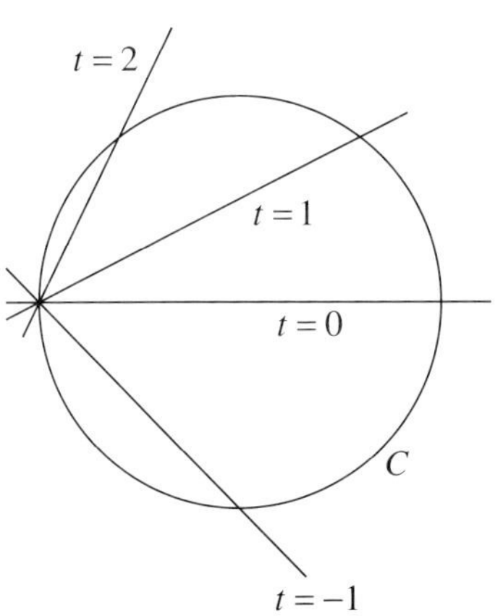

Fig. 1. Parametrization with a pencil

By this approach, we obtain in fact a proper parametrization, and the parameter t can be recovered as the one corresponding to the unique curve in the pencil through the point in question.

We are left with the question of finding a suitable pencil of curves.

For simplicity's sake, we consider only curves without infinitely near singularities and without singularities on the infinite line. The second restriction is not severe. One can always find a line containing no singular point of C. A suitable projective transformation will transform this line to infinity, and then we have no singularities on the infinite line.

The first restriction is indeed a loss of generality. However, the treatment of infinitely near singularities differs just slightly from the treatment of the singularities in the affine plane, and the main ideas are better explained in this simpler case. A good reference for infinitely near singularities is Walker (1950).

Let C be a rational curve, given by its equation $C(x, y) = 0$, where $\deg C = d$. Suppose that there are no infinitely near singularities and no singularities on the infinite line. Then the set of its singular points is the zero set of the algebraic equation system

$$C(x, y) = 0, \qquad \frac{\partial C(x, y)}{\partial x} = 0, \qquad \frac{\partial C(x, y)}{\partial y} = 0.$$

Let B be a formal sum of points on C. We will call this a cycle. We can write

$$B = \sum_{P \in C} m_P P$$

with positive integers m_P. m_P will be zero for all but finitely many points $P \in C$.

Remark. Usually, one does not work with points here, but with places of C. Each regular point corresponds to a place, and an ordinary k-fold point corresponds to different places, one for each branch passing through the point. But since we will in the following treat each branch equally, we can make the above simplification. The reader familiar with the concept of places may replace any point occurring in a cycle by the sum of places centered at that point.

Definition. Let $B = \sum m_P P$ be a cycle on C. The set of all curves of degree $\leq m$ having multiplicity $\geq m_P$ at each point P is called the linear system of curves of degree m associated with B.

A general curve of degree $\leq m$ can be written as

$$H(x, y) = \sum_{i,j=0}^{i+j \leq m} a_{ij} x^i y^j, \qquad a_{ij} \in k.$$

This representation is unique up to multiplication with a constant factor. The property of H having a m_P-fold point $P = (x_0, y_0)$ can be expressed as a set of linear equations in the a_{ij}'s. This justifies the term "linear system": curves in a linear system depend linearly on finitely many parameters.

A linear system depending only on one parameter is called a pencil. Every pencil can be written as

$$H(x, y, t) = H_0(x, y) + tH_1(x, y).$$

If $d \leq m$, the above definition has to be understood modulo C. I.e., curves $H_1(x, y)$, $H_2(x, y)$ that do only differ by a multiple of C are considered as to be the same. Also, the multiplicity at a point P has to be computed modulo C (the highest multiplicity of a curve in an equivalence class modulo C is the multiplicity modulo C of this class). For more details, cf. Schicho (1994).

The number of equations imposed by the demand that P should be an m_P-fold point can be calculated in terms of μ_P and m_P. If $m_P \leq \mu_P$, this number is $\frac{m_P(m_P-1)}{2}$, and the equations can be found by plugging P into all derivatives of a general curve H up to order $m_P - 1$ and setting them equal zero. Otherwise, the number of equations is $\mu_P m_P - \frac{\mu_P(\mu_P-1)}{2}$ (cf. Schicho 1994).

The number of free intersections of the linear system with C can also be estimated in terms of m, d, m_P, μ_P. An upper bound is

$$(*) f = md - \sum m_P \mu_P,$$

where the sum ranges over all terms with $m_P \neq 0$.

The following theorem is proved in Schicho (1994). Given B and m, it allows to decide whether the associated linear system is a suitable pencil for the parametrization. As a corollary, we can compute explicitly such a pencil. The corollary is classically known.

Theorem. Let B be a cycle on C and $m \in \mathbf{Z}^+$. The following are equivalent.
(I) The linear system of curves of degree d associated with B is a pencil intersecting C in one variable point.
(II) The lower bound of free linear parameters in this system computed via the above facts is 1 and the upper bound in $(*)$ is also 1.

Corollary. Let $m := d - 2$ and let B be the cycle given by

$$B = \sum_{P \in Sing} (\mu_P - 1)P + (n-2) \text{ regular points.}$$

Then the associated linear system is a pencil with one free intersection.

The algorithm based on the corollary is often used. The most expensive step is the calculation of the $n-2$ regular points. It is expensive in two ways: First it is time consuming, and secondly in general one has to introduce algebraic numbers at this step. This slows down severely all computations that are performed afterwards. Also, the result becomes less useful.

The power of the above theorem is that it allows to compute pencils having at most one regular point in the base cycle. If d is odd, we need no regular points at all. An algorithm to compute a better pencil can be found in Schicho (1994). Here also the whole parametrization algorithm is described explicitly.

Parametrization algorithms for curves are implemented in various computer algebra systems. For an implementation in Maple, cf. Gebauer et al. (1991).

4 Surfaces

We consider irreducible surfaces over an algebraically closed field k of characteristic 0.

A rough birational classification of surfaces can be obtained by defining numerical birational invariants. Two of them are important to decide rationality of a surface: the arithmetical genus g_a and the bigenus P_2.

There exist algorithms to evaluate these two invariants for a given surface. For the arithmetical genus of smooth surfaces, an algorithm is implemented in the computer algebra system CoCoA. Algorithms for the general case can be found in Schicho (1992).

Theorem. Let S be a surface. The following are equivalent.
(I) S is rational.
(II) S is unirational.
(III) $p_a = P_2 = 0$.

This theorem was proved by Castelnuovo (1893) for smooth surfaces. His proof is constructive, i.e., it contains implicitly an (efficient) algorithm for the parametrization of such surfaces. This is not so with the modern proofs of the theorem.

As we know today, proving the theorem for smooth surfaces means proving it for all surfaces, by the following.

Theorem. Every surface is birationally equivalent to a smooth surface.

The problem of finding a smooth variety equivalent to a given one is called the resolution of singularities. For surfaces, the solution is due to Walker (1935). Hironaka (1964) proved the existence of a resolution of singularities for arbitrary dimensional varieties in characteristic 0.

This author (Schicho 1994) designed an algorithm for the parametrization of surfaces. This algorithm has two main ingredients: an algorithm for the resolution of singularities and Castelnuovo's algorithm for the parametrization of smooth surfaces.

Obviously, the concatenation of these two algorithms would be an algorithm for surface parametrization. Nevertheless, it turns out that it is possible to do some shortcuts here. For instance, it is not necessary to resolve so-called ADE-singularities (these singularities can be classified with the Coxeter–Dynkin diagrams A_n, D_n, E_n).

To give a flavour of this algorithm, we treat here the case of cubic surfaces in $\mathbf{P}^3$. We state most results without proof. For the proofs, we refer to Schicho (1992).

Theorem. A cubic surface is rational, unless it is the cone over an elliptic cubic curve.

The singularities of a cubic surface S are either 2-fold or 3-fold. If S has a triple point P, it is unique and S is the cone over a cubic curve with vertex P. The cubic curve can be rational or elliptic. In the first case, S will have a double line through P. In the second case, P will be the only singularity.

If S does not have a triple point, it can either have a double line or a finite number of ADE-singularities (double points) or be smooth.

This shows, whenever we have a rational non-smooth cubic surface, we can find a double point on it. Projection from the double point then gives a birational map onto $\mathbf{P}^2$.

Every smooth surface contains 27 lines forming a famous configuration. Two skew lines out of these can be used for a parametrization: Each of two parameters specifies a point on one line. Draw a line through these two points and intersect it with S. One gets one point of intersection, depending rationally on the parameters (cf. Fig. 2).

These ideas combine to the following algorithm.

Algorithm CUBPAR
Input: $S(x_0, x_1, x_2, x_3)$, an irreducible form of degree 3.
Output: Three rational functions $\xi(s,t), \eta(s,t), \zeta(s,t)$ such that $(1 : \xi : \eta : \zeta)$ is a general solution to S, or a string "not rational surface."

1. Compute the singularities and their multiplicity.
2. If S has a double point
   then
      choose a double point P,
      let (s, t) parametrize the lines through P,
      compute the intersection point with S in terms of s and t.
3. Else if S has a triple point
      then
         return "not rational surface."
4. Else
         find two lines g, h in S,
         let $g(s)$ be a parametric representation for g,
         let $h(t)$ be a parametric representation for h,
         compute the intersection of the line through $g(s)$ and $h(t)$ with S in terms of s and t.

Remark. A similar method as the one in step 4 can be applied in the case of surfaces of degree 5 having two double lines, or of surfaces of degree 4 having a double line, since one can find a conic in the second case.

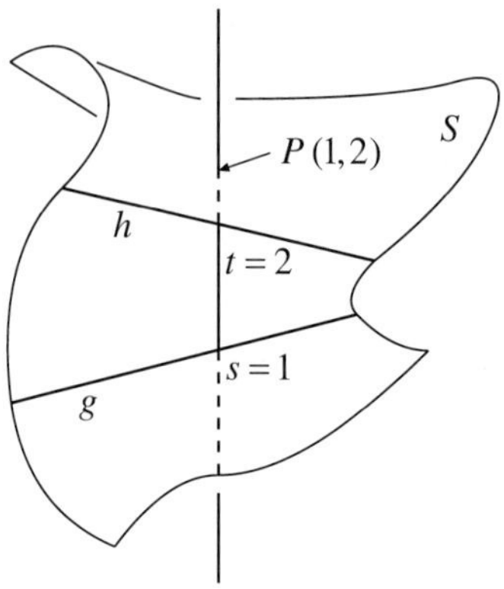

Fig. 2. Using two lines on a cubic surface

This algorithm always computes a proper parametrization. This is clear in the case where you project from a double point. In the smooth case, this follows from the following fact.

Proposition. A point in $\mathbf{P}^3$ lies on a unique line meeting given skew lines, unless it lies on either of the two given lines.

This can be easily seen by considering the projection from the point.

5 Higher dimensional varieties

For dimension ≥ 3, the problem of finding a proper parametrization is essentially harder than the problem of finding a parametrization. Given a parametric representation of a variety, the problem of finding a proper parametrization is called the Lüroth problem. The Lüroth problem is solvable for a class of varieties iff the implication

$$\text{unirational} \rightarrow \text{rational}$$

holds in this class.

For curves, the implication was proved by Lüroth (cf. also Sect. 2). For surfaces, the implication was proved by Castelnuovo (cf. Sect. 3). (For surfaces, the assumption $\operatorname{char} k = 0$ is essential.) Much later, Iskovskih and Manin (1971) gave counterexamples for the implication in the 3-dimensional case.

It would be useful to have parametrization algorithms for unirational varieties of dimension 3, 4, also. However, one important application field – graphics – does not take place: We cannot hope to picture nicely three-dimensional curved objects.

References

Castelnuovo, G. (1937): Sulle superficie di genere zero (1893). In: Castelnuovo, G.: Memorie scelte. Zanichelli, Bologna.

Clebsch, A. (1991): Über die Abbildung algebraischer Flächen, insbesondere der vierten und fünften Ordnung. Math. Ann. 1: 253–316.

Gebauer, R., Kalkbrener, M., Wall, B., Winkler, F. (1991): CASA: a computer algebra package for constructive algebraic geometry. In: Watt, S. (ed.): Proc. ISSAC '91, Bonn, Germany, 1991, pp. 403–410.

Hironaka, H. (1964): Resolution of singularities of an algebraic variety over a field of characteristic zero I, II. Ann. Math. 79: 187–326.

Iskovskih, J.-I., Manin, Y. (1971): Three-dimensional quartics and counterexamples to the Lüroth problem. Mat. Sb. 15: 141–166.

Kalkbrener, M. (1991): Three contributions to elimination theory. Ph. D. thesis, University of Linz, Linz, Austria.

Ocken, S., Schwartz, J. T., Sharir, M. (1987): Precise implementation of CAD primitives using rational parametrizations of standard surfaces. In: Schwartz, T., et al. (eds.): Planning, geometry, and complexity of robot motion. Ablex, Norwood, pp. 245–266.

Schicho, J. (1992): On the choice of pencils in the parametrization of curves. J. Symb. Comput. 14: 557–576.

Schicho, J. (1994): An algorithm for the parametrization of rational surfaces. Ph. D. thesis, University of Linz, Linz, Austria.

Shafarevich, I. R. (1974): Basic algebraic geometry. Springer, Berlin Heidelberg New York.

Walker, R. (1935): Reduction of singularities of an algebraic surface. Ann. Math. 36: 336–365.

Walker, R. (1950): Algebraic curves. Springer, Berlin Göttingen Heidelberg.

Towards a categorical calculus for critical-pair/completion

Karel Stokkermans

1 Introduction

The ultimate aim of the research reported here is to provide a general framework for algorithms that show the following two characteristics: critical pairs and completion. Here completion means extending a certain set of reductions (given by, e.g., rewrite rules, or polynomials from an ideal) until that set fulfills some completeness property. Critical pairs are used for the selection of elements for which the reduction relation to be completed is not yet confluent. The selection is essentially done by superposing left hand sides of basic reduction rules, and testing whether applying the applicable reduction rules yield the same reducts. If not, one forces confluence by adding a reduction rule between the differing reducts (if possible without violating certain conditions on the reduction relation).

The prime examples of such algorithms are:

- The *Gröbner basis algorithm* in polynomial ideal theory. Its main object is to construct (by a terminating algorithm) a finite basis for an ideal. This construction has the characteristics of a normal form procedure (i.e., all polynomials can be reduced to a normal form by means of the constructed finite basis). Formally, the algorithm completes a given (finite) set F of multivariate polynomials over a field K. From the completed set G one can form the set A of (the residue classes of) all power products that are not multiples of leading power products of polynomials in G. This A then serves as a linearly independent generating set (basis) for the associative algebra $K[x_1, \ldots, x_n]/\,\mathrm{Ideal}(F)$, where $\mathrm{Ideal}(F)$ is the ideal generated by F. In the univariate case, the Gröbner basis algorithm turns out to generalize Euclid's algorithm for finding the greatest common divisor of two or more polynomials.
- The *Knuth–Bendix algorithm*. This algorithm completes a given (finite) set F of equations between two first order terms, i.e., words composed of variables and operators. From the completed set G we can determine whether a given identity $s = t$ can be derived from the original set F. Namely, such a derivation exists if and only if the normal forms (with respect to the completed set G) of the two terms are identical. However, this completion algorithm does not always terminate.

For both algorithms, algorithmic specifications are given in Sect. 2.

In the ESPRIT BRA 3125, MEDLAR, some subtasks included research on the connections between the Gröbner basis algorithm and the Knuth–Bendix algorithm, specifically tasks γ 1.6 and 2.3 (cf. MEDLAR Consortium 1989). In the past, several attempts have been undertaken to incorporate the Gröbner basis algorithm as a subprocedure of the Knuth–Bendix algorithm. The research presented here concentrates on finding a (category theoretic) framework for all critical-pair/completion procedures. Such a framework would provide more insight in the common features of and essential differences between the procedures.

The paper starts with an overview of the critical-pair/completion algorithms we are dealing with (Sect. 2), and an explanation of the axiomatic framework for dealing with critical-pair/completion (CPC)-algorithms as suggested in Buchberger (1985b) (Sect. 3). Then, the basic categorical notions used in this paper are defined (Sect. 4), followed by the introduction of a variant of the well-established categorical notion of limit, which has proved useful for modeling normal forms and confluence, notions naturally arising in the study of CPC-procedures (Sect. 5). For lack of a more appropriate name, this notion is here called reversed limit as it is obtained from reversing the universal arrow in the limit diagram. By duality, reversed colimits are introduced. As will be shown, one can give an elegant definition of this notion within the categories of cones (respectively cocones) of a given diagram. The paper is concluded by the construction and discussion of our categorical model for CPC-procedures (Sect. 6), in which we find an application for the reversed limit notion.

Part of the paper, namely the discussion of the CPC-procedures, the axiomatic framework and the categorical model, has appeared in shortened form (Stokkermans 1992). Here, apart from the introduction to the elementary notions of category theory and the elaboration of the variant of the limit notion as well as its applications to modeling CPC-procedures, some literature references are added, and in general we have taken this opportunity for revision.

This work, which is currently being continued, is closely linked to the work on the mathematical foundations of the general framework in ESPRIT BRA 6471, MEDLAR II, which is a continuation of the MEDLAR project.

2 Overview of CPC-procedures

This section consists of algorithmic specifications for the two CPC-algorithms discussed here and a general algorithmical framework for such procedures. What the completion (of the set of reduction rules, such that confluence can be guaranteed) consists of in these procedures should be clear from the algorithmic descriptions below. For the (general) concept of critical pairs we give a short intuitive and graphical explanation, which should enable the reader to understand how the critical pairs are built in the individual algorithms. A precise definition will follow in Sect. 3.

In general, a critical pair is constructed from two reduction rules p_1: $l_1 \to r_1$ and p_2: $l_2 \to r_2$. One looks for a "most general common instance" for the left hand sides of the two rules, say L, and then reduces L according to both rules, obtaining $p_1(L)$ and $p_2(L)$ respectively as reducts. These two reducts form a critical pair. They are equivalent with respect to the equivalence relation induced by the reduction relation. Hence, to obtain a unique normal form NF(L) for L, they should either *be* equal, or *be made* equal, which is enforced by adding a new reduction rule.

Pictorially,

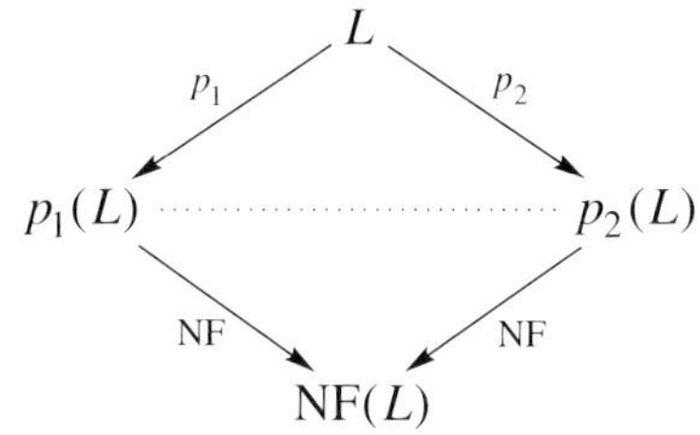

where the NF arrows correspond to the simplification algorithm that will serve as the normal form algorithm for the completed system in which confluence and termination are guaranteed.

Some references to introductory texts on the algorithms are given, more information about the relations between (extended versions of) CPC-algorithms mentioned above can be found in Buchberger (1985b) and Stokkermans (1991).

2.1 The Knuth–Bendix procedure

The Knuth–Bendix procedure was developed in Knuth and Bendix (1967). Good introductions to the Knuth–Bendix procedure and its applications are Dershowitz (1983) and Klop and Middeldorp (1988).

We present a simple version of the Knuth–Bendix algorithm, cf. Klop (1990). In this algorithm, a critical pair is generated from a most general superposition situation (cf. Sect. 3) between the left hand sides of two rewrite rules.

Algorithm.
Input: An equational specification (Σ, E), and a reduction ordering $>$ on Ter(Σ) (i.e., a program that computes $>$).
Output: A complete TRS R such that for all $s, t \in \text{Ter}(\Sigma)$: $s =_R t \Leftrightarrow (\Sigma, E) \vdash s = t$.

```
R := ∅
while E ≠ ∅ do
  choose an equation s = t ∈ E;
  reduce s and t to respective normal forms s′ and t′ with respect to R;
  if s′ ≡ t′
    then E := E − {s = t}
  else
    if s′ = t′
      then α := s′; β := t′
    else
      if t′ > s′
```

```
        then α := t′;  β := s′
      else
      failure
    fi;
    CP := {P = Q | (P, Q) is a critical pair between the rules in R and
    α → β};
    R := R ∪ {α → β};
    E := E ∪ CP − {s = t}
  fi
od;
success
```

2.2 The Gröbner basis algorithm

Easy introductions to the algorithm for computing Gröbner bases are given in, among others, Becker and Weispfenning (1993), Buchberger (1985a), and Cox et al. (1992).

The following description is taken from Buchberger (1985a). The critical pairs in this algorithm arise from unifying two polynomials in the given basis by taking the least common multiple of their leading monomials, and taking the difference the polynomials constructed by the corresponding multiplications (this is the *S*Polynomial in the algorithm below).

Definition 1. F is called a *Gröbner basis* if and only if for all g, h_1, h_2 in a given polynomial ring $K[x_1, \ldots, x_n]$: if h_1 and h_2 are normal forms of g modulo F then $h_1 = h_2$.

Algorithm.
Input: A finite subset F of the polynomial ring $K[x_1, \ldots, x_n]$.
Output: A finite subset G of the polynomial ring $K[x_1, \ldots, x_n]$, such that $\text{Ideal}(F) = \text{Ideal}(G)$ and G is a Gröbner basis.

```
G := F;
CP := {(f1, f2)|f1, f2 ∈ G, f1 ≠ f2};
while CP ≠ ∅ do
  (f1, f2) := a pair in CP;
  CP := CP − {(f1, f2)};
  h := SPolynomial(f1, f2);
  h′ := the normal form of h modulo G;
  if h′ ≠ 0
  then
    CP := CP ∪ {(g, h′)|g ∈ G};
    G := G ∪ {h′}
  fi
od
```

2.3 The CPC frame algorithm

We now give a framework for all CPC-procedures (which will also incorporate the resolution algorithm, but treatment of that is postponed to a later paper). How to fit the individual procedures into it should be clear from the algorithmic skeletons given above. The set G is the set generated during the completion of the set of original patterns (cf. Sect. 3) P. The set CP keeps track of all critical pairs still to be considered. The set $cp(f, g)$ denotes all critical pairs between the patterns f and g, the set $cp(f, G)$ all critical pairs arising from computing $cp(f, g)$ for all $g \in G$.

Algorithm.
Input: A set P of patterns in a universe T and an ordering $>$ on T.
Output: An extended set of patterns such that the reduction relation induced by the patterns allows a canonical normal form algorithm.

```
G := P;
CP := ⋃_{f,g∈G} cp(f, g);
while CP ≠ ∅ do
   (s, t) := an element in CP;
   CP := CP − {(s, t)};
   (s, t) := (Sim(s), Sim(t));
   if s ≠ t
   then
      analyze(s, t);
      l := left hand side of rule to be added;
      r := right hand side of rule to be added;
      h := (l, r);
      CP := CP ∪ ⋃ cp(h, G);
      G := G ∪ {h}.
   fi
od
```

`Sim` is a simplification algorithm, computing (weak) normal forms of elements of the universe T with respect to the reduction relation generated by the patterns in P (and any additional patterns added during the algorithm). In the subalgorithm `analyze` the procedure tests whether a reduction from `Sim`(s) to `Sim`(t) or vice versa can be added without violating the noetherianity of the reduction relation.

3 An axiomatic framework

The objective of this work is to capture the notions suggested in Buchberger (1985b) for an axiomatic treatment of CPC-procedures in a categorical framework. This section introduces these notions, namely *pattern*, *multiplier*, and *place*. They will be rephrased categorically in Sect. 6.

Given are a set T of objects and a binary reduction relation $\rightarrow$ on T that is generated by a set F of (finitely) many *patterns* F.

To be solved are *word problems* of the kind:

$$\text{“for } s, t \in T\text{:}$$

$$\text{is } (s, t) \text{ in the reflexive, symmetric, transitive closure of } \rightarrow \text{?”}$$

or problems that can be reduced to such problems.

Patterns are the basic reductions that define $\rightarrow$. We define the set of patterns F by the *pattern rule*:

$$\text{for all } s, t \in T\text{:} \quad \text{if } (s, t) \in F \text{ then } s \rightarrow t.$$

Multipliers are the substitutions or operations that can be applied to objects in T and produce objects in T. We write Σ for the (infinite) set of multipliers. For the application of substitutions to patterns we have the *multiplier rule*:

$$\text{for all } s, t \in T, \sigma \in \Sigma\text{:} \quad \text{if } (s, t) \in F \text{ then } \sigma s \rightarrow \sigma t.$$

Then, in objects of T there is a concept of *places*. We write P for the set of possible places in objects and r/u for the object placed at place u in object r. Then a *replacement* is denoted by $r[u \leftarrow t]$ (the object produced by replacing the subobject placed at place u in r by the object t). The *replacement rule* now runs as follows:

$$\text{for all } r, s, t \in T, \sigma \in \Sigma, u \in P\text{:}$$

$$\text{if } (s, t) \in F \text{ and } r/u = \sigma s \text{ then } r \rightarrow r[u \leftarrow \sigma t].$$

The above notions will be formalized, and from them the basic notions for CPC-procedures are defined.

In general, CPC-procedures deal with a structure $(T, >, \rightarrow_P, M, E)$. Below, we describe the components of this quintuple, and give their basic properties.

3.1 The fundamental concepts

The universe T

The universe T describes the domain from which the elements to which we will apply the CPC-procedure are taken. For the Knuth–Bendix algorithm the elements of T are the terms in the term algebra $\mathrm{Ter}(\Sigma)$, for a given signature Σ. In the Gröbner basis algorithm T consists of the polynomials in $K[x_1, \ldots, x_n]$.

Places

To identify subobjects of a given object from the universe T, on which a specific reduction pattern (cf. the discussion of the pattern set below) can be applied we have to define a concept of *places* on the elements of T (cf. Buchberger 1985b). Thus we obtain a labeling by natural numbers of the positions within objects.

In the case of Knuth–Bendix completion, the places are the positions where the subterms can occur, coded by a chain of positive natural numbers describing the path from the outermost symbol (at the root position) to the head of the subterm under consideration (Dewey notation). It is trivial to check that the conditions on places set out below are fulfilled (cf. Huet 1980).

In the Gröbner basis algorithm the places are the positions where terms can be added, i.e., they are coded by the power products less than or equal to the leading power product of the polynomial in question.

The set of places within a term t is denoted by $P(t)$. The subterm occurring at place p of term t is denoted by $t|_p$, and the result of replacing this subterm by another term s is denoted by $t[s]_p$. The set of all terms u that are the same as t except at place p, i.e., all terms u such that for some term s, $u[s]_p = t$, is called the *context* of the replacement. This set of terms is denoted by $u[\_]_p$.

Furthermore, we will use the convention that the root position of a term t (coding the whole term itself as its subterm) is denoted by the place $p = 0$. So, $t[s]_0$ denotes the replacement of the term t by the term s (and $t[s]_0 = s$).

The following axiomatic restrictions apply for the concept of places.

For any term $t \in U$, $P(t)$ is a set of chains of positive natural numbers fulfilling the following conditions:

(pl-1) $$\langle k_1 k_2 \ldots k_{n-1} k_n\rangle \in P(t)(n \geq 1) \Rightarrow \langle k_1 k_2 \ldots k_{n-1}\rangle \in P(t);$$

(pl-2) $$\langle k_1 k_2 \ldots k_{n-1} k_n\rangle \in P(t)(n \geq 1) \Rightarrow \\ \Rightarrow (\forall 1 \leq k < k_n)\langle k_1 k_2 \ldots k_{n-1} k\rangle \in P(t).$$

The first condition guarantees that all nodes on the path to a given node exist and represent some subobject, the second that on any given level the labeling does not "skip" numbers.

To illustrate the definition, consider the term $t = f(x, h(y, z), g(y))$. Then $t|_{\langle\rangle} = t|_0 = t$, $t|_1 = x$, $t|_2 = h(y, z)$, $t|_{21} = y$, $t|_{22} = z$, $t|_3 = g(y)$, and $t|_{31} = y$.

The *place operator* $|_{\langle k_1 \ldots k_n\rangle}$, which for any object $t \in U$ returns the subobject occurring at the given place, fulfills the following associativity axiom:

(pl-3) $$t|_{\langle k_1 k_2 \ldots k_n\rangle} = (t|_{\langle k_1\rangle})|_{\langle k_2 \ldots k_n\rangle}.$$

Ordering on T

The universe T must be equipped with an ordering, either partial or total. This ordering will serve to guarantee that in the course of the algorithm the terms generated decrease in complexity. This is necessary for proving termination.

In the Knuth–Bendix case, the reduction ordering $<$ on $\mathrm{Ter}(\Sigma)$ is given in advance as a parameter to the completion procedure. Note that a different ordering may influence the outcome of the completion. In this case the ordering normally is partial, which means termination is not guaranteed.

In the case of the Gröbner basis algorithm, we stipulate that the ordering (inferred from a total ordering on the power products) is total. In fact, we require one more property, related to the reduction, to obtain the concept of *admissible orderings*, see, e.g., Buchberger (1983). A common choice is the total degree ordering.

We will demand noetherianity of the ordering, bearing in mind the algorithmic context we are dealing with.

(o-noe) There is no infinite chain $x_1 > x_2 > x_3 > \ldots > x_n > x_{n+1} > \ldots$

The pattern set P and the generated reduction relation $\rightarrow_P \subset T \times T$
In the terminology of Buchberger (1985b), we have a set of *patterns* that generate the reduction relation. For the Knuth–Bendix algorithm, the patterns are derived from the equations in E respecting the ordering relation: if $s = t \in E$ then if $s > t$ we have the pattern $s \rightarrow_P t$, and if $t > s$ we have the pattern $t \rightarrow_P s$. In the Gröbner basis algorithm the patterns are formed from the elements of F as follows. If f is some polynomial in F, we have the pattern $LM(f) \rightarrow_P LM(f) - f$, where $LM(f)$ is the leading monomial of f.

For practical applications, the set P of all pairs (l, r) such that $l \rightarrow_P r$ is finite (this corresponds to a finite number of generators for an ideal in the Gröbner basis algorithm and a finite number of rewrite rules in Knuth–Bendix).

In order to be a true *reduction* relation, $\rightarrow_P$ has to fulfill the following property:

(p-red) $$x \rightarrow_P y \Rightarrow x > y.$$

The transitive closure of $\rightarrow_P$ will be denoted by $\rightarrow_P^+$, its transitive and reflexive closure by $\rightarrow_P^*$. From the noetherianity of the ordering and (p-red) we obtain noetherianity of the reduction relation $\rightarrow_P^+$.

There is no infinite chain $x_1 \rightarrow_P x_2 \rightarrow_P x_3 \rightarrow_P \ldots \rightarrow_P x_n \rightarrow_P x_{n+1} \rightarrow_P \ldots$
(p-noe)

The multiplying operation
In CPC-algorithms, we have a concept of *multiplier*, which essentially expresses substituting on an atomic term, that can later be incorporated into a composite term by a replacement (see below).

In the Knuth–Bendix algorithm the multipliers correspond to all variable substitutions on the terms (defined on the variables and extended to the whole signature; the composition of two substitutions is defined by their combined effect on the variables). In the Gröbner basis algorithm the multipliers correspond to all multiplications by monomials (which includes coefficients, monomials with an empty power product).

Definition 2. We define $M = \{\mu\colon T \rightarrow T\}$ as the set of all *multipliers*. Below, μ and its subscribed versions will denote multipliers.

We stipulate that M contains the identity operation and preserves the ordering, (mul-1), (mul-2). We also demand that the composition of two multipliers is again a multiplier, (mul-3). Furthermore, we demand that the multipliers behave properly with respect to the identity operation and that they are associative, (mul-4), (mul-5). Two more technical conditions are added and explained below.

(mul-1) $\mathrm{id}_T \in M$;

(mul-2) $x > y \Rightarrow (\forall \mu)\, \mu x > \mu y$;

(mul-3) $\mu, \nu \in M \Rightarrow \mu \circ \nu \in M$;

(mul-4) $\mu \in M \Rightarrow \mu \circ \mathrm{id}_T = \mu = \mathrm{id}_T \circ \mu$;

(mul-5) $\mu, \nu, \pi \in M \Rightarrow \mu \circ (\nu \circ \pi) = (\mu \circ \nu) \circ \pi$;

(mul-6) $s := \mu_{u,v}(t) \Rightarrow (t|_{\langle k_1 \ldots k_n \rangle} = v \Rightarrow s|_{\langle k_1 \ldots k_n \rangle} = u)$;

(mul-7) $\forall p\colon l \to r \;\; \forall \mu_1, \mu_2\colon \;\; \mu_1(l) = \mu_2(l) \Rightarrow \mu_1(r) = \mu_2(r)$.

Condition (mul-6) ensures that the result of multiplying a subterm at an arbitrary place within the multiplied term gives the correct result at that place. This also implies that the set of places of the term formed by the multiplier is defined correctly, more specifically: $P(s) = P(t) \cup \{\langle k_1 \ldots k_n l_1 \ldots l_m \rangle | \langle l_1 \ldots l_m \rangle \in P(u)\}$.

Condition (mul-7) guarantees that any two multipliers that have the same effect on the left hand side of a pattern also have the same effect on the right hand side ((mul-7) would for instance follow from the condition that the right hand side does not contain any free variables not occurring in the left hand side).

The operation of embedding
Having given a concept of places within an object, we now define an operation on objects which enables us to isolate subobjects (which may then be reduced by a pattern from the pattern set P).

In the case of Gröbner bases, the operations in question (embedders) are only used for the definition of the generalized reduction relation $\to_G$, they are not important for the determination of critical pairs.

For every context $u[\_]_p$ we define a function on T that embeds a term t at the empty place in the context.

Definition 3. $\eta_{up}\colon T \to T$ is defined by

$$\eta_{up}(t) := u[t]_p.$$

If $p \notin P(u)$ then $\eta_{up}(t) := u$. We also define the set of all embedding functions:

$$E = \{\eta_{up} \mid u \in T,\;\; p \in P(u)\}.$$

Elements of E will be called *embedders*. Below, η and appropriately subscribed versions will denote embedders.

E contains the identity operation on T (namely embedding in an empty context), and the embedders η in E should preserve the order. Furthermore, we demand that embedding a term t at a given place and then extracting that subterm with the place operator should return t again, (emb-3). Finally, we regulate the interplay between embedders and multipliers by stipulating that multiplying the result of an embedding yields the same object as first applying the same multiplier simultaneously to the embedded subobject and the context and subsequently embedding the multiplied subobject into the multiplied context, (emb-4).

(emb-1) $\quad \mathrm{id}_T \in E;$

(emb-2) $\quad x > y \Rightarrow (\forall\eta)\eta x > \eta y;$

(emb-3) $\quad \forall t\colon\ \eta_{u,\langle k_1 \ldots k_n\rangle}(t)|_{\langle k_1 \ldots k_n\rangle} = t;$

(emb-4) $\quad \forall\eta, \mu\colon\ \eta_{\mu(a),\langle k_1 \ldots k_n\rangle}(\mu(b)) = \mu(\eta_{a,k_1 \ldots k_n}(b)).$

The extended reduction relation $\rightarrow_G$
We proceed to define an extension of the reduction relation $\rightarrow_P$.

First we define by M and E a relation G expressing that the second object is more general than the first.

Definition 4. $(x, y) \in G$ if and only if $(\exists\mu \in M \exists\eta \in E)\ y = \eta(\mu(x))$.

In the context of reduction, $(x, y) \in G$ means that if x can be reduced by a pattern $p \in P$, then the same pattern p can be used to reduce y. In addition, if the reduct of x under p is $p(x)$, then the reduct $p(y)$ of y under p is equal to $\eta(\mu(p(x))$, for the η and μ for which $y = \eta(\mu(x))$. This is expressed by the following definition of the extended reduction relation $\rightarrow_G$.

Definition 5. $\rightarrow_G$ will denote the reduction relation generated by $\rightarrow_P$ and the following two rules:

(gen-1) $\quad x \rightarrow_G y \Rightarrow (\forall\mu)\mu x \rightarrow_G \mu y;$

(gen-2) $\quad x \rightarrow_G y \Rightarrow (\forall\eta)\eta x \rightarrow_G \eta y.$

The two rules (gen-1) and (gen-2) correspond to the *multiplier* and *replacement rules* in Buchberger (1985b), or the *fully invariant property* and *replacement property* in Dershowitz and Jouannaud (1990), respectively. In the case of Gröbner bases the generated reduction relation is not compatible with embedding (so (gen-2) would not hold), only *semi-compatible* (cf. Buchberger and Loos 1982), i.e., that if $x \rightarrow_G y$ then ηx and ηy have a common normal form. Considering the completion of the reduction relation modulo a noetherian confluent and stable simplification relation (cf. Kandri-Rody et al. 1989) would take care of this problem. It would also enable to consider rewriting modulo certain equivalence relations – but this will be part of later work.

Lemma 6.

(g-red) $$x \to_G y \Rightarrow x > y.$$

Proof. The lemma is easily proved by induction on the number of multipliers and embedders (i.e., generalizing steps) involving x and y.

For the base case, if $x \to_P y$, then by (p-red) $x > y$. Otherwise, either 1 or 2 below holds.

1. There exists a μ in M and x', y' in T such that $x = \mu x'$, $y = \mu y'$, and $x' \to_G y'$. Then by induction $x' > y'$, and by (mul-2) $x > y$.
2. There exists an η in E and x', y' in T such that $x = \eta x'$, $y = \eta y'$, and $x' \to_G y'$. Then by induction $x' > y'$, and by (emb-2) $x > y$. □

Definition 7. The transitive closure of $\to_G$ is denoted by $\to_G^+$, its transitive and reflexive closure by $\to_G^*$.

Lemma 8. The transitive closure of $\to_G$ is noetherian.

There is no infinite chain $x_1 \to_G^+ x_2 \to_G^+ x_3 \to_G^+ \ldots \to_G^+ x_n \to_G^+ x_{n+1} \to_G^+ \cdots$
(g-noe)

Proof. Directly from (p-noe) and the fact that only finite numbers of (non-identity) multiplying and embedding steps are carried out between subsequent applications of $\to_P$. □

The quintuple $(T, >, \to_P, M, E)$ will be used in our definition of the basic category CPC in Sect. 6.1.

3.2 Derived basic notions

We define the basic concepts of CPC-procedures within the framework $(T, >, \to_P, M, E)$.

Weak normal form

A weak normal form for $x \in T$ is a $y \in T$ such that $x \to_G^* y$ and it is not possible to reduce y any further. The weakness expresses that uniqueness is not guaranteed. In other words, y is a minimal element with respect to $\to_G^*$. Formally:

(wnf) $$\mathrm{WNF}(x, y) \text{ if and only if } x \to_G^* y \wedge \neg(\exists z)\, y \to_G z.$$

Normal form

The normal form of $x \in T$ is a $y \in T$ such that y is a weak normal form for x

and uniquely determined. Formally:

(nf) $y = \mathrm{NF}(x)$ if and only if $\mathrm{WNF}(x, y) \wedge [(\forall z)\, \mathrm{WNF}(x, z) \Rightarrow z = y]$.

We will denote the normal form of an element of the universe $t \in T$ by $\underline{t}$.

Termination condition
The completion of the set of patterns P is finished when all terms have a (unique) normal form. We therefore have the termination condition:

(tc) $$(\forall t \in T \exists \underline{t} \in T)\, \underline{t} = \mathrm{NF}(t).$$

Completion step
Completion is the creation of a set of generating arrows such that for all objects (any) normal form algorithm yields a (unique) normal form. A single completion step consists of adding, if necessary and possible, one new reduction pattern. Below an algorithmic description of the completion step is given. (It is a further specification of the analysis step in the CPC frame algorithm.)

Precondition: $(\exists x)\, \mathrm{WNF}(x, x_1) \wedge \mathrm{WNF}(x, x_2) \wedge x_1 \neq x_2$.
Action: if $x_1 > x_2$ then $\rightarrow_P := \rightarrow_P \cup \{(x_1, x_2)\}$
elif $x_2 > x_1$ then $\rightarrow_P := \rightarrow_P \cup \{(x_2, x_1)\}$
elif *failure*.
Continue with the extended relation $\rightarrow_P$.

Most general unifier and superposition situation
In order to find critical pairs, a CPC-algorithm computes most general superposition situations between two patterns (in fact, the same pattern may be used to be superposed on itself). Such situations occur when there are two multipliers μ_1, μ_2 such that, for some patterns p_1: $l_1 \rightarrow_P r_1$, p_2: $l_2 \rightarrow_P r_2$, $\mu_2(l_2)$ occurs as a subterm in $\mu_1(l_1)$. To capture the *most general* demand, we insist that if two other multipliers (μ_3, μ_4) can be found such that $\mu_4(l_2)$ occurs as a subterm in $\mu_3(l_1)$ *at the same place* u, we can find a multiplier exposing (μ_3, μ_4) as a special instance for (μ_1, μ_2). (Note that multipliers do not change the arrangement of places of subterms within a term (mul-6).) Formally, we have the following definition.

Definition 9. A *most general superposition situation* for two patterns $p_1 = l_1 \rightarrow_P r_1$ and $p_2 = l_2 \rightarrow_P r_2$ is a quadruple (μ_1, μ_2, η, u) such that: $\mu_1 l_1 = \eta_{\mu_1(l_1),u}(\mu_2(l_2))$, and for all (μ_3, μ_4) such that $\mu_3 l_1 = \eta_{\mu_3(l_1),u}(\mu_4(l_2))$ there exists a μ_5 such that $\mu_3(l_1) = \mu_5(\mu_1(l_1))$ and $\mu_4(l_2) = \mu_5(\mu_2(l_2))$.

In the case of the Gröbner basis algorithm, the embedder η is always taken to be the identity embedder $\eta_{\mu_1(l_1),0}$, at the root position 0 of the term $\mu_1(l_1)$, so that $\mu_1(l_1) = \mu_2(l_2)$. This yields the simpler concept of *most general unifier*.

Definition 10. A *most general unifier* for two patterns $p_1 = l_1 \rightarrow_P r_1$ and $p_2 =$

$l_2 \to_P r_2$ is a pair of multipliers (μ_1, μ_2) such that: $\mu_1(l_1) = \mu_2(l_2)$ and for all (μ_3, μ_4) such that $\mu_3(l_1) = \mu_4(l_2)$ there exists a μ_5 such that $\mu_3(l_1) = \mu_5(\mu_1(l_1))$ (and therefore $\mu_4(l_2) = \mu_5(\mu_2(l_2))$).

Note that most general unifiers need not be unique. A most general unifier will correspond to a weak coproduct in categorical terms (cf. Lemma 44).

Critical pair
From most general superposition situations we can compute critical pairs, which play an essential role in bringing down the complexity of CPC-procedures.

A critical pair is computed by reducing the most general superposition situation for two patterns by these patterns. The two terms obtained form the critical pair. The pattern to be added in the completion step is then established by reducing the critical pair to (weak) normal forms.

Deviating from ordinary terminology, we will find it convenient to refer to the unreduced critical pair as *provisional critical pair*, and to the reduced forms used for computing the new pattern as *critical pair*.

Consequently, we get the following definition.

Definition 11. A *critical pair* for two patterns $p_1 = l_1 \to_P r_1$ and $p_2 = l_2 \to_P r_2$ is a pair of objects $(\underline{s}, \underline{t}) \in T \times T$ such that $s = \mu_1 r_1$ and $t = \eta_{\mu_1(l_1),u}(\mu_2(r_2))$ is a most general superposition situation for the two patterns, and $\underline{s}$ and $\underline{t}$ are (weak) normal forms of s and t, respectively. The pair of objects (s, t) will be called *provisional critical pair*.

Two examples: For the Knuth–Bendix case, suppose we have two patterns (rewrite rules) $p_1 = a.(b.c) \to (a.b).c$ and $p_2 = a.a^{-1} \to e$. Then we have $l_1 = a.(b.c)$, $r_1 = (a.b).c$, $l_2 = a.a^{-1}$, $r_2 = e$, $\mu_1 = b^{-1}/c$ (read: b^{-1} substituted for c), $\mu_2 = b/a$, $s = (a.b).b^{-1}$, $u = 2$, $t = \eta_{a.(b.b^{-1}),2}(e) = a.e$, and, in the presence of a third pattern $p_3 = a.e \to a$, $\underline{t} = a$, whereas s cannot be reduced any further. So the critical pair is $((a.b).b^{-1}, a)$.

For Gröbner bases, take two polynomials $p_1 = xy - x^2$ and $p_2 = y^2 - x$. With lexicographic ordering we obtain as respective left and right hand sides $l_1 = xy$, $r_1 = x^2$, $l_2 = y^2$, $r_2 = x$, $\mu_1 = y$ (read: multiplying by y), $\mu_2 = x$, $s = x^2y$, $u = 1$, $t = \eta_{xy^2,1}(x^2) = x^2$ (note that the embedder is always the identity operator in the case of Gröbner bases), and, because of p_1, $\underline{s} = x^3$. We can't reduce t further, so the critical pair is (x^3, x^2).

4 A little category theory

In order to make the paper self-contained, this section introduces the notions from category theory that we will need in the development of our categorical model for CPC-procedures.

Most of the definitions below are taken from Goldblatt (1984). We also refer to Lambek and Scott (1986) and MacLane (1971) for more background material.

Definition 12. A *category* $\mathtt{C}$ consists of:

1. A collection of things called $\mathtt{C}$-*objects*. These will be denoted by capitals $A, B, C, D, \ldots$ below.
2. A collection of things called $\mathtt{C}$-*morphisms*. These will be denoted by f, g, $h, \ldots$ below. We will take the terms *morphism* and *arrow* to mean the same thing.
3. Operations *dom* and *cod* assigning to each $\mathtt{C}$-morphism f a $\mathtt{C}$-object $\mathrm{dom}(f)$ and a $\mathtt{C}$-object $\mathrm{cod}(f)$. We will use the notation $\mathtt{C}(C, D)$ for the collection of all morphisms between two objects C and D.
4. An operation assigning to each pair (g, f) of $\mathtt{C}$-morphisms with $\mathrm{dom}(g) = \mathrm{cod}(f)$ a $\mathtt{C}$-morphism $g \circ f$, the *composite* of f and g, such that $\mathrm{dom}(g \circ f) = \mathrm{dom}(f)$ and $\mathrm{cod}(g \circ f) = \mathrm{cod}(g)$ and such that the *associative law* holds. That is, for all $\mathtt{C}$-morphisms f, g, h such that

   $$A \xrightarrow{f} B \xrightarrow{g} C \xrightarrow{h} D$$

   we have

   $$h \circ (g \circ f) = (h \circ g) \circ f.$$

5. An assignment to each $\mathtt{C}$-object B of a $\mathtt{C}$-morphism $1_B\colon B \to B$, the *identity arrow* on B, such that the *identity law* holds. That is, for all $\mathtt{C}$-morphisms $f\colon A \to B$, $g\colon B \to C$ we have

   $$1_B \circ f = f \quad \text{and} \quad g \circ 1_B = g.$$

Definition 13. A category is called *small* if both the collections of objects and of arrows are sets. A category is called *locally small* if for any two objects A, B the collection of morphisms between A and B is a set. Many categories occurring in everyday mathematics are small categories.

As an aside, one could alternatively define a category in terms of an abstract graph with orientation of the edges (to obtain domain and codomain) and then imposing the categorical structure (identity and associativity laws).

As examples of categories occurring in everyday mathematics, we name the following.

- Any poset is a category by taking the elements as objects and defining a morphism from an object A to an object B if and only if $A \leq B$.
- `SET`, the category of sets, whose objects are sets, and whose morphisms are functions between sets.
- `MON`, the category of monoids, whose objects are monoids, and whose morphisms are morphisms between monoids (i.e., preserving the monoidal structure).

Definition 14. A $\mathtt{C}$-arrow $f\colon A \to B$ is called *iso*, or *invertible*, if there is a

C-arrow $g\colon B \to A$ such that $g \circ f = 1_A$ and $f \circ g = 1_B$. Two C-objects A and B are called *isomorphic*, denoted $A \cong B$, if there is a C-arrow $f\colon A \to B$ that is iso in C.

There are several fundamental constructions with categories. Here, we will define only three of those, the product category, the comma category and the freely generated category, since they will be used in the later parts of this paper. For other constructions the reader is referred to the standard texts, e.g., Goldblatt (1984), Lambek and Scott (1986), and MacLane (1971).

Definition 15. Given two categories C and D the *product category* $\mathtt{C} \times \mathtt{D}$ has as objects all pairs $\langle A, B\rangle$ where A is a C-object and B a D-object. The $\mathtt{C}\times\mathtt{D}$-arrows $\langle A, B\rangle \to \langle C, D\rangle$ are exactly the pairs $\langle f, g\rangle$ where $f\colon A \to C$ is a C-arrow and $g\colon B \to D$ is a D-arrow. Composition is defined componentwise.

Definition 16. Of *comma categories* (or *slice categories*) we distinguish two variations.

- The category of all morphisms with a common domain A (denoted by $A \downarrow \mathtt{C}$), which has as objects all arrows in C with domain A and as arrows (from an object $q\colon A \to B$ to another object $r\colon A \to C$) all arrows $p\colon B \to C$ in C such that $r = pq$. This category is also called the *category of objects under* A.
- The category of all morphisms with a common codomain A (denoted by $\mathtt{C} \downarrow A$), which has as objects all arrows in C with codomain A and as arrows (from an object $q\colon B \to A$ to another object $r\colon C \to A$) all arrows $p\colon B \to C$ in C such that $q = rp$. This category is also called the *category of objects over* A.

Definition 17. The *category* $\mathtt{F}(G)$ *freely generated* by the (directed) graph G is the smallest category with as objects the nodes of G and as arrows all edges from G and closed under conditions 4 and 5 in the definition of *category* above.

A special case of a freely generated category is a polynomial category, a concept we will employ when discussing the categorical model for CPC-algorithms.

Definition 18. Given a category C and an arrow $x\colon A \to B$ between two objects $A, B \in \mathtt{C}$, the *polynomial category* $\mathtt{C}[x]$ is the category freely generated by the underlying graph of C to which the arrow x has been adjoined. (If x already is an arrow of C, then obviously $\mathtt{C}[x] = \mathtt{C}$.)

The notion of polynomial category has an application in the theory of deductive systems, cf. Lambek and Scott (1986).

A very important standard concept in category theory which will be used frequently is that of a *functor*, a mapping between two categories.

Definition 19. A *functor* F from category C to category D is a function assigning a D-object $F(A)$ to each C-object A and a D-arrow $F(f)\colon F(A) \to F(B)$ to each C-arrow $f\colon A \to B$ such that

- $F(1_A) = 1_{F(A)}$ for all C-objects A and
- $F(g \circ f) = F(g) \circ F(f)$ whenever $g \circ f$ is defined.

An *endofunctor* is a functor from a category C onto itself.

We continue with the definition of diagrams, cones and limits. Again, for the basic results on these notions the reader is referred to the standard texts.

Definition 20. A *diagram* Δ in a category C is a collection of C-objects D_i, $D_j, \dots$ together with a set D_{ij} of C-morphisms $g\colon D_i \to D_j$ between certain of the objects D_i (where the i's are taken from an index set I) in Δ. (Clearly, $D_{ij} \subseteq \mathrm{C}(D_i, D_j)$. Furthermore, D_{ij} is allowed to be empty, cf. the examples below.)

Definition 21. A *cone* $\mathbb{D}$ for a diagram Δ consists of a C-object C (called the *top of the cone*) together with a C-morphism $f_i\colon C \to D_i$ for every object D_i in Δ such that

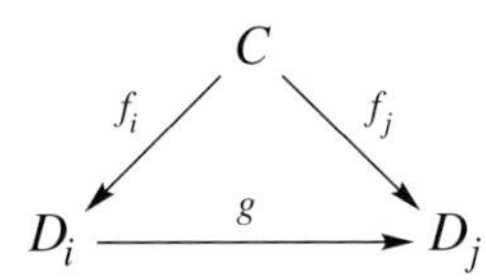

commutes, whenever g is a morphism in the diagram Δ.

To denote a cone we use $\{f_i\colon C \to D_i\}$.

Definition 22. A *limit* for a diagram Δ is a Δ-cone $\mathbb{D} = \{f_i\colon C \to D_i\}$ with the property that for any other Δ-cone $\mathbb{D}' = \{f_i'\colon C' \to D_i\}$ there is exactly one morphism $f\colon C' \to C$ such that

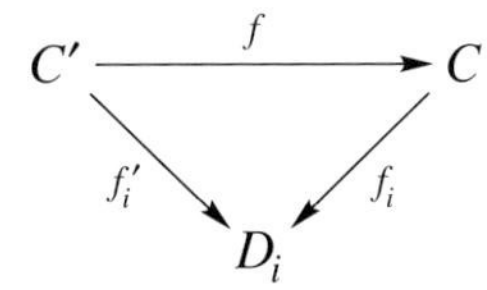

commutes for every object D_i in Δ.

This is the *universal property* of the limit (limiting cone). The limit of a diagram Δ is traditionally denoted by $\overset{\lim}{\leftarrow}\Delta$. By the universal property, a limit object is unique up to isomorphism.

Finally, a limit is called *weak* if the morphism f is not required to be unique.

Example 1. A *terminal object* in a category C is a limit of the empty diagram.

So, a terminal object is an object T such that for every object A in C there is a unique morphism (usually denoted by $!_A$ or simply !) from A to T. Pictorially: $A \stackrel{!}{\rightarrow} T$.

In a poset (the) terminal object is the maximal element (supposing that that element is comparable with all other elements, otherwise there is no terminal object). In SET any singleton set is a terminal object, in MON any 1-element monoid (containing the unit element).

Example 2. A *product* of two C-objects A and B is a limit of the diagram consisting of the objects A and B (and containing no morphisms).

So, a product of two objects A and B is an object, denoted by $A \times B$, for which there are unique morphisms (projections) π_A: $A \times B \rightarrow A$ and π_B: $A \times B \rightarrow B$, such that for any two morphisms f: $C \rightarrow A$ and g: $C \rightarrow B$ there is a unique h: $C \rightarrow A \times B$ through which f and g factor, i.e., $f = \pi_A \circ h$ and $g = \pi_B \circ h$. (This is the universal property of a product.)

In a poset (the) product of two elements is their greatest lower bound (if they have one), in SET it is the ordinary cartesian set product, and in MON the product monoid (that is, the cartesian product defined by pairwise multiplication).

Example 3. A *pullback* of a pair of C-morphisms with a common codomain f: $A \rightarrow C$, g: $B \rightarrow C$ is a limit in C for the diagram

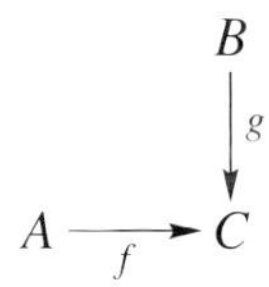

The pullback, also known as fibered product, is a fundamental mathematical notion (cf. Goldblatt 1984, MacLane and Moerdijk 1992), turning out to be basic in topos and sheaf theory. The following examples may help to illustrate the importance of the concept.

In SET the pullback of two set functions f: $A \rightarrow C$ and g: $B \rightarrow C$ is defined by $A \times_C B = \{(x, y) \mid x \in A,\ y \in B \text{ and } f(x) = g(y)\}$, with the obvious projections as morphisms from $A \times_C B$ to A and B respectively. $A \times_C B$ is a subset of $A \times B$, called the *product of A and B over C*.

If, more specifically, C is a subset of B and g the inclusion, then the pullback D is the inverse image of C under f, i.e., $D = f^{-1}(C) = \{y \in D \mid f(y) \in C\}$.

In MON consider a monoid homomorphism f: $M \rightarrow N$ and its kernel $K = \{x \mid f(x) = e\}$ (where e denotes the unit element of N). Then the kernel K can be characterized by the following pullback square:

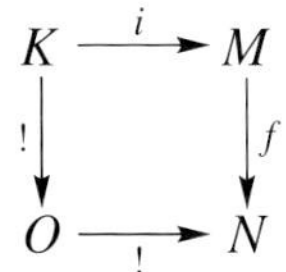

where i is the inclusion of K into M and $O = \{1\}$ a one-element monoid consisting of a unit element (O is terminal and also initial, see the subsection on colimits).

In any category with a terminal object T, if D with the morphisms $f\colon D \to A$ and $g\colon D \to B$ is a pullback of the diagram consisting of A, B, T and the unique morphisms from A respectively B to T, then $D \cong A \times B$.

Example 4. An *equalizer* of two C-morphisms $f, g\colon A \to B$ is a limit of the diagram

$$A \underset{g}{\overset{f}{\rightrightarrows}} B$$

In SET the equalizer of two functions with common domain A is the inclusion function $i\colon E \hookrightarrow A$ where $E := \{x \in A \mid f(x) = g(x)\}$, the subset of the domain A on which f and g are equal (hence the name). In a poset, the only equalizers are the identity functions.

By duality, i.e., reversing all the arrows in the previous definitions, one can define the dual notions cocones and colimits.

Definition 23. A *cocone* $\mathbb{D}$ for a diagram Δ consists of a C-object C (called the *bottom of the cone*) together with a C-morphism $f_i\colon D_i \to C$ for every object D_i in Δ such that

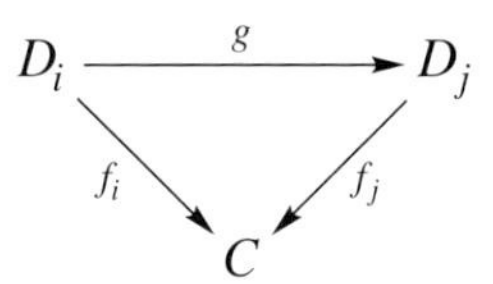

commutes, whenever g is a morphism in the diagram Δ.

To denote a cocone we use $\{f_i\colon D_i \to C\}$.

Definition 24. A *colimit* for a diagram Δ is a Δ-cocone $\mathbb{D} = \{f_i\colon D_i \to C\}$ with the property that for any other Δ-cocone $\mathbb{D}' = \{f_i'\colon D_i \to C'\}$ there is exactly one morphism $f\colon C \to C'$ such that

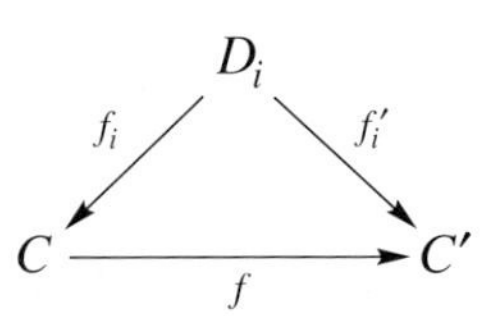

commutes for every object D_i in Δ.

This is the *universal property* of the colimit (colimiting cocone). The colimit of a diagram Δ is traditionally denoted by $\overset{\lim}{\to}\Delta$.

Finally, a colimit is called *weak* if the morphism f is not required to be unique.

Since colimit is the dual notion of $\overset{\lim}{\leftarrow}$ we are led to notions dual to terminal object, product, etc. Below, we summarize these.

Example 5. An *initial object* is a colimit of the empty diagram.

If an object is both initial and terminal, it is called a *zero object.*

Example 6. A *coproduct* of two C-objects A and B is a colimit of the diagram consisting of the objects A and B (and containing no morphisms).

Example 7. A *pushout* of a pair of C-morphisms with a common domain $f\colon A \to B$, $g\colon A \to C$ is a colimit in C for the diagram

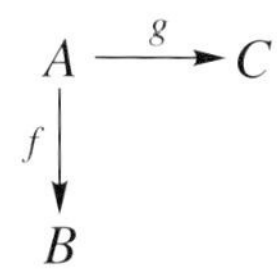

Pushouts are often denoted as $B +_A C$ (the sum of B and C over A).

Example 8. A *coequalizer* is a colimit of the diagram

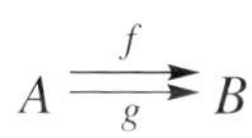

In Rydeheard and Burstall (1985) (weak) coequalizers are used to characterize most general unifiers in a categorical presentation of unification.

All the above is elementary category theory. In the next section we are going to introduce a modified notion of limit which arises naturally in our study of CPC-procedures. To illuminate the idea behind this modification of the limit notion defined previously, it is convenient to give a different (but of course equivalent) definition of limits and colimits by means of the categories of cones and cocones of a given diagram.

Definition 25. The *category of cones* of a given diagram Δ, denoted by CON(Δ), has as its objects all Δ-cones, and as morphisms between two Δ-cones $\mathbb{D}_1$ and $\mathbb{D}_2$ with tops C_1 and C_2, respectively, all morphisms $f\colon C_1 \to C_2$ such that

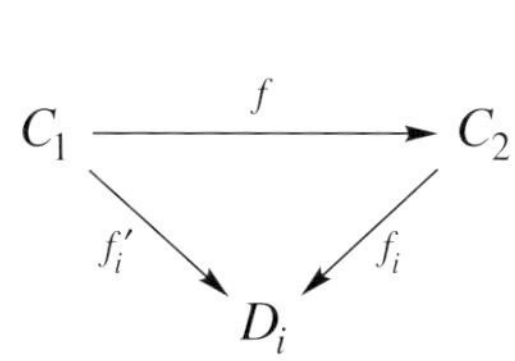

commutes for every object D_i in Δ.

Analogously, the *category of cocones* of a given diagram Δ, denoted by

$\mathtt{COC}(\Delta)$, has as its objects all Δ-cocones, and as morphisms between two Δ-cocones $\mathbb{D}_1$ and $\mathbb{D}_2$ with bottoms C_1 and C_2, respectively, all morphisms $f\colon C_1 \to C_2$ such that

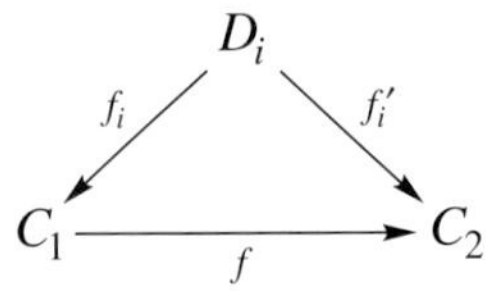

commutes for every object D_i in Δ.

The following proposition follows directly from the definition above and the definitions of limit and colimit respectively.

Proposition 26. A Δ-cone $\{f_i\colon C \to D_i\}$ is a limit of Δ if and only if it is a terminal object in $\mathtt{CON}(\Delta)$.

Analogously, a Δ-cocone $\{f_i\colon D_i \to C\}$ is a colimit of Δ if and only if it is an initial object in $\mathtt{COC}(\Delta)$.

5 Reversed limits

We now will extend the concepts of limit and colimit by taking initial objects in the category of cones (obtaining what we shall call reversed limits), and, dually, terminal objects in the category of cocones (obtaining reversed colimits).

We can then view the cones of a diagram as ranging between the limit (the "closest cone") and the reversed limit (the "most remote cone"). In this sense, limit and reversed limit form "boundaries" between which the cones of a diagram range. Analogously, colimit and reversed colimit form "boundaries" for the cocones.

The new notions will be of assistance in the characterization of completed reduction systems, cf. Sect. 6.3.

5.1 Definitions

The following definition expresses that a reversed limit of a given diagram Δ factors uniquely through all cones for Δ.

Definition 27. A *reversed limit* for a diagram Δ is a Δ-cone $\{f_i\colon C \to D_i\}$ with the property that for any other Δ-cone $\{f_i'\colon C' \to D_i\}$ there is exactly one morphism $f\colon C \to C'$ such that

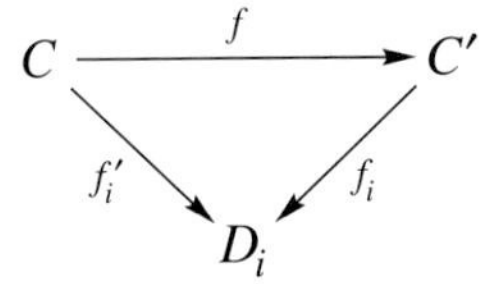

commutes for every object D_i in Δ.

This is the *universal property* for the reversed limit, and as in the case for ordinary limits and by the same argument, the universal property defines a reversed limit object up to isomorphism.

Conversely, all cocones for a diagram Δ factor uniquely through its reversed colimit.

Definition 28. A *reversed colimit* for a diagram Δ is a Δ-cocone $\{f_i\colon D_i \to C\}$ with the property that for any other Δ-cocone $\{f_i'\colon D_i \to C'\}$ there is exactly one morphism $f\colon C' \to C$ such that

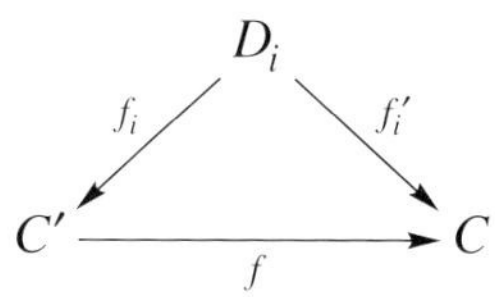

commutes for every object D_i in Δ.

This is the *universal property* for the reversed colimit, and as in the case for ordinary colimits and by the same argument, the universal property defines a reversed colimit object up to isomorphism.

The following proposition gives an elegant, alternative presentation of reversed limits and their relation to ordinary limits, and follows directly from the above definitions.

Proposition 29. A Δ-cone $\{f_i\colon C \to D_i\}$ is a reversed limit of Δ if and only if it is an initial object in $\mathtt{CON}(\Delta)$.

Analogously, a Δ-cocone $\{f_i\colon D_i \to C\}$ is a reversed colimit of Δ if and only if it is a terminal object in $\mathtt{COC}(\Delta)$.

Example 9. A *terminal object* is a reversed colimit of the empty diagram.

Example 10. An *initial object* is a reversed limit of the empty diagram.

Definition 30. A *normalizer* (for a given object A) is a reversed colimit of the diagram consisting of the object A. Pictorially, $a\colon A \to \underline{A}$ is a normalizer for A if for any arrow $f\colon A \to B$ a unique arrow $g\colon B \to \underline{A}$ can be found such that the diagram

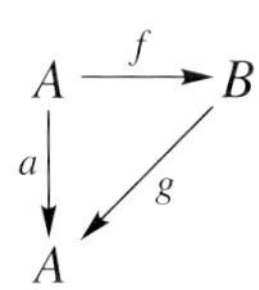

commutes (i.e., $a = g \circ f$).

Note that the corresponding limit (or colimit) would be the object A itself, with its identity morphism as limiting (or colimiting) arrow.

A normalizer of an object A in a category $\mathtt{C}$ is a terminal object in the category $A \downarrow \mathtt{C}$. The term *normalizer* is chosen here because in the category CPC which we will define in Sect. 6, the normalizer of an object A corresponds to its normal form.

The dual notion corresponds to an object which cannot be made more complex (with respect to the reduction relation defining the arrows in the category CPC), and therefore is "maximally reducible" in this sense.

Definition 31. A *maximally reducible form* (for a given object A) is a reversed limit of the diagram consisting of the object A.

Again, there is an alternative formulation: a maximally reducible form of an object A in a category $\mathtt{C}$ is an initial object in the category $\mathtt{C} \downarrow A$.

The following definition gives us a general construction of reversed limits (or reversed colimits) from the corresponding standard limits (or colimits).

Definition 32 (Standard construction of reversed limits). For every limit and colimit we define the corresponding reversed limit (and reversed colimit) by reversing the direction of the unique morphism f in the defining universal property. Hence we obtain the concepts of reversed products and reversed coproducts, reversed pullbacks and reversed pushouts, and reversed equalizers and reversed coequalizers. We already saw above that a "reversed initial object" is nothing but a terminal object, and vice versa.

5.2 Some basic properties of reversed limits

This section lists some properties of reversed limits.

The first lemma is similar to a lemma for ordinary limits, in Freyd and Ščedrov (1990: 1.433; pullbacks and a terminal object imply binary products). A difference is that in the present context the role of terminal object is taken by the reversed initial object, which is just the terminal object as explained above.

Lemma 33. The existence of all reversed pullbacks and a terminal object T guarantees the existence of all reversed binary products.

Proof. Given two objects A and B, we first construct the unique morphisms $f\colon A \to T$ and $g\colon B \to T$, where T is the terminal object. Then we can construct the reversed pullback for the diagram of f and g, obtaining an object C and morphisms $h\colon C \to A$ and $k\colon C \to B$. Then it is readily checked that (C, h, k) is the reversed product of A and B. □

The following lemma shows that maximally reducible forms and normalizers are the basic types of reversed limits and colimits, respectively.

Lemma 34. The existence of all maximally reducible forms guarantees the existence of all reversed pullbacks, and more generally, of all reversed limits of diagrams that are connected (in the graph-theoretical sense).

Proof. First we give the proof for the pullback case, then the more general one. In the argument, repeated use is made of the universal property of the (reversed) limits. Since no familiarity with this type of argument is assumed, it is more elaborated than in category theory texts (where it is standard).

Given the diagram consisting of two morphisms with common codomain $f\colon B \to D$, $g\colon C \to D$, we can construct the objects B', C', D' as the maximally reducible forms of B, C, D respectively, with corresponding morphisms $b\colon B' \to B$, $c\colon C' \to C$, and $d\colon D' \to D$. Clearly there is a morphism $f \circ b$ from B' to D, so we find a unique morphism $h\colon D' \to B'$, such that

$$f \circ b \circ h = d. \tag{1}$$

Moreover, since $f\colon B \to D$, we obtain a unique arrow j from D' to B such that

$$f \circ j = d. \tag{2}$$

Because j is the unique such arrow we immediately obtain by (1) and (2) that

$$b \circ h = j. \tag{3}$$

Moreover, since we have the arrow $j\colon D' \to B$, we obtain a unique $k\colon B' \to D'$ such that

$$j \circ k = b. \tag{4}$$

Now we can prove that B' and D' are isomorphic.

First we have $d \circ k = f \circ j \circ k = f \circ b$ (using the associativity law and (2) and (4) above).

Combining this with (1), we obtain

$$d \circ k \circ h = d. \tag{5}$$

On the other hand, we have, because of (3) and (4)

$$b \circ h \circ k = b. \tag{6}$$

We now use the universal property of D' on itself. This property states that there is a unique arrow i from D' to D' such that $d \circ i = d$. Now, obviously $i = 1_{D'}$ fulfills this equation, but from (5) we see that so does $k \circ h$. Hence, $k \circ h = i = 1_{D'}$.

Analogously, using the universal property on B', from (6) we conclude that $h \circ k = 1_{B'}$.

This proves that B' and D' are isomorphic. Write b' for the universal arrow $b \circ h\colon D' \to B$.

By an analogous argument C' and D' are isomorphic. Write c' for the corresponding universal arrow from D' to C.

Now, it is easy to prove that D', together with b' and c', is a reversed pullback. The commutativity of the square

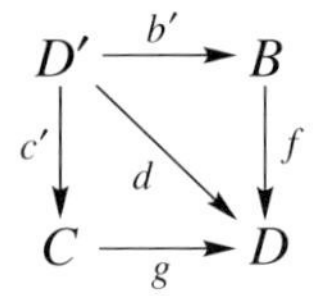

follows from the commutativity of the two triangles it is composed of. If for any other object A and morphisms l, m the square

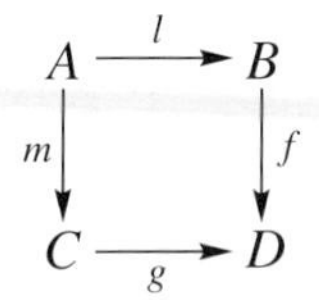

would be commutative, we immediately find the required unique morphism a from D' to A such that $f \circ l \circ a = f \circ b'$, by virtue of the fact that $D' \cong B'$ is the maximally reducible form of B. (And, again by using the universal property, now on $D' \cong C'$, we find that $f \circ b' = f \circ l \circ a = g \circ m \circ a = g \circ c'$, showing that the outer diagram is commutative.) This proves that (D', b', c') is a reversed pullback.

Now consider a diagram Δ whose objects all are connected by morphisms (i.e., Δ is a connected graph). For any two objects A, B such that we have a morphism $f\colon A \to B$ in Δ, we construct:

- the maximally reducible form B' together with a morphism $b\colon B' \to B$ and, by definition, the unique arrow $g\colon B' \to A$ such that $f \circ g = b$;
- the maximally reducible form A' together with a morphism $a\colon A' \to A$ and, because of g, the unique arrow $h\colon A' \to B'$ such that $g \circ h = a$;
- the unique morphism $k\colon B' \to A'$ such that $f \circ a \circ k = b$.

Now, as above, A' and B' are shown to be isomorphic (by h and k). (The proof, as above, uses the universal property on g and on $1_{A'}$ and $1_{B'}$ – the case is completely analogous.)

By continuing this process, we find that the maximally reducible forms of the objects in Δ are all isomorphic, say to a reversed limit C. Then, analogously to the case of reversed pullbacks it is now trivial to prove (by the commutativity of all relevant triangles) that C is the reversed limit of Δ. □

The dual result for reversed colimits, stating that the existence of all normalizers guarantees the existence of all reversed colimits of diagrams whose graph is connected, and specifically of all reversed pushouts, can be used in the categorical framework (defined in Sect. 6) for modeling (completion of) reduction systems to show that the existence of all normal forms with respect to a given reduction relation proves confluence of the relation (provided no infinite reduction sequences exist, i.e., it is impossible to compose (non-identity) arrows indefinitely). This will be discussed in more detail in Sect. 6 below.

6 A categorical model for CPC-procedures

There have been several attempts to model rewrite systems by categorical means. In Rydeheard and Stell (1987) some results on equational deduction are raised to a categorical level using the machinery of 2-categories. This includes the derivation of a unification algorithm from constructions of colimits, solving equations in the presence of term rewriting systems and the combination of unification algorithms. Known results from these areas are extended to 2-categories essentially by reworking known proofs. In Stell (1992), to which my attention has been drawn recently, a generalization of 2-categories, called sesqui-categories, is used for the categorical investigation of (the completion of) rewriting systems and unification. It appears that some analogies can be found to the approach discussed here.

In Power (1990) the fact that *pasting* (a fundamental operation for 2-categories) is well-defined is proved. This is a prerequisite for the study of (classes of) rewrite problems by 2-categories. Based on this, Power (1989) proposes to discuss rewrite systems as special 2-categories. A theorem is stated that gives conditions under which rewrite derivations exist, and the paper gives further conditions under which a normal form for a derivation exists, using the theory of 2-categories.

The 2-categorical approach was introduced by Johnson (1987). As it was then pursued (Johnson 1991), apparently independent from the earlier work by Benson (see below), string rewriting systems were modeled by 2-categories. Then, the approach is extended by modeling linear term rewriting systems by 3-categories. One major problem is that the multiple appearance of the same function symbol is hard to cover in this framework. Nevertheless, possibly the axiomatization of Buchberger (patterns, multipliers and replacements, cf. Buchberger 1985b) can be carried out in such 3-categories.

Benson (1975) constructed so-called categories of derivations from string rewriting systems. The categories obtained are free strict monoidal categories, simple forms of 2-categories. Morphisms in these categories generalize the notion of "derivation tree." Here also, only string rewriting is modeled.

Jay (1991) modeled already completed (hence confluent) reduction systems by so-called *confluent categories*, whose objects are confluent orders and morphisms are order-preserving functions. A pre-order P is defined to be confluently ordered if the set of reducts of any element are all pairwise compatible, i.e., have a common reduct. In that setting, one obtains a categorical semantics for the reduction, and a simple functorial relationship between the operational semantics (the reduction process computing normal forms) and the denotational semantics (obtained by identifying any term with its reducts and in particular its normal form).

Reichel (1990), by narrowing a 2-cell against a 1-cell, gives a 2-categorical formulation of the critical pair situation occurring in CPC-algorithms. Completion itself is not modeled.

Finally, in Huet (1986) the *computation category* associated with a *regular* term rewriting system is defined as its derivation category, quotiented by the permutation equivalence. It has as objects the terms, and as arrows between terms the permutation class of parallel derivations from the domain to the codomain. This theory of derivations was first developed in the framework of λ-calculus (Lévy 1978), and adapted to the framework of regular term rewriting systems (Huet and Lévy 1979). A more general framework of combinatory reduction systems allowing binding operators and providing a general theory encompassing λ-calculus was investigated (Klop 1980).

This condition of regularity of the term rewriting system essentially stipulates that it is left-linear (no variables occur twice in the left hand side of a rule) and does not contain critical pairs. This enables one to show confluence.

This is not what we are after. Such conditions may serve as criteria within the framework to be developed for distinguishing between certain instances of CPC-procedures but certainly not as preconditions for the framework itself. Therefore we now present an alternative categorical model for CPC-procedures.

The basic category is CPC. Based on it, we will model CPC-procedures and the endofunctors representing the multipliers and embedders discussed in Sect. 3. We will conclude with a discussion of basic CPC-notions in the categorical model.

6.1 Construction of the category CPC

The basic category CPC is defined by taking the elements of the universe T (cf. Sect. 3) as its objects, and let the arrows be induced by the reduction relation.

Definition 35. CPC is constructed as follows:

- The objects are the elements in the universe T.
- The arrows in CPC are generated from the patterns in P. We take the transitive and reflexive closure of $\rightarrow_P$ and extend it with the reductions that can be carried out because of the multiplier and replacement rules. In other words, the arrows are based on the $\rightarrow_G^*$ relation. So, there is an arrow with as domain an $x \in T$ and as codomain a $y \in T$ if and only if $x \rightarrow_G^* y$. Because of this, there is always at most one arrow between two objects, i.e., no distinction is made between different sequences of reductions leading to $x \rightarrow_G^* y$.

Theorem 36. CPC is a category.

Proof. We have to check the defining properties for categories.

1. Identity morphism for objects: this is defined by the reflexivity of the defining relation $\rightarrow_G^*$.
2. Composition of arrows: this is defined by the transitivity of $\rightarrow_G^*$.

3. The identity and associativity rules trivially hold because if there are two arrows between given objects A and B, they are the same by definition. □

Alternatively, we may construct CPC by taking the discrete category consisting of the objects from the universe and the identity arrows, and adding the generating patterns defining $\rightarrow_P$ as indeterminates.

Proposition 37. The category CPC can equivalently be described by constructing the category freely generated by the graph generated by the reduction relation $\rightarrow_G$, where the objects are the objects of the universe, and all arrows with common domain and codomain are identified.

Proof. Direct from the definition of freely generated categories in Sect. 4 and the identification of all the arrows with identical source and target. □

6.2 Constructing functors on CPC

We now define two types of functors from CPC to CPC.

- *Multiplier* functors (`mul`) corresponding to the *multipliers*.
- *Embedder* functors (`emb`) corresponding to the *embedders*.

Definition 38. Every *multiplier* μ defines a *multiplier functor* $\mathtt{mul}(\mu)$ from CPC to CPC such that

- for every object $A \in \mathtt{CPC}$ $\mathtt{mul}(\mu)(A) = \mu(A)$, and
- for every arrow $f\colon A \rightarrow B$ $\mathtt{mul}(\mu)(f) = \mu(f)\colon \mu(A) \rightarrow \mu(B)$. Rule (gen-1) guarantees that this arrow exists.

Definition 39. Every *embedder* η defines an *embedder functor* $\mathtt{emb}(\eta)$ from CPC to CPC such that

- for every object $A \in \mathtt{CPC}$ $\mathtt{emb}(\eta)(A) = \eta(A)$, and
- for every arrow $f\colon A \rightarrow B$ $\mathtt{emb}(\eta)(f) = \eta(f)\colon \eta(A) \rightarrow \eta(B)$. Rule (gen-2) guarantees that this arrow exists.

Theorem 40. All functors $\mathtt{mul}(\mu)$ and $\mathtt{emb}(\eta)$ fulfill the functor properties.

Proof. Trivial, since all required arrows exist because of (gen-1) and (gen-2), respectively, and are uniquely determined by the definition of CPC. □

These functors will have to fulfill certain conditions, induced by corresponding axiomatic properties of multipliers and embedders. Investigations into a suitable categorical formulation of these are still underway.

Below, we will often use the notations `mul` and `emb` to denote $\mathtt{mul}(\mu)$ and

$\mathtt{emb}(\eta)$ respectively. Subscribed versions will be used accordingly, e.g., $\mathtt{mul}_1$ is an abbreviation for $\mathtt{mul}(\mu_1)$.

6.3 Discussion of CPC

In this subsection we formulate the relevant notions of CPC-algorithms in categorical terms, starting from the category CPC, invoking categories derived from it for some of the concepts, and making use of the variant of the limit notion developed in Sect. 5.

Weak normal form

In the categorical model, a weak normal form of an object A is an object B such that there exists an arrow $f\colon A \to B$ and such that there are no arrows with domain B except the identity arrow 1_B. In arrow notation,

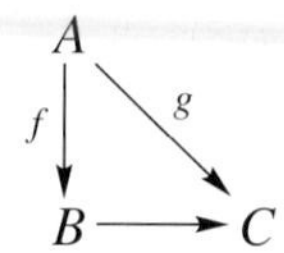

implies $B = C$ (or $g = f$).

Normal form

The canonical normal form of an object A is characterized as a terminal object in the comma category $A \downarrow \mathtt{CPC}$.

To be precise, the canonical normal form $\underline{A}$ of the object A is the unique object fulfilling, for all B, the commutativity of

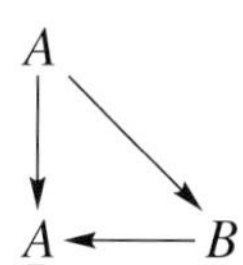

As explained in Sect. 5, a terminal object in the comma category $A \downarrow \mathtt{CPC}$ corresponds to the normalizer of A in CPC.

Lemma 41. If the reduction system is strongly normalizing, any object A has as its normal form the object $\underline{A}$ characterized by being the terminal object in the comma category $A \downarrow \mathtt{CPC}$.

Proof. If $\underline{A}$ is the canonical normal form of A, it clearly holds that for any object B such that A reduces to B, B can be reduced to $\underline{A}$. This fact yields the required diagram in $A \downarrow \mathtt{CPC}$, where the uniqueness of the arrow from $A \to B$ to $A \to \underline{A}$ is induced by the uniqueness of the arrow $B \to \underline{A}$ in CPC.

Conversely, if $\underline{A}$ is the terminal object in $A \downarrow \mathtt{CPC}$, we know that any object B such that A reduces to B has a reduction to $\underline{A}$. Under the condition that all reduction sequences are finite (i.e., the reduction relation $\rightarrow_G$ is strongly normalizing), this implies that $\underline{A}$ is the canonical normal form of A. □

Most general unifier and superposition situation

The categorical characterization of most general superposition situations is based on that of most general unifiers. Essentially, one takes the left hand side of a fixed pattern and tries to unify the left hand side of any other pattern (possibly the same) with any of its subterms. If this is possible, one only considers a most general pair of multipliers (for the precise definition, cf. Sect. 3).

Hence, a most general superposition situation is given by an embedder functor emb and two multiplier functors $\mathtt{mul}_1$, $\mathtt{mul}_2$ such that the pair $(\mathtt{mul}_1, \mathtt{mul}_2)$ is a most general unifier in the (product) category of multipliers on CPC. For the precise definition, we first give the (simpler) case of plain most general unifiers (as used in the Gröbner basis algorithm) and then generalize to most general superposition situations.

A most general unifier of two objects (left hand sides of patterns) is a weak coproduct in the category of multiplier functors on CPC. First, we define this *category of multipliers* μCPC.

Definition 42. μCPC is constructed as follows:

- The objects are the elements in the universe T, the same objects as in CPC.
- The arrows in μCPC are generated by the multiplier functors $\mathtt{mul}(\mu)$. I.e., for all A, B in CPC, there is an arrow $\mathtt{mul}(\mu)$: $A \rightarrow B$ if and only if $\mathtt{mul}(\mu)(A) = B$, for a multiplier μ in M.

Note that the above definition leaves us with identically labeled arrows with different domains and codomains. For a correct labeling we should index the arrows with their domain (which determines their codomain uniquely, as the multiplier is given). We shall refrain from doing so, indicating the domain and codomain of all arrows whenever necessary.

Lemma 43. μCPC is a category.

Proof. We check the properties defining a category.

1. Identity morphism for objects: this is defined by (mul-1): the set of all multipliers contains the identity operation, so $\mathtt{mul}(\mathrm{id}_T)$ yields the identity arrow for all objects.
2. Composition of arrows: this is defined by (mul-3): the compositions of two multipliers is again a multiplier, so for two arrows $\mathtt{mul}(\mu_1)$: $A \rightarrow B$ and $\mathtt{mul}(\mu_2)$: $B \rightarrow C$, the composition $\mathtt{mul}(\mu_2) \circ \mathtt{mul}(\mu_1)$: $A \rightarrow C$ exists and is defined by the multiplier $\mathtt{mul}(\mu_2 \circ \mu_1)$.
3. The identity and associativity rules: immediately from (mul-4) and (mul-5). □

Now, a most general unifier is a weak coproduct in this category.

Lemma 44. A most general unifier of two objects A, B in T (so objects in CPC, and μCPC) is a weak coproduct of A and B in μCPC.

Proof. The defining property of a most general unifier (namely that any other unifier is just a special instance of it, attainable by an intermediate multiplier (here $\mathtt{mul}_5$)) is exactly what is expressed by the weak coproduct diagram for μCPC, below (note that $\mathtt{mul}_5$ is not required to be unique, hence the weakness).

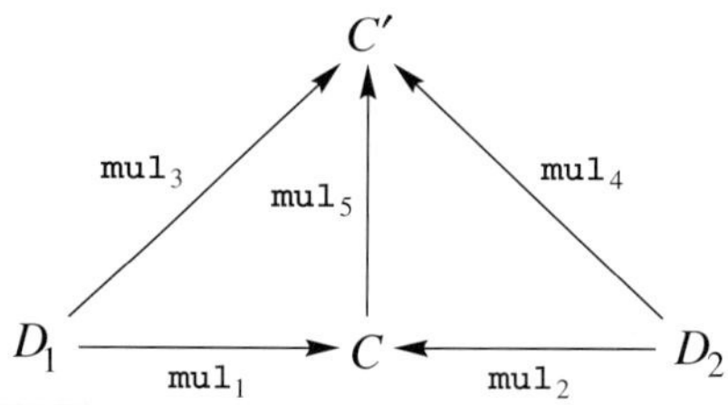

□

From this, we derive the definition of a *most general superposition situation* within the product category $\mu\mathrm{CPC} \times \mu\mathrm{CPC}$.

Lemma 45. The most general superposition situation of two objects A, B in T (so objects in CPC, and μCPC) is given by a triple of endofunctors on CPC $(\mathtt{emb}, \mathtt{mul}_1, \mathtt{mul}_2)$ such that $\mathtt{emb} \circ \mathtt{mul}_1 = \mathtt{mul}_2$ and the pair $(\mathtt{mul}_1, \mathtt{mul}_2)$ fulfills the property that for every pair $(\mathtt{mul}_3, \mathtt{mul}_4)$ for which $\mathtt{emb} \circ \mathtt{mul}_3 = \mathtt{mul}_4$ there is a pair $(\mathtt{mul}_5, \mathtt{mul}_5)$ such that the following diagram within $\mu\mathrm{CPC} \times \mu\mathrm{CPC}$ commutes:

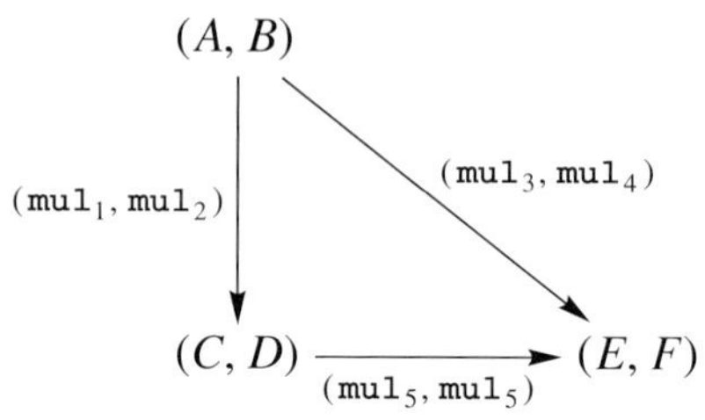

where
$(C, D) = (\mathtt{mul}_1(A), \mathtt{emb}(\mathtt{mul}_1(A)))$ and $(E, F) = (\mathtt{mul}_3(A), \mathtt{emb}(\mathtt{mul}_3(A)))$.

Proof. Directly from the definition of most general superposition situations in Sect. 3. □

Critical pair
A provisional critical pair for D_1 and D_2 with respect to the patterns f_1 and f_2 is given by the pair (A, B), a critical pair consists of $\underline{A} = \mathtt{Sim}(A)$ and $\underline{B} = \mathtt{Sim}(B)$. The computation of the critical pair is illustrated by the following diagram.

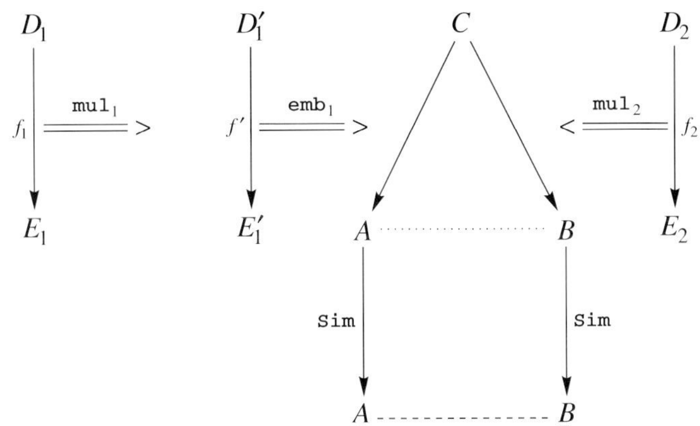

The provisional critical pair can categorically be obtained from D_1, D_2 and the patterns f_1 and f_2 by computing on the arrows of CPC. To formulate this, the *extended category of multipliers* μ^*CPC is defined.

Definition 46. μ^*CPC is constructed as follows:

- The objects are the arrows in CPC.
- The arrows in μ^*CPC are generated by the multiplier functors $\texttt{mul}(\mu)$. I.e., for all $f\colon A \to B$, $g\colon C \to D$ in CPC, there is an arrow $\texttt{mul}(\mu)\colon f \to g$ if and only if $\texttt{mul}(\mu)(f) = g$, for a multiplier $\texttt{mul}(\mu)$ in M. (That this is well-defined follows from the definition of the multiplier functors.)

Lemma 47. μ^*CPC is a category.

Proof. Completely analogous to Lemma 43 (treating μCPC). □

In this extended category of multipliers, a provisional critical pair of two patterns $f_1\colon D_1 \to E_1$ and $f_2\colon D_2 \to E_2$ is obtained from computing the most general superposition situation of D_1 and D_2 in $\mu\text{CPC} \times \mu\text{CPC}$ and then applying the defining embedder and multipliers emb, $\texttt{mul}_1$, $\texttt{mul}_2$ on the arrows f_1, f_2, objects in μ^*CPC. From the provisional critical pair (cf. the corresponding definition in Sect. 3) the real critical pair is found by calculating the weak normal forms of the codomains $\texttt{emb}(\texttt{mul}_1(E_1))$ and $\texttt{mul}_2(E_2)$ in CPC.

The completion step

The completion step consists of adding an arrow (new basic pattern) $\underline{A} \to \underline{B}$ or vice versa (compatibility with $>$), to the category CPC. This is equivalent to the construction of the category freely generated by the graph (on T) generated by the basic patterns from $\to_P$ and the additional reduction $\underline{A} \to \underline{B}$ and closed under functor (emb, mul) application. Denoting the added arrow by x, this corresponds to the (free) construction of the polynomial category CPC$[x]$, cf. Lambek and Scott (1986).

Hence, the completion process consists of successive constructions of polynomial categories, until the category is completed, i.e., fulfills the property that all objects have canonical normal forms.

As we have seen before, the existence of all canonical normal forms amounts to the existence of all normalizers (and hence all reversed pushouts) in the category. We will call such a category a *completed category*, not to be confused with a *complete category* (a category in which all small diagrams have a limit, cf. Freyd and Ščedrov 1990, Lambek and Scott 1986).

The completed category $\underline{\texttt{CPC}}$

The completion process terminates successfully if and only if all objects of CPC have uniquely determined normal forms. As no infinite reductions exist (having demanded that $\rightarrow_P^+$ and consequently $\rightarrow_G^+$ be noetherian), this means that for all objects A, if there are arrows $f\colon A \rightarrow B$ and $g\colon A \rightarrow C$ we must be able to find arrows $h\colon B \rightarrow D$ and $k\colon C \rightarrow D$. The normal form itself is given by the reversed pushout of f and g in CPC (terminology of Sect. 5). This leads to the following theorem.

Theorem 48. The completion of CPC is terminated successfully, creating the completed category $\underline{\texttt{CPC}}$, if all reversed pushouts exist (in $\underline{\texttt{CPC}}$).

Proof. The confluence of the reduction relation is expressed by the fact that for any two reductions $f\colon A \rightarrow_G^* B$ and $g\colon A \rightarrow_G^* C$ there exists an object D and arrows $h\colon B \rightarrow_G^* D$, $k\colon C \rightarrow_G^* D$ in the completed category $\underline{\texttt{CPC}}$ such that the corresponding diagram commutes (i.e., $h \circ f = k \circ g$).

The uniqueness of the normal form is then equivalent to the statement that for any D', h', k' making the pushout diagram of f and g commutative, we can find an arrow $l\colon D' \rightarrow_G^* D$ (taking D as the normal form). This last arrow is exactly inverse to the arrow defining a *pushout*, hence the label *reversed pushout*.

The above discussion can be summarized in the following commutative diagram.

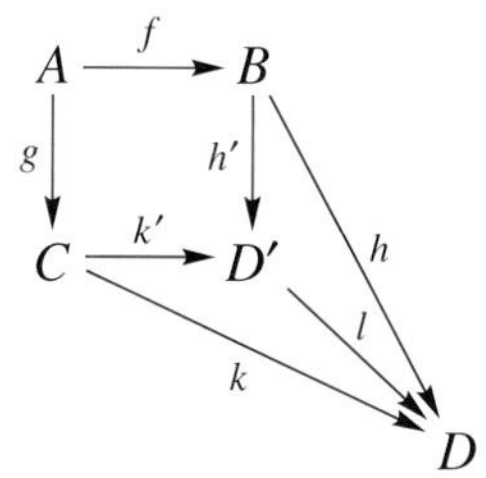

□

Acknowledgements

This work has benefited greatly from discussions with and encouragement from (first and foremost) Jochen Pfalzgraf, Barry Jay and Bruno Buchberger. I thank one of the referees for very helpful and detailed comments, especially on Sect. 5.2.

Sponsored by the Austrian Ministry of Science and Research (BMWF), ESPRIT

BRA 3125: MEDLAR, and the Austrian Science Foundation (FWF), ESPRIT BRP 6471: MEDLAR II.

References

Becker, T., Weispfenning, V. (1993): Gröbner bases. Springer, Berlin Heidelberg New York Tokyo (Graduate texts in mathematics, vol. 141).

Benson, D. (1975): The basic algebraic structures in the categories of derivations. Inf. Control 28: 1–29.

Buchberger, B. (1983): A critical-pair/completion algorithm in reduction rings. Tech. Rep. RISC Linz 83-21.

Buchberger, B. (1985a): Gröbner bases: an algorithmic method in polynomial ideal theory. In: Bose, N. (ed.): Multidimensional systems theory. Reidel, Dordrecht, pp. 184–232.

Buchberger, B. (1985b): Basic features and development of the critical-pair/completion procedure. In: Jouannaud, J.-P. (ed.): Rewriting techniques and applications. Springer, Berlin Heidelberg New York Tokyo, pp. 1–45 (Lecture notes in computer science, vol. 202).

Buchberger, B., Loos, R. (1982): Algebraic simplification. Computing [Suppl.] 4: 11–43.

Cox, D., Little, J., O'Shea, D. (1992): Ideals, varieties, and algorithms. Springer, Berlin Heidelberg New York Tokyo (Undergraduate texts in mathematics).

Dershowitz, N. (1983): Applications of the Knuth–Bendix completion procedure. Tech. Rep. The Aerospace Corporation El Segundo, California ATR-83(8478)-2.

Dershowitz, N., Jouannaud, J.-P. (1990): Rewriting systems. In: Van Leeuwen, J. (ed.): Handbook of theoretical computer science. Elsevier, Amsterdam, pp. 243–320.

Freyd, P., Ščedrov, A. (1990): Categories, allegories. North-Holland, Amsterdam.

Goldblatt, R. (1984): Topoi. The categorial analysis of logic. North-Holland, Amsterdam.

Huet, G. (1980): Confluent reductions: abstract properties and applications to term rewriting systems. J. ACM 27: 797–821.

Huet, G. (1986): Formal structures for computation and deduction. Working material for lectures at the International Summer School on Logic of Programming and Calculi of Discrete Design in Marktoberdorf, Germany, 1986.

Huet, G., Lévy, J.-J. (1979): Call by need computations in non-ambiguous linear term rewriting systems. Techn. Rep. IRIA 359.

Jay, C. B. (1991): Modelling reduction in confluent categories. Tech. Rep. Department of Computer Science, University of Edinburgh ECS-LFCS-91-187.

Johnson, M. (1987): Pasting diagrams in n-categories with applications to coherence theorems and categories of paths. Ph.D. thesis, University of Sydney, Sydney, N.S.W., Australia.

Johnson, M. (1991): Linear term rewriting systems are higher dimensional string rewriting systems. In: Rattray, C., Clark, R. (eds.): The unified computation laboratory. Oxford University Press, Oxford, pp. 3–12.

Kandri-Rody, A., Kapur, D., Winkler, F. (1989): Knuth–Bendix procedure and Buchberger algorithm – a synthesis. In: Proceedings of the ACM-SIGSAM International Symposium on Symbolic and Algebraic Computation, ISSAC '89, Portland, Oregon. ACM Press, New York, pp. 55–67.

Klop, J. W. (1980): Combinatory reduction systems. Ph.D. thesis, Mathematisch Centrum, Amsterdam, The Netherlands.

Klop, J. W. (1990): Term rewriting systems. Tech. Rep. Centrum voor Wiskunde en Informatica Amsterdam CS-R9073.

Klop, J. W., Middeldorp, A. (1988): An introduction to Knuth–Bendix completion. Tech. Rep. Vrije Universiteit Amsterdam IR-162.

Knuth, D., Bendix, P. (1967): Simple word problems in universal algebras. In: Leech, J. (ed.): Proceedings of the Conference on Computational Problems in Abstract Algebra, Oxford, 1967. Pergamon Press, Oxford, pp. 263–298.

Lambek, J., Scott, P. (1986): Introduction to higher-order categorical logic. Cambridge University Press, Cambridge (Studies in advanced mathematics, vol. 7).

Lévy, J.-J. (1978): Réductions correctes et optimales dans le λ-calcul. Thèse d'Etat, Université de Paris VII, Paris, France.

MacLane, S. (1971): Categories for the working mathematician. Springer, Berlin Heidelberg New York Tokyo (Graduate texts in mathematics, vol. 5).

MacLane, S., Moerdijk, I. (1992): Sheaves in geometry and logic. Springer, Berlin Heidelberg New York Tokyo.

MEDLAR Consortium (1989): Mechanizing deduction in the logics of practical reasoning. Technical Annex of ESPRIT BRA 3125. Tech. Rep. RISC Linz 89-49.0.

Power, A. J. (1989): An abstract formulation for rewrite systems. In: Pitt, D. H., Rydeheard, D. E., Dybjer, P., Pitts, A. M., Poigne, A. (eds.): Category theory and computer science. Springer, Berlin Heidelberg New York Tokyo, pp. 300–312 (Lecture notes in computer science, vol. 389).

Power, A. J. (1990): A 2-categorical pasting theorem. J. Algebra 129: 439–445.

Reichel, H. (1990): A 2-category approach to critical pair completion. In: Ehrig, H., Jantke, K. P., Orejas, F., Reichel, H. (eds.): Recent trends in data type specification. Springer, Berlin Heidelberg New York Tokyo, pp. 266–273 (Lecture notes in computer science, vol. 534).

Rydeheard, D., Burstall, R. (1985): A categorical unification algorithm. In: Pitt, D. H., Abramsky, S., Poigne, A., Rydeheard, D. E. (eds.): Category theory and computer programming. Springer, Berlin Heidelberg New York Tokyo, pp. 493–505 (Lecture notes in computer science, vol. 240).

Rydeheard, D., Stell, J. (1987): Foundations of equational deduction: a categorical treatment of equational proofs and unification algorithms. In: Pitt, D. H., Poigne, A., Rydeheard, D. E. (eds.): Category theory and computer science. Springer, Berlin Heidelberg New York Tokyo, pp. 114–139 (Lecture notes in computer science, vol. 283).

Stell, J. (1992): Categorical aspects of unification and rewriting. Ph.D. thesis, University of Manchester, Manchester, U.K.

Stokkermans, K. (1991): A categorical approach to critical-pair/completion procedures. Techn. Rep. RISC Linz 91-58.

Stokkermans, K. (1992): A categorical formulation for critical-pair/completion procedures. In: Rusinowitch, M., Rémy, J.-L. (eds.): Conditional term rewriting systems. Springer, Berlin Heidelberg New York Tokyo, pp. 328–342 (Lecture notes in computer science, vol. 656).

CASA: computer algebra software for computing with algebraic sets

Bernhard Wall

1 Introduction

In this report we want to illustrate with two examples how the program package "Computer Algebra Software for Constructive Algebraic Geometry" (CASA) (see Gebauer et al. 1991) can be used in order to reason about geometric objects defined by algebraic equations.

Algebraic geometry is the theory of geometric objects which are the zeros of systems of polynomial equations. In the last decades the non-constructive aspects of algebraic geometry gained more and more importance as the discussed objects became too complicated to be managed explicitly without using a machine. The availability of computer algebra systems opened the possibility to actually perform operations on a larger class of algebraic sets.

CASA was designed to enhance the capabilities of a traditional computer algebra system, Maple[1], by adding procedures for constructive algebraic geometry. Maple was chosen because it allows easy prototyping of mathematical algorithms and it seems to be quite reliable. It was used in different research projects at the Research Institute for Symbolic Computation at the University of Linz, where CASA was developed. Code was contributed to CASA from these projects. The work on CASA is not finished, yet. It can be expected that the ongoing research will improve and enlarge the system. On the other hand CASA will also benefit from the further development of Maple. Currently CASA works on top of Maple V Release 1. For instance, in this version of Maple the implementation of the Gröbner basis algorithm only works for polynomials over transcendental extension fields of the rational numbers. The Gröbner basis algorithm is fundamental for a number of algorithms implemented in CASA. Most algorithms in CASA would also work for polynomials over algebraic extension fields of the rational numbers. Once the Gröbner basis algorithm in Maple is implemented to work with this bigger class of polynomials CASA will also be able to handle a larger class of examples.

For information on related computer programs in the area of constructive

1 For information on the computer algebra system Maple see Char et al. (1992, 1991a, b).

algebraic geometry we refer to the GANITH project (Bajaj and Royappa 1989, 1990), the Macaulay system (Stillman et al. 1989), and to Bennet (1990).

In this report we want to demonstrate how CASA can be used to derive properties of algebraic sets. CASA works with algebraic sets in different representations. There are algorithms available to switch from one representation to another one. By following a specific example we will show in the first part of this report how this can be used for the computation of intersections of algebraic sets. The second part is a review of the mathematical background of a part of CASA, the series expansion of branches of algebraic curves. We will see that by series expansion methods it is possible to count the number of (real) branches of an algebraic curve at a singular point. It will be shown how this can be used to plot topologically correct pictures of a curve.

2 Intersection of algebraic sets – a case study

In this section we investigate the properties of two algebraic sets with the help of CASA. Only a part of CASA will be used during this sample session. For a description of all available functions we refer to Wall (1991a).

First of all let us fix some notions and notations. Let K be a finitely generated extension field of $\mathbb{Q}$. For a given subset F of $K[x_1, \ldots, x_n]$, Ideal(F) denotes the ideal in $K[x_1, \ldots, x_n]$ generated by F. $V(F)$ denotes the algebraic set of F, i.e., the set

$$\{a \in \mathbb{C}^n \mid f(a) = 0 \quad \text{for all} \quad f \in \mathrm{Ideal}(F)\}.$$

Since every ideal in $K[x_1, \ldots, x_n]$ is finitely generated every algebraic set in $\mathbb{C}^n$ can be given as the zero-set of finitely many polynomials. If an algebraic set is specified in this way we say it is given in *implicit form.*

Let us consider the following two algebraic sets C and S in $\mathbb{C}^3$ which are given in implicit form by polynomials in $\mathbb{Q}[x, y, z]$. C is given by the polynomials

$$y^3z^2 - 10y^3z + 25y^3 - y^2z + 5y^2 - yz + y,$$
$$10y^2z - y^2z^2 - yz^2 - 25y^2 + 6yz + x - 5y + 1;$$

S is specified by

$$x^2y + y^4 - yz^2.$$

These two algebraic sets will be defined in CASA. First we start Maple and read in CASA. (CASA is entirely written in the Maple programming language.)

```
    |\^/|     MAPLE V
._|\|   |/|_. Copyright (c) 1981-1990 by the University of Waterloo.
 \  MAPLE  /  All rights reserved.  MAPLE is a registered trademark of
 <____ ____>  Waterloo Maple Software.
      |       Type ? for help.
> read casa;
```

```
              ~~~~~~
    _________||__
   /              \
  /    C A S A     \      Version October 1992
 /------------------\
 |      |\^/|       |
 |  ._|\|   |/|_.   |
 |  \  MAPLE  /     |      Version V Release 1
 |   <____ ____>    |
 |        |         |
-+------------------+-
For on-line help on CASA, type  help(CASA); or ?CASA
--------------------------------------------------------------------------
>
```

In the next step we define C and S in CASA. This is done with the function `mkImplAlgSet` ("make implicit algebraic set," in the sequel we will see that CASA can represent algebraic sets in different ways). The first argument of `mkImplAlgSet` is the list of polynomials which describe the algebraic set. The second argument is the list of variables of the polynomial ring over K in which the polynomials are. This is used in order to distinguish between variables and parameters (i.e., elements of K).

```
> Cim := mkImplAlgSet(
>          [-y^2*z^2 + 10*y^2*z - y*z^2 - 25*y^2 + 6*y*z + x - 5*y +1,
>           y^3*z^2 - 10*y^3*z + 25*y^3 - y^2*z + 5*y^2 - y*z + y],[x,y,z]);
                          2  2       2          2       2
 Cim := algebraic_set([- y  z  + 10 y  z - y z  - 25 y  + 6 y z + x - 5 y + 1,
                          3  2       3          3    2         2
                         y  z  - 10 y  z + 25 y  - y  z + 5 y  - y z + y],
     [x, y, z], attr)
--------------------------------------------------------------------------
> Sim := mkImplAlgSet([x^2*y+y^4-y*z^2],[x,y,z]);
                                2      4      2
           Sim := algebraic_set([x  y + y  - y z ], [x, y, z], attr)
```

The two algebraic sets have been assigned to the variables `Cim` and `Sim`. Next we compute the dimension of C and of S. This is done by an algorithm described in Kredel and Weispfenning (1988) based on the computation of Gröbner bases.

```
> dimension(Cim);
                                      1
--------------------------------------------------------------------------
> dimension(Sim);
                                      2
```

C is a space curve and S is a two-dimensional surface. Figure 1 shows a picture of S produced by the CASA function `plotAlgSet`. See Gebauer (1990) for a description of the algorithms used in CASA for the plotting of algebraic sets in two and three-dimensional space.

```
> plotAlgSet(Sim,x=-1..1,y=-1..1,z=-1..1,numpoints=40);
```

One obtains an ideal I for which $V(I) = C \cap S$ by computing the union of ideals which define C and S. In CASA this is done by the function `implIntersect`. Also there is the function `implUnionLCM` available in order

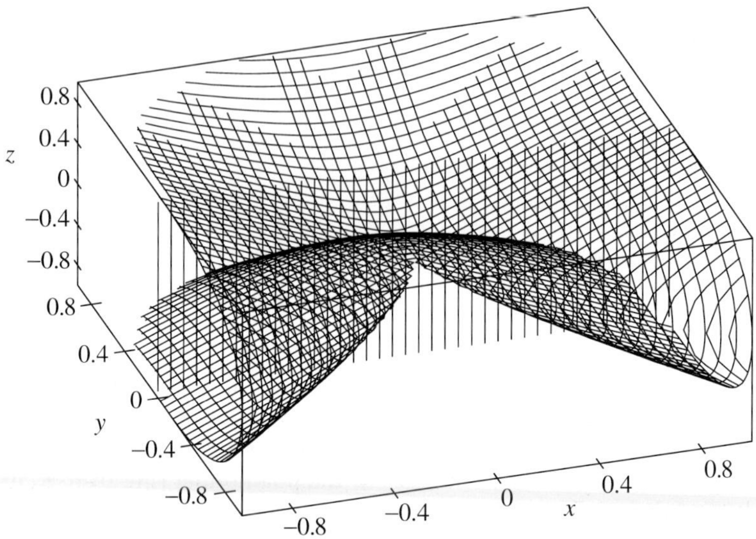

Fig. 1. Graph of S

to determine the union of algebraic sets by computing the least common multiple of ideals.

```
> C1im := implIntersect(Cim,Sim);
C1im := algebraic_set(
       2      4      2     2  2       2        2       2
    [x  y + y  - y z , - y  z  + 10 y  z - y z  - 25 y  + 6 y z + x - 5 y + 1,
         3  2       3        3    2       2
        y  z  - 10 y  z + 25 y  - y  z + 5 y  - y z + y],
    [x, y, z], attr)
--------------------------------------------------------------------------------
> dimension(C1im);
                                       1
```

A curve and a surface in "generic" position intersect in a finite number of points. In our case $\texttt{C1im} = C \cap S$ is a one-dimensional algebraic set. However, it may contain zero-dimensional components. The function `tsolve` splits the ideal of an algebraic set A (i.e., the ideal of *all* polynomials which vanish on A) into the union of algebraic sets whose ideals are given by triangularized bases. For a detailed description of `tsolve` see Kalkbrener (1991b).

```
> tsolve(C1im);
algebraic_set(
     2  2       2        2       2
[- y  z  + 10 y  z - y z  - 25 y  + 6 y z + x - 5 y + 1,
 12       11        10        9         8         7          6          5
z   - 36 z   + 560 z   - 4908 z  + 26502 z  - 90847 z  + 199055 z  - 286342 z

              4          3          2
     + 295547 z  - 161148 z  - 262344 z  + 551601 z - 251001,
 10         9        8        8        7        7          6          6
z   y - 35 z  y + 3 z  + 535 z  y - 76 z  - 4691 z  y + 26117 z  y + 771 z

             5         5           4         4           3          3
     - 96988 z  y - 3900 z  + 247678 z  y + 9626 z  - 445977 z  y - 7509 z

                 2        2
     + 569830 y z  - 9360 z  + 12525 z - 476526 y z + 188376 y],
```

```
[x, y, z], attr),
algebraic_set(
       2  2       2        2      2                                   2
   [- y  z  + 10 y  z - y z  - 25 y  + 6 y z + x - 5 y + 1, 260 y , z - 1],
   [x, y, z], attr),
algebraic_set(
   2      4      2           2  2      2        2      2
 [x  y + y  - y z , y, - y  z  + 10 y  z - y z  - 25 y  + 6 y z + x - 5 y + 1,
     3  2       3         3    2         2
    y  z  - 10 y  z + 25 y  - y  z + 5 y  - y z + y],
 [x, y, z], attr)
-----------------------------------------------------------------------------
> Groebnerbasis("[3]);     #       " refers to the previous output of Maple.
                                   [1 + x, y]
```

One can see that the first two algebraic sets in the output of `tsolve` are zero-dimensional (because their bases contain a univariate polynomial in z), the third is one-dimensional. The function `Groebnerbasis` computes a Gröbner basis for the ideal generated by the defining polynomials of an algebraic set in CASA. We see that the ideal of the third algebraic set in the previous output is generated by the polynomials $x + 1$ and y. Hence the algebraic set is a line.

Summarizing we have derived the following knowledge on C and S: The space curve C and the two-dimensional surface S intersect in a line and in a finite set of points. C is not an irreducible algebraic set. One of its components is a line which lies on S.

The next operation we will perform is a decomposition of `Cim` into irreducible components. This means we want to write `Cim` as the union of algebraic sets which are irreducible, i.e., which cannot be written as a union of two proper algebraic subsets. The function `decompose` computes a decomposition of `Cim` over the rational numbers. This means that the irreducible algebraic sets are described by polynomials with rational coefficients. Clearly, irreducible algebraic sets over the rational numbers can be reducible over some algebraic extension of $\mathbb{Q}$. For instance the planar curve defined by $x^2 - 2y^2$ is irreducible over $\mathbb{Q}$ but splits into the algebraic sets defined by $x - \sqrt{2}y$ and $x + \sqrt{2}y$ over $\mathbb{Q}(\sqrt{2})$.

The algorithm used in CASA to compute the decomposition is based on the computation of Ritt's characteristic sets and Gröbner bases, see Ritt (1950), Wang (1989, 1992) and Wu (1984).

```
> decompose(Cim);
algebraic_set(
    2                     2  2       2              2
[4 z  + z x - 23 z - 2 y  x  + 22 y  x + 152 y  + 106 y + 41 y x + 36 + 16 x
        2
     - x  y,
                                           2        2          2      2  2
  20 y z + z x + 5 z - 54 y - 19 y x - 22 y  x - x  y - 152 y  + 2 y  x  - 4,
                                           2        2           2       3      2
  - 44 x - 438 y + 65 z - 197 y x - 306 y  x - 16 x  y - 1064 y  - y x  + z x
           2  2           2  3
      - 8 y  x  + 2 z x + 2 y  x  - 108,
        3        3    3  2       2        2
  - 11 y  x - 76 y  + y  x  - 15 y  x - 15 y  - 3 y - 3 y x - 1 - x],
[x, y, z], attr),
    algebraic_set([y, 1 + x], [x, y, z], attr)
-----------------------------------------------------------------------------
```

```
> C2im := mkImplAlgSet(Groebnerbasis("[1]),[x,y,z]);
 C2im := algebraic_set(
               2                                 2         2  2       2
     [x - y z  - z + 5 y z + 2, 5 y - z - y z - 10 y  z + y  z  + 25 y  + 1],
     [x, y, z], attr)
```

The second algebraic set in the output of decompose is the line lying on S. A Gröbner basis was computed for the ideal of the first algebraic set; this basis was used to define the algebraic set C2im. By using the function dimension it can be verified that C2im is a space curve.

An algebraic set is unmixed-d-dimensional if all its irreducible components have dimension d. Such an unmixed-d-dimensional algebraic set A in n-dimensional space, A having no multiple components, is (after a suitable linear change of coordinates) birationally projectable onto a d-dimensional algebraic set A' in $d+1$-dimensional space. A' is a hypersurface, hence its ideal is generated by a single polynomial. Since A' has no multiple components we have that the defining polynomial of A' is square-free.

If an algebraic set A is given by a square-free polynomial f and a list of rational functions $\frac{p_1}{q_1}, \ldots, \frac{p_n}{q_n}$ (i.e., the birational mapping) we say that it is represented in *projected form*. More precisely (for the case of three-dimensional space), let Ideal$(\{f\}) = P_1 \cap \ldots \cap P_k$, where the P_j's are prime ideals. Ideal$(\{f\})$ has such a representation because it does not contain multiple components. Let (a_{j1}, a_{j2}, a_{j3}) be a generic point of P_j for $j \in \{1, \ldots, k\}$. Then

$$A = V\Big(\big\{g \in K[x, y, z] \mid \\ \mid g\big(\tfrac{p_1(a_{j1},a_{j2},a_{j3})}{q_1(a_{j1},a_{j2},a_{j3})}, \tfrac{p_2(a_{j1},a_{j2},a_{j3})}{q_2(a_{j1},a_{j2},a_{j3})}, \tfrac{p_3(a_{j1},a_{j2},a_{j3})}{q_3(a_{j1},a_{j2},a_{j3})}\big) = 0 \quad \forall j \in \{1, \ldots, k\}\big\}\Big).$$

In CASA the function impl2proj computes the projected form of an algebraic set in implicit form. However, if the algebraic set is not unmixed-dimensional then only the components of highest dimension will be projected. The algorithm used for projection is a generalization of the one described in Kalkbrener (1990a) and is based on Gröbner bases computation. The algorithm described in Kalkbrener (1990a) works for irreducible algebraic set. Also in Abhyankar and Bajaj (1988a, 1989) an algorithm for computing the projection is given. It is based on resultant computations and requires an irreducible space curve a input. Slightly different approaches are discussed in Hoffmann (1988, 1989). The inverse function proj2impl to switch from projected to implicit representations is also available. It is a generalization of the algorithm described in Kalkbrener (1990b, 1991a).

```
> C2pr := impl2proj(C2im);
  C2pr := algebraic_set(
             2       3                      2      3                 3  2
    [[- 15 y  - 76 y  - 1 - 3 y + (- 15 y  - 11 y  - 1 - 3 y) x + y  x ],
                             2
        [x, y, 7 y + 25 y  + 1 + y x]],
               -------------------
                      2
                   5 y  + 1 + 2 y
    [x, y], attr)
```

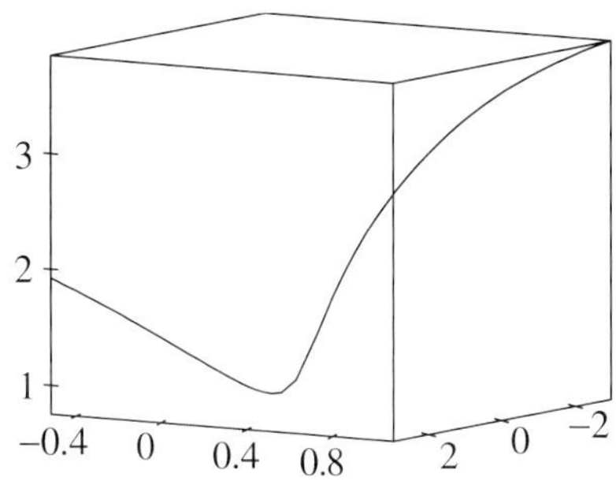

Fig. 2. Graph of a component of C

C2pr is the same algebraic set as C2im but in a different representation. A number of algorithms which work on planar curves can be applied to space curves which are represented in projected form. For instance it is possible to plot implicitly given planar curves with CASA. This algorithm is used to plot the planar curve in the representation of a space curve and the resulting points are mapped into n-dimensional space by means of the birational mapping. The zeros of the denominators of the rational functions and the singularities of the planar curve have to be treated carefully. Figure 2 shows a picture of C2pr produced by the CASA function plotAlgSet.

```
> plotAlgSet(C2pr,x=-3..3,y=-3..3,numpoints=100);
```

Another algorithm which is available for space curves is the computation of a rational parametrization of a curve, if the curve is parametrizable in rational functions. The planar curve is parametrized by an algorithm described in Sendra and Winkler (1991). (Another, similar algorithm is given in Abhyankar and Bajaj 1988b, 1989.) The resulting rational functions are plugged into the rational functions describing the birational mapping. The result is a list of rational functions which parametrize the curve. This leads to another representation of algebraic sets in CASA. An algebraic set which is given by a list of rational functions $\frac{p_1}{q_1}, \ldots, \frac{p_n}{q_n}$ (where $p_i, q_i \in K[t_1, \ldots, t_s]$) is said to be in *parametric form*. More precisely (for the case of curves in three-dimensional space), the algebraic space curve defined by the parametrization $\frac{p_1(t)}{q_1(t)}, \frac{p_2(t)}{q_2(t)}, \frac{p_3(t)}{q_3(t)}$ is

$$V\left(\left\{g \in K[x, y, z] \mid g\left(\frac{p_1(t)}{q_1(t)}, \frac{p_2(t)}{q_2(t)}, \frac{p_3(t)}{q_3(t)}\right) = 0\right\}\right).$$

```
> C2pa := proj2para(C2pr);
 C2pa := algebraic_set(
                                                 - 7 + t          2
        [- t3 + 21 t2 - 147 t + 342, - -------------, t  - 13 t + 43], [t], attr)
                                          2
                                         t  + 38 - 13 t
```

At this point one might ask the question if it is possible in CASA to obtain the representation of C2im from C2pa. The answer is: in principle yes. There is the function para2impl based on Gröbner bases computation (Kalkbrener 1990b) which does this job. However, the computations tend to be very time consuming.

On a DEC station 5000 CASA could not compute the implicit equations for C2pa in 1000 CPU seconds. If one reparametrizes C2pa in a way such that the rational functions are sparser (i.e., contain fewer terms) then the implicit equations can be computed in a few CPU seconds.

```
> C2pa := reparametrize(t=t+7,C2pa);
                                 3                t          2
     C2pa := algebraic_set([- t  - 1, - ------------, t  + t + 1], [t], attr)
                                                    2
                                        - 4 + t + t
-----------------------------------------------------------------------------
> para2impl(C2pa);
algebraic_set(
         2       3                       2          3                   3  2
[- 15 y  - 76 y  - 1 - 3 y - 15 x y  - 11 x y  - x - 3 x y + y  x ,
                                         2                        2            2      2  2
- 197 x y - 438 y + 65 z - 108 - 16 x  y + 2 z x - 1064 y  - 306 x y  - 8 x  y
                3         2      3  2
     - 44 x - x  y + z x  + 2 x  y ,
   2                                                   2          2     2         2  2
4 z  + z x - 23 z + 16 x + 106 y + 41 x y + 22 x y  + 152 y  - x  y - 2 x  y
     + 36,
                                             2                    2          2      2  2
- 19 x y + 20 y z - 54 y + 5 z - 4 - x  y + z x - 152 y  - 22 x y  + 2 x  y ],
[x, y, z], attr)
-----------------------------------------------------------------------------
> implEqual(",C2im);
                                     true
```

The function implEqual tests the equality of the two ideals by which two algebraic sets in implicit form are given.

Another representation of algebraic sets in CASA is a list of *places*. These places are equivalence classes of power series expansions of the algebraic set around a specific point on the curve, called *center* of the place. Around a regular center there is only one place but around a singular center there may be more than one place. A set of places which all center around a specific point give a representation of an algebraic set. The power series are convergent around the center, thus finite parts of the series give an approximation of the algebraic set in a suitable neighborhood of the center. The mathematical background and applications of places are the topic of the next section.

3 Puiseux expansion in CASA

3.1 Mathematical background

Series expansion of branches of algebraic curves

Let us consider a plane algebraic curve C which passes through the origin, given by a polynomial $f \in \mathbb{C}[x, y]$. We want to study all local parametrizations of f around the origin. If the origin is a regular point we may assume that $\frac{\partial f}{\partial y}(0, 0) \neq 0$. Then, by the implicit function theorem, there exists only one unique local parametrization of f in analytic functions, i.e., there exists a function $y(x)$, analytic in some neighborhood of $x = 0$, such that $y(0) = 0$, $f(x, y(x)) = 0$ and for every point (x_0, y_0) on C in a suitable neighborhood of $(0, 0)$: $y_0 = y(x_0)$. The analytic function $y(x)$ can be expanded into a Taylor series in x, which is convergent in a neighborhood of 0. That means $y(x) = \sum c_i x^i$, $c_i \in \mathbb{C}$ for $i \in \mathbb{Z}$.

It is possible to derive a local (in a suitable neighborhood convergent) parametrization in power series of the curve from this expansion. Let t be a new variable, let $x_1(t) = t$ and $y_1(t) = \sum c_i t^i$. It holds that $f(x_1(t), y_1(t)) = 0$ and x_1 and y_1 are convergent around $t = 0$.

If the origin is a singular point then, by Newton's theorem (Newton 1969), there exist finitely many local parametrizations, i.e., there exist finitely many pairs of functions $(x(t), y(t))$, analytic in some neighborhood of $t = 0$, such that (1) $x(0) = 0$, $y(0) = 0$, (2) $f(x(t), y(t)) = 0$ and (3) for every point $(x_0, y_0) \neq (0, 0)$ lying on C in a suitable neighborhood of $(0, 0)$ there is exactly one of the pairs of functions $(x(t), y(t))$ for which there exists a unique t_0 such that $x(t_0) = x_0$ and $y(t_0) = y_0$.

Analogous to the case of a non-singular $(0, 0)$, an analytic function $y(x)$ is also defined implicitly around a singular point by the equation $f(x, y)$, but not uniquely. The $y(x)$ can still be expanded into power series, but with rational exponents. These expansions correspond to the local parametrizations of the branches of the curve C defined by f. Let $(\lambda t^e, \sum c_i t^i)$ be the parametrization of a branch of C, that means $f(\lambda t^e, \sum c_i t^i) = 0$. Let $\lambda t^e = x$, thus $t = \omega(\frac{1}{\lambda}x)^{1/e}$, where ω is an e-th root of unity. The power series expansion of $y(x)$ then is $y(x) = \sum c_i \omega(\frac{1}{\lambda}x)^{i/e}$. There are e different $y(x)$ corresponding to the same branch (depending on the choice of ω). It follows that $f(x, y(x)) = 0$. The denominators of the exponents of the power series expansion $y(x)$ are bounded. These power series are elements of the field $\mathbb{C}\langle\langle x\rangle\rangle = \bigcup_{n\in\mathbb{N}} \mathbb{C}((x^{1/n}))$, the field of *Puiseux series* over $\mathbb{C}$. ($\mathbb{C}((x))$ denotes the field of formal Laurent series with coefficients in $\mathbb{C}$.) In the following we will study formal power series with coefficients in an arbitrary, algebraically closed field Ω of characteristic 0. Hence, we define more generally $\Omega\langle\langle x\rangle\rangle = \bigcup_{n\in\mathbb{N}} \Omega((x^{1/n}))$, the field of *Puiseux series* over Ω.

Let us view $f \in \Omega[x, y]$ as a polynomial in y with coefficients in $\Omega\langle\langle x\rangle\rangle$. Computing a power series expansion for y can be seen as the solving of a polynomial equation in one variable over the field of Puiseux series. Puiseux's theorem (Puiseux 1850) states that *$\Omega\langle\langle x\rangle\rangle$ is algebraically closed if Ω is algebraically closed.* One can find different proofs of this theorem in textbooks and lecture notes in algebraic geometry, such as Eichler (1966), van der Waerden (1973), Abhyankar (1975), Walker (1978), Brieskorn and Knörrer (1986).

Example 1. Let $f = y^5 - 4y^4 + 4y^3 + 2x^2y^2 - xy^2 + 2x^2y + 2xy + x^4 + x^3$. Let us plot the real part of the curve defined by f with CASA.

```
> A := mkImplAlgSet([y^5 - 4*y^4 + 4*y^3 + 2*x^2*y^2 - x*y^2 + 2*x^2*y +
>                    2*x*y + x^4 + x^3],[x,y]);
A := algebraic_set(
      5      4      3      2  2      2      2                4    3
    [y  - 4 y  + 4 y  + 2 x  y  - x y  + 2 x  y + 2 x y + x  + x ], [x, y], attr
    )
--------------------------------------------------------------------------------
> plotAlgSet(A,x=-1.5..0.5,y=-1..2.5,numpoints=100);
```

Figure 3 shows the plot.

f defines implicitly around $(0, 0)$ two different pairs of functions $(x(t), y(t))$

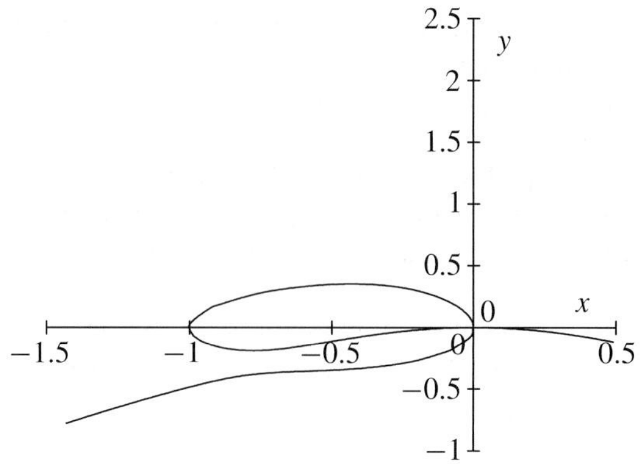

Fig. 3. Graph of $y^5 - 4y^4 + 4y^3 + 2x^2y^2 - xy^2 + 2x^2y + 2xy + x^4 + x^3$

corresponding to the two branches of f around the origin. Power series expansion of these functions are

$$(x_1(t), y_1(t)) = \left(t, -\tfrac{1}{2}t^2 + \tfrac{1}{8}t^4 - \tfrac{1}{8}t^5 + \tfrac{1}{16}t^6 + \tfrac{1}{16}t^7 + \ldots\right),$$
$$(x_2(t), y_2(t)) = \left(-2t^2, t + \tfrac{1}{4}t^2 - \tfrac{27}{32}t^3 - \tfrac{7}{8}t^4 - \tfrac{4057}{2048}t^5 + \ldots\right).$$

The Puiseux series expansions of the implicitly defined $y(x)$ around the origin are

$$y_1(x) = -\tfrac{1}{2}x^2 + \tfrac{1}{8}x^4 - \tfrac{1}{8}x^5 + \tfrac{1}{16}x^6 + \tfrac{1}{16}x^7 + \ldots,$$
$$y_2(x) = \tfrac{\sqrt{-2}}{2}x^{\frac{1}{2}} - \tfrac{1}{8}x + \tfrac{27\sqrt{-2}}{128}x^{\frac{3}{2}} - \tfrac{7}{32}x^2 - \tfrac{4057\sqrt{-2}}{16384}x^{\frac{5}{2}} + \ldots,$$
$$y_3(x) = -\tfrac{\sqrt{-2}}{2}x^{\frac{1}{2}} - \tfrac{1}{8}x - \tfrac{27\sqrt{-2}}{128}x^{\frac{3}{2}} - \tfrac{7}{32}x^2 + \tfrac{4057\sqrt{-2}}{16384}x^{\frac{5}{2}} + \ldots,$$
$$y_4(x) = 2 + \left(\tfrac{1}{8} + \tfrac{\sqrt{-95}}{8}\right)x + \left(\tfrac{15}{32} - \tfrac{47\sqrt{-95}}{3040}\right)x^2 + \left(\tfrac{756199}{4620800} - \tfrac{167913\sqrt{-95}}{4620800}\right)x^3 - $$
$$- \left(\tfrac{655}{2048} - \tfrac{66672639\sqrt{-95}}{1755904000}\right)x^4 + \ldots,$$
$$y_5(x) = 2 + \left(\tfrac{1}{8} - \tfrac{\sqrt{-95}}{8}\right)x + \left(\tfrac{15}{32} + \tfrac{47\sqrt{-95}}{3040}\right)x^2 + \left(\tfrac{756199}{4620800} + \tfrac{167913\sqrt{-95}}{4620800}\right)x^3 - $$
$$- \left(\tfrac{655}{2048} + \tfrac{66672639\sqrt{-95}}{1755904000}\right)x^4 + \ldots$$

In this case $y_1(x)$ corresponds to the branch described by $(x_1(t), y_1(t))$ and $y_2(x)$ and $y_3(x)$ correspond to $(x_2(t), y_2(t))$. The Puiseux series $y_4(x)$ and $y_5(x)$ correspond to branches of the curve around the point $(0, 2)$ because the constant term of the series expansion is equal to 2.

The problem of computing terms of Puiseux series in computer algebra.
Given: A plane algebraic curve C described by a bivariate polynomial f over some finitely generated extension field K of the rational numbers, $f \in K[x, y]$ and a positive integer ν.
Find: The number of branches of C around the origin and for each branch the terms of a power series expansion of the branch up to order ν and an algebraic extension field L of K which contains the computed coefficients.

The restriction on the ground field K is put in order to make the coefficient representable on a computer. In fact, K could be any field of characteristic 0 whose elements can be represented in a finite amount of storage.

Computer algebra methods for Puiseux expansion
In the following we briefly describe the algorithms which were used in CASA for the implementation of Puiseux expansions. It was Newton's classical polygon method, a refinement of Dominique Duval to keep the necessary field extensions as small as possible and a method of Kung and Traub to speed up the computation of terms around regular points of the curve. For further information on known algorithms for series expansions of branches of curves and related topics we refer to the annotated bibliography by Wall (1991b).

Newton polygon method. We sketch a proof of Puiseux's theorem, for details we refer to Walker (1978). The proof is constructive in the sense that a method is given to compute the exponents and the coefficients of the Puiseux series.

We have to show that $\bar{K}\langle\langle x\rangle\rangle$ is algebraically closed, where $\bar{K}$ is the algebraic closure of K. So let us consider a polynomial f of positive degree in the variable y with coefficients in $K\langle\langle x\rangle\rangle$. We will show that f has at least one root, i.e., that there exists a Puiseux series $y(x) \in L\langle\langle x\rangle\rangle$ such that $f(x, y(x)) = 0$ and L is an algebraic extension of K. We will see that L is finitely generated. $f(x, y(x)) = 0$ gives rise to necessary conditions on $y(x)$.

Let $f(x, y) = a_0(x) + a_1(x)y + \ldots + a_n(x)y^n \in K\langle\langle x\rangle\rangle[y]$, $n > 0$. Let us write $a_i(x) = \bar{a}_i x^{\alpha_i} + \ldots$, with α_i being the smallest exponent of a_i. We may assume that $a_n \neq 0$ and $a_0 \neq 0$. We want to derive conditions on the exponents and coefficients of $y(x)$, so we put $y(x) = x^{\gamma}(c + y_1(x))$, $c \neq 0$, $\gamma \in \mathbb{Q}$, and plug it into $f(x, y)$. This yields

$$f(x, y(x)) = a_0(x) + a_1(x)x^{\gamma}(c + y_1(x)) + \ldots + a_n(x)x^{n\gamma}(c + y_1(x))^n.$$

The terms of lowest order must cancel. Therefore there exist at least two indices j, k with $j \neq k$ and $0 \leq j, k \leq n$ such that

$$c^j a_j(x)x^{j\gamma} = c^j \bar{a}_j x^{\alpha_j + j\gamma} + \ldots \quad \text{and} \quad c^k a_k(x)x^{k\gamma} = c^k \bar{a}_k x^{\alpha_k + k\gamma} + \ldots$$

have the same order and this order is minimal. Let $\beta = \alpha_j + j\gamma$. Comparing exponents and coefficients yields

$$\alpha_j + j\gamma = \alpha_k + k\gamma \leq \alpha_i + i\gamma, \quad i = 0, \ldots, n,$$

and

$$\sum_{\alpha_i + i\gamma = \beta} \bar{a}_i c^i = 0.$$

In order to determine possible values for γ a graphical device, the Newton polygon, is used. The points $\{(i, \alpha_i) \mid i = 0, \ldots, n\}$ are plotted in a Cartesian coordinate system. If some $a_i(x) = 0$ then the corresponding point is omitted. There are at least two points in the diagram (because $a_n \neq 0$ and $a_0 \neq 0$). Every line segment between two points of the diagram corresponds to a γ which makes at least two terms cancel (after the choice of a suitable c). In fact, γ is the negative slope of the line segment. The line segments of the lower left boundary of the convex hull of the points correspond to γ's for which the terms of lowest order cancel. In general there are different possible values for γ. These different γ's correspond to different branches of the curve lying above the origin.

For every γ we obtain the corresponding c by taking the non-zero roots (only they give terms with non-zero coefficients) of the equation $\sum_{\alpha_i + i\gamma = \beta} \bar{a}_i c^i = 0$ in $\bar{K}$. At this place it might be necessary to extend K.

Let us again consider the example of the curve defined by the polynomial $f = y^5 - 4y^4 + 4y^3 + 2x^2y^2 - xy^2 + 2x^2y + 2xy + x^4 + x^3$. Figure 4 shows the Newton polygon of this curve. The diagram consists of six points. There are three segments on the lower left boundary of the convex hull of these points.

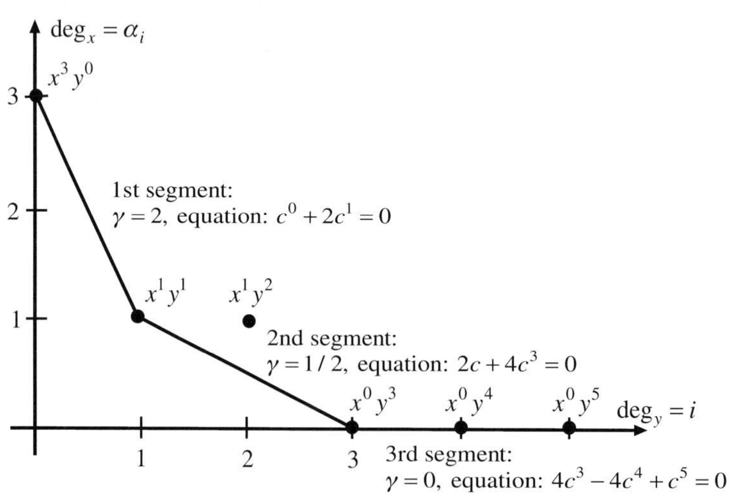

Fig. 4. Newton polygon of $y^5 - 4y^4 + 4y^3 + 2x^2y^2 - xy^2 + 2x^2y + 2xy + x^4 + x^3$

These three segments give three possible choices for γ, namely $\gamma = 2$, $\gamma = 1/2$, and $\gamma = 0$. In all three cases the corresponding equation has non-zero roots. In the case of $\gamma = 2$, the equation is $2c+1 = 0$, hence $c = -1/2$. For $\gamma = 1/2$, the equation is $4c^3 + 2c = 0$, the non-zero solutions are $\pm\frac{1}{\sqrt{-2}}$. Finally for $\gamma = 0$, the equation is $c^5 - 4c^4 + 4c^3 = c^3(c-2)^2 = 0$, the non-zero solution is 2. This gives four different smallest terms of Puiseux series solutions for the equation $f(x, y) = 0$. Since the degree of f in y is 5 and f is square free there are five different Puiseux series solutions. Hence two of these solutions must have the same smallest terms. This is the case for $y_4(x) = 2 + \left(\frac{1}{8} + \frac{\sqrt{-95}}{8}\right) x + \ldots$ and $y_5(x) = 2 + \left(\frac{1}{8} - \frac{\sqrt{-95}}{8}\right) x + \ldots$

Having found γ and c the same process we have performed with $y(x)$ is done for $y_1(x)$. However, $y_1(x)$ is not a root of the same polynomial f, but a solution of the equation

$$f_1(x, y_1) = x^{-\beta} f(x, x^{\gamma}(c + y_1)).$$

This process can be iterated until the desired number of terms are computed. For all iterations but the first one only values with $\gamma > 0$ are considered. In the example above there are four different f_1 depending on the choice of γ and c. For instance for $\gamma = 0$ and $c = 2$ (hence $\beta = 0$) we have $f_1(x, y_1) = y_1^5 + 6y_1^4 + 12y_1^3 + \left(8 - x + 2x^2\right) y_1^2 + \left(10x^2 - 2x\right) y_1 + x^3 + x^4 + 12x^2$. The Newton polygon of this polynomial has one segment with positive γ. The corresponding equation of this segment has two different non-zero roots; they show up as coefficients of x in the Puiseux series $y_4(x)$ and $y_5(x)$.

It can be proven that all Puiseux expansions of f can be computed by choosing all possible γ's and all roots of the corresponding equations.

Rational Puiseux expansion. In Duval (1987, 1989) a refinement of the classical Newton polygon method was introduced. The main idea is to compute local parametrizations of the branches instead of Puiseux series expansions with fractional exponents. Two local parametrizations $(x_1(t), y_1(t))$ and $(x_2(t), y_2(t))$ are equivalent if they have the same center, i.e., $x_1(0) = x_2(0)$ and $y_1(0) = y_2(0)$, and if there exists a power series $v(t) = a_1 t + a_2 t^2 + \ldots$, $a_1 \neq 0$ such that $x_1(t) = x_2(v(t))$ and $y_1(t) = y_2(v(t))$. Every equivalence class of parametrizations corresponds to a branch of the curve and is called a *place*. It can be shown that every place has a parametrization of the form $(\lambda t^n, y(t))$. In the example above the Puiseux series expansions

$$y_2(x) = \frac{\sqrt{-2}}{2} x^{1/2} - \frac{1}{8} x + \frac{27\sqrt{-2}}{128} x^{3/2} + \ldots \quad \text{and}$$

$$y_3(x) = -\frac{\sqrt{-2}}{2} x^{1/2} - \frac{1}{8} x - \frac{27\sqrt{-2}}{128} x^{3/2} + \ldots$$

correspond both with the place

$$(x_2(t), y_2(t)) = (-2t^2, t + \frac{1}{4}t^2 - \frac{27}{32}t^3 + \ldots).$$

In fact, in this case we obtain the local parametrization of the place from $(x, y_2(x))$ by setting $t = \frac{\sqrt{-2}}{2}x^{1/2}$ and from $(x, y_3(x))$ by setting $t = -\frac{\sqrt{-2}}{2}x^{1/2}$.

The rational Puiseux expansion algorithm detects this kind of parameter substitutions at the stage where the corresponding equation of a segment of the Newton polygon has to be solved. If it holds that all exponents in the equation

$$\sum_{\alpha_i + i\gamma = \beta} \bar{a}_i c^i = 0$$

have a greatest common divisor $q > 1$ then

$$\sum_{\alpha_i + i\gamma = \beta} \bar{a}_i c^i = \sum_{\alpha_i + i\gamma = \beta} \bar{a}_i z^{i/q} \quad \text{and} \quad z = c^q.$$

It suffices to consider the solutions of $\sum_{\alpha_i + i\gamma = \beta} \bar{a}_i z^{i/q} = 0$. All other solutions can be obtained by multiplication with q-th roots of unity. This is taken care of by setting $x(t) = t^{mq}$, if $x(t) = t^m$ has been computed so far, starting with $x(t) = t$. Additionally it is possible to avoid algebraic extension for the coefficients if one allows $x(t) = \lambda t^m$. The λ is updated together with the exponent m.

Let us again consider the example. For the computation of the first term of the parametrization we have studied the Newton polygon in Fig. 4. The segment corresponding to $\gamma = 1/2$ has the equation $4c^2 + 2 = 0$. We obtain

$$4c^2 + 2 = 4z + 2 = 0.$$

This equation has the root $z = -1/2$. It is sufficient to consider only one expansion for $y(t)$ with the first term $1 \cdot t^1$ and set $x(t) = -2t^2$. In this way the algebraic extension of $\mathbb{Q}$ by $\sqrt{-2}$ can be avoided.

A description of the algorithm in great detail as well as a complexity analysis is given in Duval (1989).

· Newton-like iteration to compute terms around regular points. In Kung and Traub (1978) a method very similar to the Newton iteration for numerical approximation of the solutions of equations is developed. It works for regular points of a curve C. Let us assume that the origin is a regular point of C and that $\frac{\partial f}{\partial y}(0, 0) \neq 0$, where $f \in K[x, y]$ is the equation for C. Let $y(x)$ be a power series expansion of f around the origin, i.e., $f(x, y(x)) = 0$. In the case of a regular center there are no fractional exponents occurring in $y(x)$. The following iteration procedure for $Y_i(x)$ converges to $y(x)$:

1. $Y_0(x) = 0$,
2. $Y_{i+1}(x) = Y_i(x) - \frac{f(x, Y_i(x))}{\frac{\partial f}{\partial y}(x, Y_i(x))}$.

It can be shown that the lowest order term of $y(x) - Y_i(x)$ has an exponent greater equal 2^i. In the paper of Kung and Traub this method is called *Newton-like* iteration.

For computing a series expansion of a curve C around a singular origin one can first use the Newton polygon method. Let f_1 be the transformed polynomial after the first Newton polygon step describing a curve C_1. If C_1 has a regular point at the origin the Newton-like iteration method can be employed. Otherwise another Newton polygon step is performed. It can be proven that after a finite number of Newton polygon steps one arrives at the regular case. So for the computation of a large number of terms the asymptotically faster method of Newton-like iteration can be used.

Furthermore it can be seen that with the Newton-like iteration no algebraic extensions of the current field of computation are needed. Therefore all algebraic extensions happen during the computation of the "singular part" by the Newton polygon method. The field L which contains all coefficients of the local parametrization of the branches of a curve is an finite extension of K.

3.2 Application of series expansion methods to the plotting of planar curves

In the following it will be outlined how Puiseux series expansions can be used to plot topological correct pictures of planar curves. First, it should be noted that there exist other algorithms to reach this goal. For instance, one can analyse the topology of an algebraic curve around a singularity with the help of a desingularization process by quadratic transformations. For algorithmic description and references to implementations of this procedure see, e.g., Henry and Merle (1987a, b) or Rybowicz (1990). In Hoffmann (1988, 1989) and Bajaj et al. (1988), an algorithm to trace an algebraic curve through a singularity by tracing the desingularized model of the curve is described.

Another possibility to analyse the singularity of an algebraic curve is by computing the equations of the tangent cone of the algebraic set (Mora 1982). This method has the advantage that it works for algebraic sets of arbitrary dimension and not only for curves.

In CASA a straightforward algorithm to plot the real part of a plane algebraic curve is implemented, see Gebauer (1990). However, this algorithm may produce topological incorrect pictures of curves because the heuristics which are implemented to decide how to connect sample points on the curve (obtained by numerical approximation) may fail. First a rough description of the algorithm in CASA is given.

Plotting of planar curves in CASA

Let us assume we want to plot the real part of a curve C defined by a polynomial $f \in K[x, y]$. The first step is to compute all critical points of C with respect

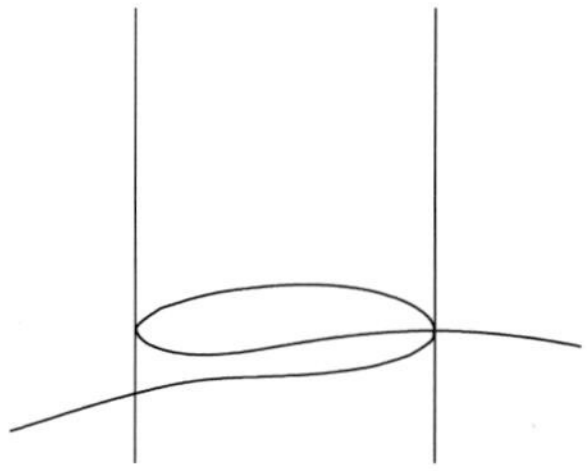

Fig. 5. Graph of $y^5 - 4y^4 + 4y^3 + 2x^2y^2 - xy^2 + 2x^2y + 2xy + x^4 + x^3$, partitioned in 3 slabs

to x, i.e., all points (x_0, y_0) on C such that (x_0, y_0) is a singularity of C or C has a tangent parallel to the y-axis in (x_0, y_0). x_0 is called a critical value of C with respect to x if there exists a y_0 such that (x_0, y_0) is a critical point of C with respect to x. (These critical values are exactly the zeros of the resultant of f and $\frac{\partial f}{\partial y}$ with respect to y.) Let $\{x_1, \ldots, x_N\}$ be the set of critical values of C with respect to x. The vertical lines $x = x_1, \ldots, x = x_N$ partition the xy-plane into slabs. Figure 5 shows the curve and the slabs for the previously considered example.

For each vertical line $x = x'$, ($x_{i-1} < x' < x_i$ for some i or $x' < x_1$ or $x' > x_N$) in the i-th slab it holds that the number of real intersections with C (that is the number of real branches of C lying over x') is constant. Plotting the branches within each slab is easy. Since there are no intersections between two branches one has just to sort the sampled points for one specific x-coordinate by the y-coordinate and to connect the corresponding points according to this order.

In the example the singularities are at $(0, 0)$ and $(0, 2)$, furthermore $(-1, 0)$ is a point with a vertical tangent. The set of critical values with respect to x is $\{-1, 0\}$. The leftmost slab contains only one real branch. The slab $]-1, 0[\times \mathbb{R}$ contains three real branches, two of them start in the point $(-1, 0)$. All three end in the singularity $(0, 0)$. The rightmost slab also contains only one real branch. At the singularity $(0, 2)$ two complex branches meet. In this example the picture produced by CASA is correct. Wrong pictures may be produced if the two singularities are closer together. The heuristics by which CASA decides which branches to connect may fail.

A theorem on the topological structure of an algebraic set around a singularity

Following J. Milnor (1968) (see also Stobbe 1992) a theorem which describes the topology of an algebraic set around a regular point or an isolated singularity is presented in the following. First some notations are introduced.

Let V be an algebraic set. Let $\bar{x} \in K^n$ be a either a simple point of V or an isolated point of the set of singularities of V. (If V is one-dimensional then the set of singularities of V is at most zero-dimensional. Hence, all singularities of curves are isolated.) Let $S_\epsilon(\bar{x})$ denote the sphere around $\bar{x}$ with radius ϵ, i.e.,

$$S_\epsilon(\bar{x}) = \{x \mid \|x - \bar{x}\| = \epsilon\},$$

$\|\cdot\|$ denoting the Euclidean norm. Likewise, let $D_\epsilon(\bar{x})$ denote the closed disk

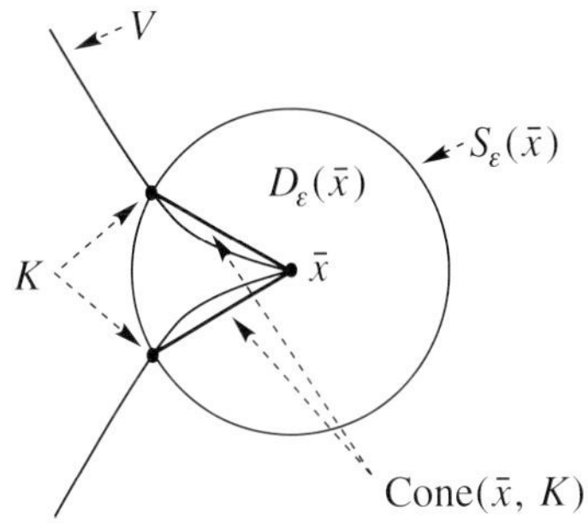

Fig. 6. $(D_\epsilon(\bar{x}), V \cap D_\epsilon(\bar{x}))$ is homeomorphic to $(\text{Cone}(\bar{x}, S_\epsilon(\bar{x})), \text{Cone}(\bar{x}, K))$

around $\bar{x}$ with radius ϵ, i.e.,

$$D_\epsilon(\bar{x}) = \{x \mid \|x - \bar{x}\| \leq \epsilon\}.$$

By $\text{Cone}(\bar{x}, K)$ we denote the cone with apex $\bar{x}$ over the set K, i.e., the set of all line segments connecting $\bar{x}$ with some point in K,

$$\text{Cone}(\bar{x}, K) = \bigcup_{k \in K} \{tk + (1 - t)\bar{x} \mid 0 \leq t \leq 1\}.$$

Note that $D_\epsilon(\bar{x}) = \text{Cone}(\bar{x}, S_\epsilon(\bar{x}))$. Now we can give the theorem.

Theorem 1 (Milnor). For small enough ϵ the intersection of V with $D_\epsilon(\bar{x})$ is homeomorphic to the cone over $K = V \cap S_\epsilon(\bar{x})$. In fact the pair $(D_\epsilon(\bar{x}), V \cap D_\epsilon(\bar{x}))$ is homeomorphic to the pair $(\text{Cone}(\bar{x}, S_\epsilon(\bar{x})), \text{Cone}(\bar{x}, K))$.

Proof. Milnor (1968). □

Figure 6 visualizes the theorem. From the proof one can see that ϵ must be chosen small enough such that $D_\epsilon(\bar{x}) \setminus \{\bar{x}\}$ contains no singularity.

This theorem is useful for the plotting of curves around singularities. Once we have given a small enough ϵ such that the theorem holds we know which branches to connect to the singularity. The branches can be easily plotted within $D_\epsilon(\bar{x})$ because they do not intersect.

Once we know the number of real branches of a curve C meeting a certain singularity $\bar{x}$ we can determine a small enough ϵ in the following way: We choose ϵ such that $D_\epsilon(\bar{x}) \setminus \{\bar{x}\}$ contains no critical point of C with respect to x or y. Then we compute the number of real intersections of $S_\epsilon(\bar{x})$ and C, counted with multiplicities. If this number corresponds to the number of real branches in $\bar{x}$ then ϵ is small enough. The question how to determine the number of real branches of a curve at a certain point is answered in the next paragraph.

A theorem on the number of real branches at a point of an algebraic curve

The *coefficient field* of a series is the smallest field which contains all coefficients of the series. In Duval (1989) it is proven that the coefficient field of the rational

Puiseux expansion of a given branch of a curve C is "the smallest one" among the coefficient fields of the parametrizations of this branch. For the real numbers, we get the following result.

Theorem 2 (Duval). Let $f \in \mathbb{R}[x, y]$ and let $\{(x_k(t), y_k(t)) \mid 1 \leq k \leq \mu\}$ be a system of rational Puiseux expansions of f. Then for each k the branch of C parametrized by $(x_k(t), y_k(t))$ is real if and only if every coefficient of $x_k(t)$ and of $y_k(t)$ is a real number.

Proof. Duval (1989). □

This theorem leads to a simple determination of the real branches of C since it can be decided whether every coefficient of $x_k(t)$ and of $y_k(t)$ is real with a finite computation. As remarked earlier it is sufficient to check that the finitely many coefficients of the "singular part" (computed by the Newton polygon method) are real numbers (cf. Sect. 3.1). This allows us to count the number of real branches for an arbitrary point on C.

Example 2. In the following we will use CASA to illustrate how to use Puiseux expansion to improve plotting curves. In Example 1, the algebraic curve A, defined by the polynomial $f = y^5 - 4y^4 + 4y^3 + 2x^2y^2 - xy^2 + 2x^2y + 2xy + x^4 + x^3$, was created in a CASA session. Now let us go on with this session and determine the singularities of A.

```
> tsolve(singLocus(A));
                algebraic_set([y - 2, - 6768 x], [x, y], attr),
                    algebraic_set([y, 2 x], [x, y], attr)
```

The function `singLocus` computes the derivatives of f with respect to x and y and creates an algebraic set consisting of these derivatives and f. The function `tsolve` splits the ideal of a given algebraic set into the union of algebraic sets with a triangularized basis. In this example it is easy to see that $(0, 0)$ and $(0, 2)$ are singularities. Around these singularities we compute expansions in power series by the rational Puiseux expansion algorithm. In other words we switch from a representation in implicit form to a *representation by places* (CASA function name `impl2plac`). We start with an expansion around $(0, 0)$.

```
> B := impl2plac(A,[0,0]);
 B := algebraic_set([[proc(powparm) ... end, proc(powparm) ... end],
                    [proc(powparm) ... end, proc(powparm) ... end]], [T],
    attr)
```

The result is a list of lists of function which evaluate the coefficients up to a given order on demand. However, the "singular part" will be always displayed. This is done by the CASA function `shAlgSet`.

```
> shAlgSet(B,5);
The algebraic set is known to have the following properties:
None are known.
It is given by the following places:
[
                2          4      5            2             2   27   3         4      5
[T, - 1/2 T  + 1/8 T  + O(T )], [- 2 T , T + 1/4 T  - --- T  - 7/8 T  + O(T )]
                                                          32
]
```

We see that all coefficients are real numbers. Hence, by Theorem 2, there are two real branches around (0, 0). Next comes the expansion around (0, 2).

```
> C := impl2plac(A,[0,2]);
 C := algebraic_set([[proc(powparm) ... end, proc(powparm) ... end],
                                [proc(powparm) ... end, proc(powparm) ... end]], [T],
     attr)
--------------------------------------------------------------------------------
> shAlgSet(C,5);
The algebraic set is known to have the following properties:
None are known.
It is given by the following places:
[
                   1/2   1/2
[(1/12 - 1/12 I 5     19   ) T,
             /   47     49       1/2   1/2\  2   / 9137     25771       1/2   1/2\  3
    2 + T + |- --- + ----- I 5     19    | T  + |----- - ------- I 5     19    | T
             \  144   13680               /      \41040   3898800               /
          /    36648193     172182383      1/2   1/2\  4      5
       + |- --------- + ----------- I 5     19    | T  + O(T )
          \  187142400   17778528000               /
    ],
                   1/2   1/2
[(1/12 + 1/12 I 5     19   ) T,
             /   47     49       1/2   1/2\  2   / 9137     25771       1/2   1/2\  3
    2 + T + |- --- - ----- I 5     19    | T  + |----- + ------- I 5     19    | T
             \  144   13680               /      \41040   3898800               /
          /    36648193     172182383      1/2   1/2\  4      5
       + |- --------- - ----------- I 5     19    | T  + O(T )
          \  187142400   17778528000               /
    ]
]
```

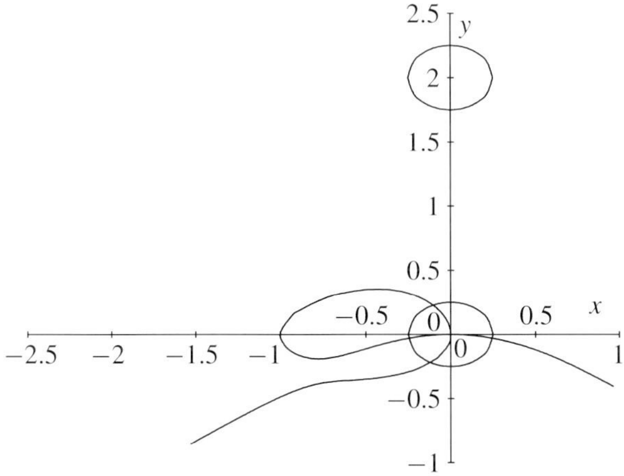

Fig. 7. The curve with circle of radius 1/4 around the singular points

Around $(0, 2)$ there are no real branches. So for all sufficiently small neighborhoods U of $(0, 2)$ it holds that $U \setminus \{(0, 2)\}$ contains no real points of A.

In order to apply Theorem 1 we have to find small enough circles around $(0, 0)$ and $(0, 2)$ such that the circle around $(0, 0)$ has four real intersections with A and the circle around $(0, 2)$ has no real intersection with A. This part is not implemented in CASA, yet. By inspection of Fig. 7 one can see that in both cases a circle of radius $1/4$ is sufficient.

In the example CASA plots a correct picture without using Puiseux series expansion. However, one can easily conceive a series of examples where the two singularities move arbitrarily close to each other. For such an example it may happen that CASA connects branches to the wrong singularity.

Acknowledgements

The work reported herein was supported by the Austrian Fonds zur Förderung der wissenschaftlichen Forschung, project number P8573-PHY, and the wiss.-techn. Abkommen Österreich – Spanien, Integrierte Aktion 12.

References

Abhyankar, S. S. (1975): Approximate roots of polynomials and special cases of the epimorphism theorem. Lecture notes by Chris Christensen, Division of Mathematical Sciences, Purdue University, West Lafayette, IN.

Abhyankar, S. S., Bajaj, C. (1988a): Automatic parametrization of rational curves and surfaces IV: algebraic space curves. Res. Rep., Computer Science Department, Purdue University, West Lafayette, IN.

Abhyankar, S. S., Bajaj, C. (1988b): Automatic parametrization of rational curves and surfaces III: algebraic plane curves. Comput. Aided Geom. Des. 5: 309–321.

Abhyankar, S. S., Bajaj, C. (1989): Computations with algebraic curves. In: Gianni, P. (ed.): Symbolic and algebraic computation. Springer, Berlin Heidelberg New York Tokyo, pp. 274–284 (Lecture notes in computer science, vol. 358).

Bajaj, C., Royappa, A. (1989): GANITH: an algebraic geometry package. Res. Rep. csd-tr-914, Computer Science Department, Purdue University, West Lafayette, IN.

Bajaj, C., Royappa, A. (1990): The GANITH algebraic geometry toolkit. In: Miola, A. (ed.): Design and implementation of symbolic computation systems. Springer, Berlin Heidelberg New York Tokyo, pp. 268–269 (Lecture notes in computer science, vol. 429).

Bajaj, C., Hoffmann, C. M., Lynch, R. E., Hopcroft, J. E. H. (1988): Tracing surface intersections. Comput. Aided Geom. Des. 5: 285–307.

Bennett, D. (1990): Interactive display and manipulation of curves and surfaces of mathematical functions. ACM SIGSAM Bull. 24 (3): 33–34.

Brieskorn, E., Knörrer, H. (1986): Plane algebraic curves. Birkhäuser, Basel.

Char, B. W., Geddes, K. O., Gonnet, G. H., Leong, B. L., Monagan, M. B., Watt, S. M. (1991a): Maple V language reference manual. Springer, Berlin Heidelberg New York Tokyo.

Char, B. W., Geddes, K. O., Gonnet, G. H., Leong, B. L., Monagan, M. B., Watt, S. M.

(1991b): Maple V library reference manual. Springer, Berlin Heidelberg New York Tokyo.

Char, B. W., Geddes, K. O., Gonnet, G. H., Leong, B. L., Monagan, M. B., Watt, S. M. (1992): First leaves: a tutorial introduction to Maple V. Springer, Berlin Heidelberg New York Tokyo.

Duval, D. (1987): Diverses questions relatives au calcul formel avec des nombres algébriques. Ph.D. thesis, Institut Fourier, Grenoble, France.

Duval, D. (1989): Rational Puiseux expansion. Compos. Math. 70: 119–154.

Eichler, M. (1966): Introduction to the theory of algebraic numbers and functions. Academic Press, London.

Gebauer, R. (1990): Plotting algebraic curves. Tech. Rep. RISC Linz 90-69.0.

Gebauer, R., Kalkbrener, M., Wall, B., Winkler, F. (1991): CASA: a computer algebra package for constructive algebraic geometry. In: Watt, S. M. (ed.): ISSAC '91, Bonn, Germany, July 1991, pp. 403–410.

Henry, J. P. G., Merle, M. (1987a): Complexity of computation of embedded resolution of algebraic curves. In: Davenport, J. H. (ed.): EUROCAL '87. Springer, Berlin Heidelberg New York Tokyo, pp. 381–390 (Lecture notes in computer science, vol. 378).

Henry, J. P. G., Merle, M. (1987b): Puiseux pairs, resolution of curves and lazy evaluation. Res. Rep., Centre de Mathématiques, École Polytechniques, Palaiseau.

Hoffmann, C. M. (1988): Algebraic curves. In: Rice, J. (ed.): Mathematical aspects of scientific software. Springer, Berlin Heidelberg New York Tokyo, pp. 101–122 (The IMA volumes in mathematics and its applications, vol. 14).

Hoffmann, C. M. (1989): Geometric and solid modelling – an introduction. Morgan Kauffmann, San Mateo, CA.

Kalkbrener, M. (1990a): Birational projections of irreducible varieties. Tech. Rep. RISC Linz 90-59.0.

Kalkbrener, M. (1990b): Implicitization by using Gröbner bases. Tech. Rep. RISC Linz 90-27.0.

Kalkbrener, M. (1991a): Implicitization of rational curves and surfaces. In: Sakata, S. (ed.): Applied algebra, algebraic algorithms, error-correcting codes. Springer, Berlin Heidelberg New York Tokyo, pp. 249–259 (Lecture notes in computer science, vol. 508).

Kalkbrener, M. (1991b): Three contributions to elimination theory. Ph.D. thesis, Research Institute for Symbolic Computation, University of Linz, Linz, Austria.

Kredel, H., Weispfenning, V. (1988): Computing dimension and independent sets for polynomial ideals. J. Symb. Comput. 6: 231–248.

Kung, H. T., Traub, J. F. (1978): All algebraic functions can be computed fast. J. ACM 25: 245–260.

Milnor, J. (1968): Singular points of complex hypersurfaces. Princeton University Press, Princeton.

Mora, F. (1982): An algorithm to compute the equation of tangent cones. In: Calmet, J. (ed.): Computer algebra. Springer, Berlin Heidelberg New York Tokyo, pp. 273–280 (Lecture notes in computer science, vol. 144).

Newton, I. (1969): Methods of series and fluxions. In: Whiteside, D. T. (ed.): The mathematical papers of Isaac Newton. Cambridge University Press, Cambridge.

Puiseux, M. V. (1850): Recherches sur les fonctions algebriques. J. Math. Pures Appl. 15: 365–480.

Ritt, J. F. (1950): Differential algebra. American Mathematical Society, New York.

Rybowicz, M. (1990): Sur le calcul des places et des anneaux d'entiers d'un corps de fonctions algebriques. Ph.D. thesis, Université de Limoges, Limoges, France.

Sendra, J. R., Winkler, F. (1991): Symbolic parametrization of curves. J. Symb. Comput. 12: 607–632.

Stillman, M., Stillman, M., Bayer, D. (1989): Macaulay user manual. Available via FTP on site 128.103.28.10 (math.harvard.edu).

Stobbe, R. (1992): Darstellung algebraischer Kurven mittels Computergrafik. Master's thesis, Fachbereich Mathematik der Universität Kaiserslautern, Kaiserslautern, Germany.

van der Waerden, B. L. (1973): Einführung in die algebraische Geometrie, 2nd edn. Springer, Berlin Heidelberg New York.

Walker, R. J. (1978): Algebraic curves, 2nd edn. Springer, Berlin Heidelberg New York.

Wall, B. (1991a): CASA: computer algebra software for constructive algebraic geometry in Maple – a primer. Tech. Rep. RISC Linz 91-34.1.

Wall, B. (1991b): Puiseux expansion: an annotated bibliography. Tech. Rep. RISC Linz 91-46.0.

Wang, D. (1989): A method for determining the finite basis of an ideal from its characteristic set with application to irreducible decomposition of algebraic varieties. Tech. Rep. RISC Linz 89-50.0.

Wang, D. (1992): Irreducible decomposition of algebraic varieties via characteristic sets and Gröbner bases. Comput. Aided Geom. Des. 9: 471–484.

Wu, W. (1984): Basic principles of mechanical theorem proving in elementary geometries. J. Syst. Sci. Math. Sci. 4: 207–235.

Reasoning about geometric problems using an elimination method

Dongming Wang

1 Introduction

The present work relates to a paper by Wang (1991) in which he explained the reasoning about a set of selected, geometry-related problems by using the algebraic methods of characteristic sets (Ritt 1950; Wu 1984a, b), Gröbner bases (Buchberger 1985) and cylindrical algebraic decomposition (Collins 1975). Its main purpose is to demonstrate how to deal with the same set of geometric problems by using another algebraic method which is based on some elimination procedures proposed by Wang (1993). We use the same formulations of the problems (with slight modifications when necessary) and the same set of illustrative examples given previously (Wang 1991). It is shown that for most of the examples our new method takes less computing time than the methods of characteristic sets and Gröbner bases do.

The discovery of our elimination method was inspired by the ideas underlying the elimination theory of Seidenberg (1956a, b, 1969) and by a thorough study of Ritt–Wu's characteristic set method. The new method differs from the methods of characteristic sets and Gröbner bases by its style and structure, but it can be applied to most of the examples to which the other two methods are applicable. The method is somewhat similar to the characteristic set method in terms of goal and applicability while it has bypassed several difficulties inherent in characteristic sets computation, resulting in a considerable advance with regard to practical efficiency.

We shall give a brief review of the elimination method in Sect. 2 for the purpose of geometric applications to be discussed in later sections. The full details of the method are given in Wang (1993). Sections 3–10 are on reasoning about selected problems using the method. The significance and importance of reasoning about such problems have been pointed out previously (Wang 1991) and will no longer be stressed. The motivation for each problem has also been explained (Wang 1991) and will not be repeated unless necessary. The materials in these sections will be presented in such a way that the reader can draw a parallel with those in the earlier report (Wang 1991) for the sake of comparison.

The methods for solving the geometric problems are described informally. Their correctness either follows from the theorems in Sect. 2 or can be seen from the relevant work in the cited references. A number of footnotes are given to explain some technical details. The experiments reported along with the examples are made by a draft implementation of the elimination method in Maple 4.3 running on an Apollo DN10000 under a UNIX operating system (the same computer algebra system and machine we used for the experiments in Wang 1991).

This work as well as our previous work on the same subject is carried out in the frame of an ESPRIT project on Mechanizing Deduction in the Logics of Practical Reasoning (MEDLAR I and II), where algebraic methods are considered of interest and representative for practical reasoning in several aspects. It is believed that the reasoning about geometric problems using algebraic methods is a challenging subject to automatic deduction and its success will contribute to the development of intelligent systems in geometry engineering.

2 An elimination method for polynomial systems

In this section we briefly review the functionality of a general elimination method for polynomial systems proposed by the author in extending the ideas of A. Seidenberg (1956a, b). A detailed description of this method is given in Wang (1993).

2.1 Definitions and notations

Let

$\boldsymbol{K}$	be a fixed field of characteristic 0,
$x_1 \prec \ldots \prec x_n$	n variables with the fixed ordering, and
$\boldsymbol{K}[x_1, \ldots, x_n]$	the ring of n-variate polynomials over $\boldsymbol{K}$.

We use the typed variables

$P, Q, F, H, \ldots$	for non-zero polynomials in $\boldsymbol{K}[x_1, \ldots, x_n]$,
$PS, QS, US, \ldots$	finite sets or lists of non-zero polynomials (or polynomial sets/lists for short),
$[PS, QS], [TF, US], \ldots$	pairs of polynomial sets or lists, and
$\boldsymbol{Q}, \boldsymbol{R}, \boldsymbol{C}$	the rational, real, complex number fields.

For any polynomial $P \in \boldsymbol{K}[x_1, \ldots, x_n]$ and a variable x_i, the degree of P in x_i is denoted by $\deg(P, x_i)$. If P is not a constant (i.e., $P \notin \boldsymbol{K}$), then the variable x_l with smallest index l such that $P \in \boldsymbol{K}[x_1, \ldots, x_l]$ is called the *leading variable* of P, denoted by $\mathrm{lvar}(P)$. For convenience, we define the leading variable of any constant to be x_0 which is $\prec x_1$. For a non-constant polynomial P, the leading coefficient of P with respect to $\mathrm{lvar}(P)$ is called the *initial* of P, denoted by $\mathrm{ini}(P)$. Sometimes, we use the triple $\mathrm{index}(P) = [t\ x\ d]$ to characterize the polynomial P, where t is the number of actual terms in P, $x = \mathrm{lvar}(P)$ and $d = \deg(P, x)$. If $\mathrm{ini}(P) = I$ and $\mathrm{index}(P) = [t\ x\ d]$, then $\mathrm{red}(P) = P - Ix^d$ is called the *reductum* of P. For two polynomials P and Q with $\text{lvar}(Q) \neq x_0$, we denote, by $\text{prem}(P, Q)$, the *pseudo-remainder* of P with respect to Q in $\text{lvar}(Q)$. For a polynomial set PS, we write $\text{prem}(PS, Q)$ for $\{\text{prem}(P, Q) \mid P \in PS\}$.

By a polynomial system we mean a pair $[PS, QS]$ of polynomial sets with $PS \neq \emptyset$. The zero set of $[PS, QS]$ (or the difference set of zeros of PS and of QS), denoted by $\text{Zero}(PS/QS)$, is the totality of those common zeros of the polynomials in PS which are not zeros of any polynomial in QS. We write $\text{Zero}(PS)$ for $\text{Zero}(PS/\emptyset)$ and $\text{Zero}(PS/Q)$ for $\text{Zero}(PS/\{Q\})$.

A finite non-empty list

$$TF = [T_1, T_2, \ldots, T_r]$$

of non-constant polynomials is called a *triangular form* if

$$\text{lvar}(T_1) \prec \text{lvar}(T_2) \prec \ldots \prec \text{lvar}(T_r).$$

Let Q be any other polynomial. It is said to be *reduced* with respect to TF if $\deg(Q, \text{lvar}(T_i)) < \deg(T_i, \text{lvar}(T_i))$ for all i. The polynomial $\text{prem}(\ldots\text{prem}(Q, T_r), \ldots, T_1)$, denoted simply by $\text{prem}(Q, TF)$, is called the pseudo-remainder of Q with respect to TF.

A *triangular system* is a pair $[TF, US]$ of which TF is a triangular form and US is a polynomial set such that $\text{Zero}(\text{ini}(T)) \cap \text{Zero}(TF/US) = \emptyset$ in any extension field of $\boldsymbol{K}$ for all $T \in TF$. A triangular system $[TF, US]$ is said to be *fine* if $\text{prem}(U, TF) \neq 0$ for all $U \in US$. It is said to be *perfect* if $\text{Zero}(TF/US) \neq \emptyset$ in some extension field of $\boldsymbol{K}$.

2.2 Zero decomposition of polynomial systems

For any polynomial system $[PS, QS]$, one can compute a sequence of fine triangular systems $[TF_1, US_1], \ldots, [TF_e, US_e]$ such that

$$\text{Zero}(PS/QS) = \bigcup_{i=1}^{e} \text{Zero}(TF_i/US_i). \tag{2.1}$$

This is done by using the algorithm PTriSys described below which computes, by eliminating the variables from x_n to x_1, a pair $[TF, US]$ and a set $\Delta = \{[PS_1, QS_1], \ldots, [PS_t, QS_t]\}$ of polynomial systems such that

$$\text{Zero}(PS/QS) = \text{Zero}(TF/US) \cup \bigcup_{i=1}^{t} \text{Zero}(PS_i/QS_i),$$

where either $[TF, US]$ is a fine triangular system, or $TF \cap \boldsymbol{K} \neq \emptyset$, or $0 \in US$. In the first case, $[TF, US]$ is called a *principal triangular system* of $[PS, QS]$ (or of PS when $QS = \emptyset$) and $\text{Zero}(TF/US)$ contains in general the majority of zeros of $[PS, QS]$. In the latter two cases, $\text{Zero}(TF/US)$ is empty and thus can be deleted from the decomposition.

Algorithm PTriSys.
Input: $[PS, QS]$; Output: $[TF, US]$, Δ.

1. Set $TF \leftarrow PS$, $US \leftarrow QS$, $\Delta \leftarrow \emptyset$.
2. For $i = n, \dots, 1$ do:
   2.1. If $TF \cap \boldsymbol{K} \neq \emptyset$ then the procedure terminates. Otherwise, set $MS \leftarrow \{M \in TF \mid \operatorname{lvar}(M) = x_i\}$. If $MS = \emptyset$ then go back to step 2 for next i.
   2.2. Let $T \in MS$ have smallest degree in x_i and set $MS \leftarrow MS \setminus \{T\}$. If $\operatorname{ini}(T) \notin \boldsymbol{K}$ then set $\Delta \leftarrow \Delta \cup \{[TF \setminus \{T\} \cup \{\operatorname{ini}(T), \operatorname{red}(T)\}, US]\}$, $US \leftarrow US \cup \{\operatorname{ini}(T)\}$.
   2.3. If $MS \neq \emptyset$ then compute $TF \leftarrow TF \setminus MS \cup \operatorname{prem}(MS, T) \setminus \{0\}$ and go to step 2.1.
   2.4. Compute $US \leftarrow \operatorname{prem}(US, T)$. If $0 \in US$ then the procedure terminates.

Applying the algorithm PTriSys to each of the produced polynomial systems $[PS_i, QS_i]$, one should get further triangular systems and polynomial systems. This procedure will terminate so that one arrives at a zero decomposition of the form (2.1). $\operatorname{Zero}(PS/QS) = \emptyset$ if $e = 0$. Hence, the following theorem can be concluded.

Theorem A (Wang 1993). There is an algorithm which computes, for any polynomial system $[PS, QS]$, a finite sequence of fine triangular systems $[TF_1, US_1]$, $\dots$, $[TF_e, US_e]$ such that the zero decomposition (2.1) holds.

2.3 Projection and irreducible zero decomposition

Since the zero set of a fine triangular system may be empty, some empty components in the zero decomposition (2.1) are not necessarily detected. In other words, by only using Theorem A we are unable to determine the emptiness of the zero set of any given polynomial system and thus unable to completely determine the solvability of any system of polynomial equations and inequations. For this determination as well as for other reasons, we have to perform elimination with projection or irreducibility test.

Let $[PS, QS]$ be any polynomial system and k $(0 \leq k \leq n)$ an integer. The projection of $\operatorname{Zero}(PS/QS)$ onto $[x_1, \dots, x_k]$, denoted sometimes as $\operatorname{Proj}_{[x_1,\dots,x_k]} \operatorname{Zero}(PS/QS)$, is defined to be the set

$$\{(x_1, \dots, x_k) \mid \exists x_{k+1}, \dots, x_n \quad \text{such that} \quad (x_1, \dots, x_n) \in \operatorname{Zero}(PS/QS)\}.$$

In particular, $\operatorname{Proj}_{[x_1,\dots,x_n]} \operatorname{Zero}(PS/QS) = \operatorname{Zero}(PS/QS)$ (without projection) and $\operatorname{Proj}\operatorname{Zero}(PS/QS)$ for the case $k = 0$ (with full projection) is understood as *true* if $\operatorname{Zero}(PS/QS) \neq \emptyset$ and *false* otherwise.

Now let us modify the elimination algorithm PTriSys described in the preceding subsection as follows: Instead of computing $US \leftarrow \operatorname{prem}(US, T)$ in step 2.4, set $US^* \leftarrow \{U \in US \mid \operatorname{lvar}(U) \succ x_i\}$. If $US^* \neq \emptyset$, then split the polynomial system $[TF, US]$ into finitely many systems $[TF, US_l]$, where each US_l is obtained from US by replacing every $U \in US^*$ with one of its coefficients with respect to those variables which actually appear in U and are $\succ x_i$. After this splitting, every US_l should contain no polynomial with leading variable $\succ x_i$. Next, let $US_l^* \leftarrow \{U \in US_l \mid \mathrm{lvar}(U) = x_i\}$ for each l. If $US_l^* \neq \emptyset$, then compute $R_l \leftarrow \mathrm{prem}(\prod_{U \in US_l^*} U^{\deg(T, x_i)}, T)$ and set $US_l \leftarrow (US_l \setminus US_l^*) \cup \{R_l\}$.

The process explained above is called *projection* for the variable x_i. One can go through this process for every split system. Moreover, for each variable x_i one can perform the elimination with or without projection. In particular, the elimination may be performed with projection for $x_n, \ldots, x_k$ and without projection for $x_{k-1}, \ldots, x_1$ for any given integer k. In this case, we have the following theorem.

Theorem B (Wang 1993). There is an algorithm which computes, for any integer k $(0 \leq k \leq n)$ and any polynomial system $[PS, QS]$, a finite sequence of triangular systems $[TF_1, US_1], \ldots, [TF_e, US_e]$ such that the zero decomposition (2.1) holds and

$$\mathrm{Proj}_{[x_1,\ldots,x_k]} \mathrm{Zero}(PS/QS) = \bigcup_{i=1}^{e} \mathrm{Zero}(TF_i^{(k)}/US_i^{(k)}), \tag{2.2}$$

where $TF_i^{(k)} = TF_i \cap \boldsymbol{K}[x_1, \ldots, x_k]$ and $US_i^{(k)} = US_i \cap \boldsymbol{K}[x_1, \ldots, x_k]$. Moreover, $\mathrm{Proj}_{[x_1,\ldots,x_k]} \mathrm{Zero}(TF_i/US_i) = \mathrm{Zero}(TF_i^{(k)}/US_i^{(k)})$ for each i. If $k = 0$, then the triangular systems are all perfect.

If the elimination is performed only for $x_n, \ldots, x_k$ with projection (in this case, let the obtained polynomial systems be denoted by $[TF_i, US_i]$ still), then $[TF_i, US_i]$ is not necessarily a triangular system, but every TF_i contains at most one polynomial with leading variable x_i for $i \geq k$ and the zero relations (2.1) and (2.2) hold as well. For some applications in later sections, this is already sufficient to meet the requirement, while the computation may be much cheaper. However, for the simplicity of presentation we shall still use the above theorem.

A triangular form $TF = [T_1, \ldots, T_r]$ is said to be *irreducible* if T_1, as a polynomial in $\mathrm{lvar}(T_1)$, is irreducible, and for any k $(2 \leq k \leq r)$ there are no polynomials D and H_1, H_2 reduced with respect to $TF_{k-1} = [T_1, \ldots, T_{k-1}]$ with $\mathrm{lvar}(D) \prec \mathrm{lvar}(T_k)$, $\mathrm{lvar}(H_1) = \mathrm{lvar}(H_2) = \mathrm{lvar}(T_k)$ such that $\mathrm{prem}(D \cdot T_k - H_1 \cdot H_2, TF_{k-1}) = 0$. A triangular system $[TF, US]$ is said to be *irreducible* if TF is irreducible. It is easy to prove that any irreducible triangular system is perfect.

Now let us perform elimination without projection as in the preceding subsection to get a zero decomposition of the form (2.1). For each triangular system $[TF_i, US_i]$ we verify whether or not TF_i is irreducible by known methods of algebraic factorization (see Wang 1992a, 1994, for example). If TF_i is reducible, we can further decompose the triangular system into finitely many irreducible triangular systems (cf. Wang 1993). In conclusion we may state the following theorem.

Theorem C (Wang 1993). There is an algorithm which computes, for any polynomial system $[PS, QS]$, a finite sequence of irreducible triangular systems $[TF_1, US_1], \ldots, [TF_e, US_e]$ such that the zero decomposition (2.1) holds.

The set or sequence of (irreducible) triangular systems $[TF_1, US_1], \ldots, [TF_e, US_e]$ in the theorems will be called an *(irreducible) triangular series* of the polynomial system $[PS, QS]$ or the polynomial set PS when $QS = \emptyset$. Note that in case the triangular form TF_i is irreducible, the corresponding US_i in the decomposition can be replaced by the set of initials of the polynomials in TF_i for every i. The reader may refer to Wang (1993) for this and the correctness of the above theorems.

3 Mechanical geometry theorem proving

Research interests on this subject have been renewed since the breakthrough of Wu's algebraic method (Wu 1978, 1984a) in proving hundreds of non-trivial geometric theorems. We refer to Buchberger et al. (1988), Chou (1988), Kapur and Mundy (1989), Wu (1984a, b) for history, motivation, significance, importance, introduction and survey on various algebraic methods for geometry theorem proving.

3.1 Problem

By introducing coordinate systems as to establish a correspondence between standard geometric relations and algebraic expressions, the hypothesis and the conclusion of a geometric theorem may be expressed by means of polynomial equations (=), inequations (≠) and inequalities (≤, <). Let us restrict ourselves to such a class of theorems, called theorems of *equality type*, for which the algebraic formulations of the hypotheses and conclusions involve only polynomial equations and inequations, say of the form

$$\text{HYP} \quad \begin{array}{l} H_1(x_1, \ldots, x_n) = 0, \ldots, H_s(x_1, \ldots, x_n) = 0, \\ D_1(x_1, \ldots, x_n) \neq 0, \ldots, D_t(x_1, \ldots, x_n) \neq 0, \end{array}$$

$$\text{CON} \quad C(x_1, \ldots, x_n) = 0,$$

where $x_1, \ldots, x_n$ are geometric entities such as the coordinates of points and areas of triangles. These variables usually consist of two kinds: one of parameters and the other of geometric dependents. Proving the theorem amounts to deciding whether the formula

$$\begin{aligned} (\forall x_1, \ldots, x_n)[H_1(x_1, \ldots, x_n) = 0 \wedge \ldots \wedge H_s(x_1, \ldots, x_n) = 0 \\ \wedge D_1(x_1, \ldots, x_n) \neq 0 \wedge \ldots \wedge D_t(x_1, \ldots, x_n) \neq 0 \\ \Longrightarrow C(x_1, \ldots, x_n) = 0] \end{aligned} \tag{3.1}$$

is valid, and if not, finding some subsidiary conditions $D_1^*(x_1, \ldots, x_n) \neq 0, \ldots,$

$D^*_{t^*}(x_1, \ldots, x_n) \neq 0$ (which ensure the configuration of the geometric hypotheses to be in a generic position) so that the formula

$$\begin{aligned}(\forall x_1, \ldots, x_n)[H_1(x_1, \ldots, x_n) = 0 \wedge \ldots \wedge H_s(x_1, \ldots, x_n) = 0 \\ \wedge D_1(x_1, \ldots, x_n) \neq 0 \wedge \ldots \wedge D_t(x_1, \ldots, x_n) \neq 0 \\ \wedge D^*_1(x_1, \ldots, x_n) \neq 0 \wedge \ldots \wedge D^*_{t^*}(x_1, \ldots, x_n) \neq 0 \\ \Longrightarrow C(x_1, \ldots, x_n) = 0]\end{aligned} \tag{3.2}$$

becomes valid over the geometry-associated field $\boldsymbol{K}$ or some extension of $\boldsymbol{K}$.

3.2 Methods

In this section we present three methods based on our elimination procedures for the above algebraic decision problem of geometry theorem proving. For this purpose, set $PS = \{H_1, \ldots, H_s\}$ and $QS = \{D_1, \ldots, D_t\}$.

Method A (coarse form for confirming theorems).

1. Compute $[TF, US] \leftarrow$ PTriSys(PS, QS). If $TF \cap \boldsymbol{K} \neq \emptyset$ or $0 \in US$, then the hypothesis of the theorem is self-contradictory and the procedure terminates.
2. Compute $R \leftarrow \operatorname{prem}(C, TF)$. If $R \equiv 0$, then the theorem is true under the subsidiary conditions[1] $U \neq 0$ for $U \in US$. Otherwise, the theorem is not confirmed and the procedure terminates.
3. Analyze whether the subsidiary conditions are non-degeneracy conditions.

Usually, the geometric meanings of the algebraic subsidiary conditions can be easily explained,[2] and one is able to see from the geometric explanation whether a subsidiary condition is a non-degeneracy condition. In order to speak about genericity we sometimes separate the variables $x_1, \ldots, x_n$ into parameters and geometric dependents, and assume for simplicity that $x_1, \ldots, x_d$ are the former and $x_{d+1}, \ldots, x_n$ the latter. The identification between parameters and dependents can be done according to the geometric statement of the theorem and usually is easy. When the identification is necessary, we assume that it is done correctly and consider any inequation in $x_1, \ldots, x_d$ as a non-degeneracy condition. Thus, the triangular systems need to be computed only with respect to the geometrically dependent variables.

Whether or not the theorem is true in a degenerate case can be determined by using the above method in regarding the degeneracy condition as an additional hypothesis of the theorem.

---

1 Actually, if no polynomial is removed as a factor during the computation, only the initials of the polynomials in TF need to be considered for the subsidiary conditions, because Zero(PS) $\subset$ Zero(TF).

2 In our geometry theorem prover GEOTHER, most non-degeneracy conditions are provided in geometric form by means of predicates that can be automatically translated into English.

Method B (fine form for the algebraic decision problem of geometry theorem proving by using irreducible zero decomposition).

1. Compute an irreducible triangular series Ψ of $[PS, QS]$ over[3] $\boldsymbol{K}$. If $\Psi = \emptyset$, then the hypothesis of the theorem is self-contradictory and the procedure terminates. Otherwise, let $\Psi \leftarrow \{TF \mid [TF, US] \in \Psi\}$ (with some redundant TF removed as possible).

2. Compute $R_i \leftarrow \text{prem}(C, TF_i)$ for each $TF_i \in \Psi$. If $R_i \equiv 0$ for some i, then the theorem is true for the component TF_i. If $R_i \equiv 0$ for all i, then the theorem is universally true. If $R_i \not\equiv 0$ for all i, then the theorem is universally false. If $R_i \equiv 0$ for at least one but not all i, then the theorem is conditionally true. In this case, the subsidiary conditions for the theorem to be true are determined by excluding those triangular forms in Ψ for which the theorem is false.

3. If the theorem is conditionally true, then analyze whether the subsidiary conditions are non-degeneracy conditions.

To confirm theorems, Method B above can also be modified for computing the irreducible triangular series of $[PS, QS \cup \{C\}]$, see Method C described in Wang (1995).

Method C (fine form for determining whether or not a geometric theorem is generically true by using projection).

1. Compute a triangular series Ψ of $[PS, QS]$ with projection for $x_n, \ldots, x_1$ (i.e., $k = 0$) over $\boldsymbol{K}$. If $\Psi = \emptyset$, then the hypothesis of the theorem is self-contradictory and the procedure terminates.[4]

2. Compute a triangular series Ψ of $[PS, QS \cup \{C\}]$ with projection for $x_n, \ldots, x_{d+1}$ over $\boldsymbol{K}$ (cf. the remark following Theorem B). If $\Psi = \emptyset$, then the theorem is universally true. If $TF_i \cap \boldsymbol{K}[x_1, \ldots, x_d] \neq \emptyset$ for all $[TF_i, US_i] \in \Psi$, then the theorem is generically true. In this case, let $D_i^* = D_i^*(x_1, \ldots, x_d)$ be any polynomial in $TF_i \cap \boldsymbol{K}[x_1, \ldots, x_d]$ for each i; then all $D_i^* \neq 0$ constitute the non-degeneracy conditions for the theorem to be true. Otherwise, the theorem is not generically true.

3.3 Examples

Example A (Arnon 1986). Let $ABCD$ be a square, CG parallel to the diagonal BD, E on CG such that $BE = BD$ and F the intersection point of BE and DC (Fig. 1). Then $DF = DE$.

---

3 The computation can also be performed over $\boldsymbol{K}(x_1, \ldots, x_d)$ when $x_1, \ldots, x_d$ are correctly identified parameters from the variables and the theorem is considered only for the non-degenerate case.

4 This step is only to examine whether the hypothesis of the theorem is self-contradictory. It is not necessary if the theorem is already well-stated.

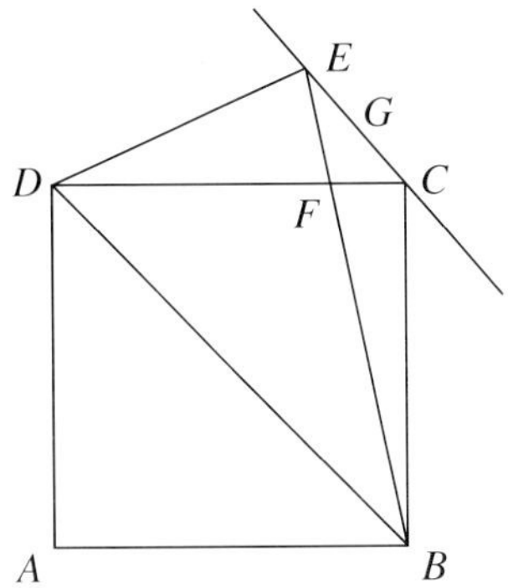

Fig. 1

We take the coordinates of the points as $A(0, 0)$, $B(u_1, 0)$, $C(u_1, u_1)$, $D(0, u_1)$, $E(x_1, x_2)$ and $F(x_3, u_1)$ as in Arnon (1986) and Wang (1991). Then the hypothesis and conclusion of the theorem may be expressed as

$$\begin{array}{lll} \text{HYP} & H_1 = x_1^2 + x_2^2 - 2u_1x_1 - u_1^2 = 0, & (BE = BD) \\ & H_2 = x_2 + x_1 - 2u_1 = 0, & (CG \| BD) \\ & H_3 = x_2x_3 - u_1x_2 - u_1x_1 + u_1^2 = 0, & (F \text{ lies on } EB) \\ \text{CON} & C = x_3^2 - x_2^2 + 2u_1x_2 - x_1^2 - u_1^2 = 0. & (DE = DF) \end{array}$$

With respect to the natural variable ordering $x_1 \prec x_2 \prec x_3$ (with u_1 as a parameter), the principal triangular system [*TF*, *US*] of HYP = $\{H_1, H_2, H_3\}$ is

$$[[2x_1^2 - 6u_1x_1 + 3u_1^2, x_2 + x_1 - 2u_1, -x_2x_3 + u_1x_2 + u_1x_1 - u_1^2], \{x_1 - 2u_1\}],$$

in which the triangular form *TF* is quite similar to the characteristic set and Gröbner basis of HYP given in Wang (1991). Computing prem(C, *TF*), we immediately get 0 and thus the theorem is true under the subsidiary condition $x_1 - 2u_1 \neq 0$. The geometric meaning of the condition $x_1 - 2u_1 = 0$ is not quite evident. However, some simple analysis shows that $x_1 - 2u_1 = 0$ only if $u_1 = 0$, i.e., the square becomes a point, which is certainly a degenerate case and has no geometric interest.

For Method B, we compute an irreducible triangular series Ψ of HYP. It is found that Ψ contains only one irreducible triangular system that is the above principal one. So the theorem is again proved to be true and the subsidiary condition $x_1 - 2u_1 \neq 0$ is examined algebraically to be a non-degeneracy condition indeed.

For Method C, we compute a triangular series Ψ of [HYP, {C}] with projection for x_3, x_2, x_1 over $\boldsymbol{Q}(u_1)$. It is found that $\Psi = \emptyset$, so the theorem is true under some non-degeneracy conditions. If the computation is done over $\boldsymbol{Q}$, then Ψ contains one triangular system that is $[[u_1, x_1, x_2], \{C\}]$. Therefore, the theorem is true under the non-degeneracy condition $u_1 \neq 0$ (i.e., the square does

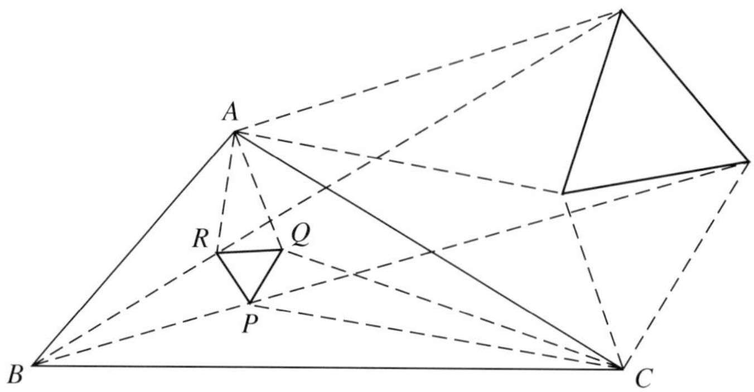

Fig. 2

not degenerate to a point). The proof of this theorem by using Methods A, B and C took 0.366, 0.466 and 0.484 CPU seconds respectively.

Example B (Morley's theorem; Wu 1984a). The neighbouring trisectors of the three angles of any triangle intersect to form 27 triangles in all, of which 18 are equilateral (Fig. 2).

Using the algebraic specification given in Wang (1991) which follows a trick of Wu (1984b), this theorem can be proved also easily by using the methods described in Sect. 3.2. To further illustrate our methods, let us consider a natural formulation of the theorem, where the hypothesis consists of

$$\angle ABC = 3\angle PBC, \quad \angle ACB = 3\angle PCB, \quad \angle CAB = 3\angle RAB,$$
$$\angle ABR = \angle PBC, \quad \angle ACQ = \angle PCB, \quad \angle BAR = \angle QAC$$

and the conclusion to be proved consists of

$$PQ = PR, \quad PQ = QR.$$

Let the coordinates of the points be chosen as $A(y_2, y_1)$, $B(u_1, 0)$, $C(u_2, 0)$, $P(0, 1)$, $Q(y_6, y_5)$, $R(y_4, y_3)$. Then by taking tangent for the equalities of angles the hypothesis and the conclusion can both be expressed as polynomial equations with index triples

HYP: $[6\ y_2\ 1]$, $[6\ y_2\ 1]$, $[90\ y_4\ 3]$, $[9\ y_4\ 1]$, $[9, y_6\ 1]$, $[41\ y_6\ 1]$,

CON: $[6\ y_6\ 2]$, $[6\ y_6\ 2]$

with respect to the variable ordering $y_1 \prec \ldots \prec y_6$. The set of hypothesis-polynomials can be decomposed[5] over $\boldsymbol{Q}(u_1, u_2)$ into two irreducible triangular

5 The decomposition over $\boldsymbol{Q}$ yields the same two triangular forms, provided that the inequations $u_1 - u_2 \neq 0$, $y_1 \neq 0$, $u_1^2 + 1 \neq 0$, $u_2 y_1 + y_2 - u_2 \neq 0$, $u_1 y_1 + y_2 - u_1 \neq 0$ are added to the hypothesis to exclude the degenerate cases.

forms

$$TF = [T_1, T_2, T_3, T_4, T_5, T_6], \qquad TF^* = [T_1, T_2, T_3^*, T_4, T_5, T_6],$$

where

$$\begin{aligned}
T_1 &= 3u_1^2 - 9u_1^2u_2^2 + 3u_1^2y_1u_2^2 - u_1^2y_1 + 8u_1y_1u_2 + 3u_2^2 + 3y_1 - y_1u_2^2 - 1,\\
T_2 &= y_1u_2^3 - 3y_1u_2 + 3u_2^2y_2 - 3u_2^3 - y_2 + u_2,\\
T_3 &= -4u_1^2 - 16y_3u_1u_2 - y_3^2u_1^2 + 4y_3u_1^2 + 3y_3^2 + 12u_1^2u_2^2 - y_3^2u_2^2 + 8u_2u_1y_3^2 +\\
&\quad + 3y_3^2u_1^2u_2^2 - 12y_3u_1^2u_2^2,\\
T_4 &= y_3u_1^2 - 2u_1^2 + 2y_4u_1 - y_3,\\
T_5 &= 3u_2^2y_3u_1^3y_5 - 6u_1^3u_2^2y_5 + 2u_1^3y_5 - u_1^3y_3y_5 - 6u_1^2u_2^3y_3 + 3u_1^2u_2^3y_5y_3 -\\
&\quad - 6u_2u_1^2y_3 + 7u_1^2y_5y_3u_2 - 6u_2^2u_1y_5 + 7u_2^2u_1y_5y_3 + 3y_3u_1y_5 +\\
&\quad + 2u_1y_5 + 2u_2^3y_3 - u_2^3y_3y_5 + 3y_3y_5u_2 + 2y_3u_2,\\
T_6 &= y_1u_2^2 - u_2y_1y_6 + u_2y_2y_5 - u_2^2y_5 - y_1y_5 - y_2y_6 + y_2u_2 + u_2y_6 - u_2^2,\\
T_3^* &= 3y_3 - y_3u_1^2 + 8y_3u_1u_2 + 3y_3u_1^2u_2^2 - u_2^2y_3 - 2u_2u_1 + 6u_2^3u_1 + 2u_1^2 - 6u_1^2u_2^2.
\end{aligned}$$

It is easy to verify that the pseudo-remainders of the two conclusion-polynomials are both 0 with respect to TF, but not 0 with respect to TF^*. Therefore, under some non-degeneracy conditions the theorem is true for one component and false for the other.

Let us recall the tricky formulation of Wu, in which the following additional constraint was imposed:

$$\angle CBP + \angle PCB + \angle BAR \equiv \theta \bmod 2\pi$$

with $\tan^2\theta = 3$ (i.e., $\tan^2(\angle CBP + \angle PCB + \angle BAR) = 3$). We have examined that after the addition of this constraint the component TF^* is then excluded, so that only one component TF remains. Therefore, we have arrived at the same conclusion as Wu without using his trick in the formulation.

Note that T_3 is of degree 2 and T_3^* of degree 1 in y_3. This can be explained in the following way. After the trisectors are fixed for two angles of the triangle, the trisectors for the third angle will have three possibilities in forming the triangle PQR. T_3 corresponds to two of the three possibilities for which the triangle PQR is equilateral, and T_3' to the third possibility for which PQR is not equilateral in general. This can be seen more clearly if we slightly modify the formulation for proving the conclusion-relations

$$\tan^2\angle QPR = 3, \qquad \tan^2\angle PQR = 3$$

instead of $PQ = PR$, $PQ = QR$. Let us introduce a new variable y_0 and add the polynomial $T_0 = y_0^2 - 3$ into the set of hypothesis-polynomials. Then the polynomial T_3 can be factorized (cf. Wang 1994), over the extension field $\boldsymbol{Q}(u_1, u_2, y_0)$ with the algebraic element y_0 having minimal polynomial T_0, as

$$T_3 = \frac{T_3'T_3''}{D} = \frac{(H + 2u_1y_0 + 2u_1y_0u_2^2)(H - 2u_1y_0 - 2u_1y_0u_2^2)}{3-u_1^2-u_2^2 + 8u_2u_1 + 3u_1^2u_2^2},$$

where

$$H = 3y_3-y_3u_1^2-u_2^2y_3 + 8y_3u_1u_2 + 3y_3u_1^2u_2^2 + 2u_1^2-8u_2u_1-6u_1^2u_2^2.$$

So $\{T_0\} \cup TF_1$ can be further decomposed into two irreducible triangular forms

$$TF' = [T_0, T_1, T_2, T_3', T_4, T_5, T_5], \qquad TF'' = [T_0, T_1, T_2, T_3'', T_4, T_5, T_5].$$

It is easy to see that the conclusion-equations can now be written as

$$(\tan \angle QPR+y_0)(\tan \angle QPR-y_0) = 0, \quad (\tan \angle PQR+y_0)(\tan \angle PQR-y_0) = 0.$$

We may verify that $\tan \angle QPR + y_0 = 0$ and $\tan \angle PQR - y_0 = 0$ are true for TF', and $\tan \angle QPR - y_0 = 0$ and $\tan \angle PQR + y_0 = 0$ are true for TF''. That is, on both of the components that correspond to the two possibilities of T_3 in forming the triangle PQR the theorem is true.

As for the computing time, the irreducible decomposition over $\boldsymbol{Q}(u_1, u_2)$ and over $\boldsymbol{Q}$ took 51.716 and 2504.75 s respectively. If the inequations indicated in footnote 5 are added to the hypothesis, then the time for the irreducible decomposition over $\boldsymbol{Q}$ can be reduced to 495.85 s. The factorization of T_3 over $\boldsymbol{Q}(u_1, u_2, y_0)$ took 7.217 s. The formation of the pseudo-remainders of the two conclusion-polynomials with respect to TF and TF^* all together took 17.216 s. The proof of this theorem using Method C was rejected by the Maple system for "object too large."

Before closing this section, we consider another example.

Example C (Pedoe's inequality; Wu 1988). Let ABC and $A'B'C'$ be two triangles in the same plane with sides a, b, c; a', b', c' and areas Δ, Δ' respectively (Fig. 3). Then

$$a'^2(b^2 + c^2 - a^2) + b'^2(c^2 + a^2 - b^2) + c'^2(a^2 + b^2 - c^2) \geq 16\Delta'\Delta. \tag{3.3}$$

Moreover, the equality holds only when the two triangles are similar.

Wu (1988) proved this geometric inequality by using his method in combination with the technique of Lagrangean multipliers. The inequality was proved again in Wang (1991) by using the CAD method (Collins 1975). Without loss of generality, we assume that the two triangles have a common vertex, say $B = B'$, and the side BC coincides with the side $B'C'$. Take the coordinates of the points

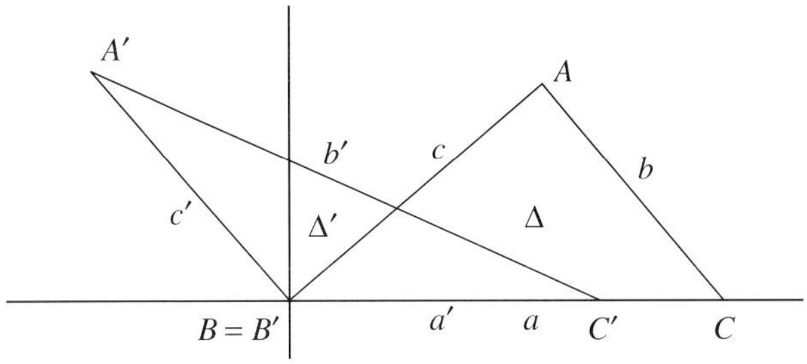

Fig. 3

as $A(x, y)$, $A'(x', y')$, $B = B'(0, 0)$, $C(a, 0)$ and $C'(a', 0)$, see Fig. 3. Then we have[6]

$$b^2 = (x-a)^2 + y^2, \qquad c^2 = x^2 + y^2,$$
$$b'^2 = (x'-a')^2 + y'^2, \qquad c'^2 = x'^2 + y'^2,$$
$$\Delta = \tfrac{1}{2}ay, \qquad \Delta' = \tfrac{1}{2}a'y'.$$

Substituting them into (3.3), the inequality to be proved becomes

$$a'^2x^2 + a'^2y^2 - 2x'a'xa + a^2x'^2 + y'^2a^2 \geq 2a'y'ay. \tag{3.4}$$

To see how our method is used to prove this inequality, we follow the approach of Wu (1988) by determining the extremal values.

Let

$$F = a'^2x^2 + a'^2y^2 - 2x'a'xa + a^2x'^2 + y'^2a^2 - 2a'y'ay.$$

We want to prove that the minimum of F is 0 and it takes place when the two triangles are similar. To do so, let us consider the polynomial set

$$PS = \left\{\frac{\partial F}{\partial a}, \frac{\partial F}{\partial a'}, \frac{\partial F}{\partial x}, \frac{\partial F}{\partial x'}, \frac{\partial F}{\partial y}, \frac{\partial F}{\partial y'}\right\}$$

and compute an (irreducible) triangular series of PS. It was found in 1.567 s that the series consists of three triangular systems

$$[TF_1, US_1] = [[a'x - ax', a'y - ay'], \{a\}], \qquad [TF_2, US_2] = [[a, a'], \emptyset],$$
$$[TF_3, US_3] = [[a, x, y], \emptyset].$$

From them we know that the polynomial F as a function in a, a', x, x', y, y' takes maximum or minimum only if $a'x - ax', a'y - ay'$, or $a = a' = 0$, or $a = x = y = 0$. Some verifications show that F indeed takes minimum in

6 Δ and Δ' here may have a sign difference from the areas of the two triangles in the usual sense. However, this does not bother us in proving the inequality because it holds still if Δ and/or Δ' take(s) negative sign.

these cases and we omit the details. The first case says that the two triangles are similar, and the other two are degenerate cases of the geometric problem which have no interest to be considered. The geometric inequality is therefore proved to be generically true.

4 Automatic derivation of unknown relations

4.1 Problem

The automatic derivation of unknown relations among geometric entities has been investigated by several authors, see Chou (1987), Chou and Gao (1990), Wang (1991), Wu (1986b), for example. The problem consists in determining some unknown algebraic relations among geometric entities, given a proper description of the geometric conditions. The idea is to first algebraize the geometric conditions as systems of polynomial equations and inequations, then compute some kind of triangular forms from the polynomial systems using an appropriate variable ordering and finally get the desired relations from the triangularized systems. A typical example, as given by Chou (1987), Wang (1991), and Wu (1986b) and to be seen again as Example A below, is the automated derivation of Qin–Heron's formula (the representation of the area of a triangle in terms of its three sides). First, let us formulate the problem as follows.

Given two sets of geometric entities $u_1, \ldots, u_e$ (abbreviated to u) and $x_1, \ldots, x_n$ associated with some geometric conditions expressed as a system of polynomial equations $P_1 = 0, \ldots, P_s = 0$ and inequations $Q_1 \neq 0, \ldots, Q_t \neq 0$ in $u, x_1, \ldots, x_n$ with coefficients in $\boldsymbol{K}$, determine for a fixed i whether there is an algebraic relation $R(u, x_i) = 0$ between u and x_i such that $R = 0$ is a formal consequence of $P_1 = 0, \ldots, P_s = 0, Q_1 \neq 0, \ldots, Q_t \neq 0$ (possibly under some non-degeneracy conditions $D_i \neq 0$), and if so, find such $R(u, x_i)$.

4.2 Method

Without loss of generality, we assume that x_1 is the fixed variable. The problem is to derive an algebraic relation between u and x_1. Let $PS = \{P_1, \ldots, P_s\}$ and $QS = \{Q_1, \ldots, Q_t\}$. Then based on our elimination procedures we may describe a method for solving this problem roughly as follows.

Method (for automatic derivation of unknown relations).

1. Compute $[TF, US] \leftarrow \mathrm{PTriSys}(PS, QS)$. If $TF \cap \boldsymbol{K} \neq \emptyset$ or $0 \in US$, then the geometric conditions are self-contradictory and the procedure terminates. If TF contains a polynomial $R(u, x_1)$ involving the variables u and x_1 only and $TF \cap \boldsymbol{K}[u]$ is empty or irreducible as a triangular form, then return the relation[7] $R(u, x_1) = 0$ and the procedure terminates.

---

7 If some polynomials, say $D_1, \ldots, D_q$, have been removed as factors during the computation, then one has to analyze whether every $D_i = 0$ corresponds to a degenerate

2. Compute an irreducible triangular series Ψ of $[PS, QS]$. IF $\Psi = \emptyset$, then the geometric conditions are self-contradictory and the procedure terminates. If the triangular form of every triangular system in Ψ contains a polynomial $R_i(u, x_1)$ involving the variables u and x_1 only, then return the relation $R(u, x_1) = \prod_i R_i(u, x_1) = 0$ and the procedure terminates. If there is one triangular system in Ψ for which the triangular form contains no polynomial involving the variables u and x_1 only, then there is in general no algebraic relation between u and x_1 for the proposed specification of the problem. In this case one may try to get possible relations by adding proper polynomials as subsidiary conditions to QS to exclude some components of the triangular series.

4.3 Examples

Example A (Qin–Heron's formula; Wu 1986b). Determine the area Δ of a triangle ABC in terms of its three sides a, b, c (Fig. 4).

Let us choose the coordinates of the points as $A(x_1, 0)$, $B(0, 0)$, $C(x_2, x_3)$. Then the geometric conditions can be expressed as the following polynomial equations

$$\begin{aligned}
H_1 &= x_1^2 - c^2 = 0, && (c = AB)\\
H_2 &= x_2^2 + x_3^2 - a^2 = 0, && (a = BC)\\
H_3 &= (x_2 - x_1)^2 + x_3^2 - b^2 = 0, && (b = AC)\\
H_4 &= x_3^2 x_1^2 - 4\Delta^2 = 0. && (\Delta = \tfrac{1}{2} AB \cdot AD)
\end{aligned}$$

With respect to the ordering $\Delta \prec x_1 \prec x_2 \prec x_3$, the principal triangular system $[TF, US]$ of $PS = \{H_1, \dots, H_4\}$ can be easily computed, yielding

$$\begin{aligned}
TF = [&a^4 - 2a^2b^2 - 2a^2c^2 + b^4 - 2c^2b^2 + c^4 + 16\Delta^2,\\
&- x_1^2 + c^2, a^2 - 2x_2x_1 - b^2 + c^2, x_2^2 + x_3^2 - a^2],\\
US = \{&x_1\},
\end{aligned}$$

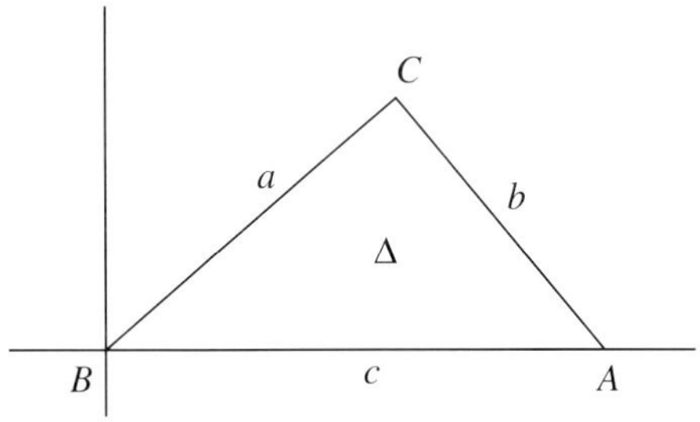

Fig. 4

case of the geometric problem. If so, then the desired relation $R(u, x_1) = 0$ is obtained under the non degeneracy conditions $D_i \neq 0$. Otherwise, one needs to proceed with step 2.

where the triangular form *TF* is the same as the quasi-characteristic set of *PS* given in Wang (1991). The vanishing of the first polynomial in *TF* gives the desired algebraic relation. This relation can be written as the well-known Qin–Heron formula (Wu 1986b)

$$\Delta^2 = s(s-a)(s-b)(s-c),$$

where $s = (a+b+c)/2$. Its derivation took 0.4 s by using the method above.

Example B (Brahmagupta's formula; Chou and Gao 1990, Wang 1991). Let $ABCD$ be a cyclic quadrilateral. Determine the signed areas of the oriented quadrilateral $ABCD$ in terms of its four sides (Fig. 5).

Let the coordinates of the points be chosen as $A(0,0)$, $B(u_1,0)$, $C(x_1,x_2)$, $D(x_3,x_4)$, let $u_2 = BC$, $u_3 = CD$, $u_4 = DA$, and denote the sum of the signed areas of ABC and ACD by k as in Chou and Gao (1990). Then the geometric conditions associated with these geometric entities can be expressed as

$$\begin{aligned}
H_1 &= x_2^2 + x_1^2 - 2u_1x_1 - u_2^2 + u_1^2 = 0,\\
H_2 &= x_4^2 - 2x_2x_4 + x_3^2 - 2x_1x_3 + x_2^2 + x_1^2 - u_3^2 = 0,\\
H_3 &= x_4^2 + x_3^2 - u_4^2 = 0,\\
H_4 &= u_1x_2x_4^2 + (-u_1x_2^2 - u_1x_1^2 + u_1^2x_1)x_4 + u_1x_2x_3^2 - u_1^2x_2x_3 = 0,\\
H_5 &= x_1x_4 - x_2x_3 + u_1x_2 - 2k = 0.
\end{aligned}$$

Now we want to find a relation among $u_1, \ldots, u_4$ and k. To this end, set $PS = \{H_1, \ldots, H_5\}$ and compute the principal triangular system [*TF*, *US*] of *PS* with respect to the ordering $k \prec x_1 \prec \ldots \prec x_4$. It is found that the triangular form *TF* contains five polynomials having the following index triples

$$[46\ k\ 4], \quad [35\ x_1\ 1], \quad [6\ x_2\ 1], \quad [8\ x_3\ 1], \quad [4\ x_4\ 1]$$

(of which the last four are similar to those in the quasi-characteristic set of *PS*

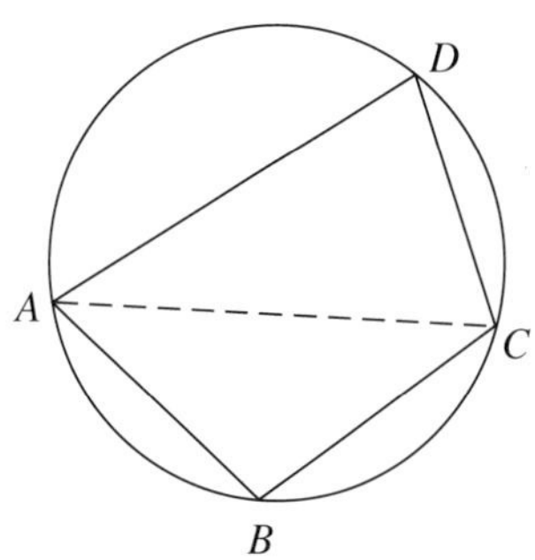

Fig. 5

given in Wang 1991) and *US* contains three polynomials having index triples

$$[11\ k\ 2], \qquad [64\ k\ 2], \qquad [24\ k\ 2].$$

During the computation three trivial factors $u_1, x_1, -u_1^2 + u_3^2 + u_4^2 - u_2^2$ are removed. The first polynomial in *TF*, consisting of 46 terms and of degree 4 in k, can be factorized as the product of the following two polynomials

$$\begin{aligned} R_1 = {} & 16k^2 + u_3^4 + u_4^4 - 2u_4^2u_3^2 - 2u_2^2u_3^2 - 2u_2^2u_1^2 - 2u_2^2u_4^2 - 2u_1^2u_3^2 - 2u_1^2u_4^2 + \\ & + u_2^4 + 8u_1u_3u_2u_4 + u_1^4, \\ R_2 = {} & 16k^2 + u_3^4 + u_4^4 - 2u_4^2u_3^2 - 2u_2^2u_3^2 - 2u_2^2u_1^2 - 2u_2^2u_4^2 - 2u_1^2u_3^2 - 2u_1^2u_4^2 + \\ & + u_2^4 - 8u_1u_3u_2u_4 + u_1^4. \end{aligned}$$

It is easy to see that $u_1 = 0$, $x_1 = 0$ and $-u_1^2 + u_3^2 + u_4^2 - u_2^2 = 0$ can all be considered as degenerate cases of the geometric problem. Therefore, we get the algebraic relation

$$R = R_1R_2 = 0$$

under the non-degeneracy condition $u_1x_1(-u_1^2 + u_3^2 + u_4^2 - u_2^2) \neq 0$. If one sets $s = (u_1 + u_2 + u_3 + u_4)/2$, the above relation leads either to

$$k^2 = (s - u_1)(s - u_2)(s - u_3)(s - u_4),$$

or to

$$k^2 = s(s - u_1 - u_3)(s - u_1 - u_2)(s - u_1 - u_4).$$

See Chou and Gao (1990) and Wang (1991) for some explanation about the two equalities. The derivation of the relation (including factorization) took 10.584 s by using our method.

If the irreducible triangular series of *PS* is computed directly, then two irreducible triangular systems can be obtained in 30.017 s. The two triangular forms are actually just those obtained from the above *TF* with its first polynomial replaced by R_1 and R_2 respectively, from which the same algebraic relation may be derived as well.

5 Automatic derivation of locus equations

The idea expressed in the preceding section can be extended to derive the locus equations of motions, whose geometric description is given. In general, one cannot tell only from the geometric description what a locus looks like. When its equations are found, the geometric figure can be much clearly analyzed and explained according to its algebraic structure (see examples in Sect. 5.3).

5.1 Problem

Now we need to determine one or several sets of algebraic relations between n variables $x_1, \ldots, x_n$ and the u's. The problem considered below and that formulated in the last section have some similarity, but they are different in essence.

Let $u_1, \ldots, u_d$ (abbreviated to u) be a set of (geometric) parameters. Determine the locus equations of a point $(x_1, \ldots, x_n)$, in terms of u, that moves in an n-dimensional space $\boldsymbol{K}^n$ constrained by geometric conditions expressed as a system of polynomial equations $P_1 = 0, \ldots, P_s = 0$ and inequations $Q_1 \neq 0, \ldots, Q_t \neq 0$ in $u, x_1, \ldots, x_n, y_1, \ldots, y_m$, where $y_1, \ldots, y_m$ are some other geometric entities.

Here by locus equations we mean a system or the disjunction of several systems of polynomial equations and inequations in the variables $x_1, \ldots, x_n$ with u as parameters such that it is a formal consequence of the geometric conditions and for any point on the locus there is at least one configuration which satisfies the geometric conditions. More concretely, let $PS = \{P_1, \ldots, P_s\}$ and $QS = \{Q_1, \ldots, Q_t\}$. The problem amounts to finding polynomial systems $[PS_1, QS_1], \ldots, [PS_e, QS_e]$ in $\boldsymbol{K}(u)[x_1, \ldots, x_n]$ such that for any $(\bar{x}_1, \ldots, \bar{x}_n, \bar{y}_1, \ldots, \bar{y}_m) \in \mathrm{Zero}(PS/QS)$, $(\bar{x}_1, \ldots, \bar{x}_n) \in \mathrm{Zero}(PS_i/QS_i)$ for some i; and for any i and any $(\bar{x}_1, \ldots, \bar{x}_n) \in \mathrm{Zero}(PS_i/QS_i)$ there are $\bar{y}_1, \ldots, \bar{y}_m$ such that $(\bar{x}_1, \ldots, \bar{x}_n, \bar{y}_1, \ldots, \bar{y}_m) \in \mathrm{Zero}(PS/QS)$. Whereas, in the case of deriving unknown relations we are satisfied by only requiring the relations to be consequences of the geometric conditions.

5.2 Method

The following method differs from the one described in Sect. 4.2 by its need of projection (rather than irreducible decomposition).

Method (for automatic derivation of locus equations).

1. Compute a triangular series[8] Ψ of $[PS, QS]$ with projection for $y_m, \ldots, y_1$ with respect to the ordering[9] $x_1 \prec \ldots \prec x_n \prec y_1 \prec \ldots \prec y_m$. If $\Psi = \emptyset$, then either the geometric conditions are self-contradictory (in this case $\mathrm{Zero}(PS/QS) = \emptyset$), or the motion is free (in this case the locus fills up the whole space, i.e.,

8 The triangular series may also be considered and computed in $\boldsymbol{K}[u, x_1, \ldots, x_n, y_1, \ldots, y_m]$.

9 Actually, we need to perform the elimination only for the variables $y_m, \ldots, y_1$ because it is sufficient when we have already obtained equations and inequations in the variables $u, x_1, \ldots, x_n$ – these equations and inequations do not necessarily have to be in triangular form (cf. the remark following Theorem B).

for any $(\bar{x}_1, \ldots, \bar{x}_n)$ there are $\bar{y}_1, \ldots, \bar{y}_m$ such that $(\bar{x}_1, \ldots, \bar{x}_n, \bar{y}_1, \ldots, \bar{y}_m) \in \mathrm{Zero}(PS/QS)$); thus the procedure terminates.

2. Remove redundant sets[10] from $\bigcup_{[TF,US]\in\Psi} \mathrm{Zero}(TF \cap \boldsymbol{K}(u)[x_1, \ldots, x_n]/US \cap \boldsymbol{K}(u)[x_1, \ldots, x_n])$, simplify it and let the obtained zero set be $\bigcup_{i=1}^{e} \mathrm{Zero}(TF_i/US_i)$. Then the disjunction

$$TF_1 = 0, US_1 \neq 0 \quad \text{or} \quad TF_2 = 0, US_2 \neq 0 \quad \ldots \quad \text{or} \quad TF_e = 0, US_e \neq 0$$

constitutes the locus equations to be derived.

5.3 Examples

Example A. Let ABC be a triangle with two vertices A and B fixed at the two poles of the unit sphere S and the third vertex C moving along a small circle which is parallel to the equator (called *parallel* in astronomical terminology) on the sphere. Determine the locus equations of the centroid M of ABC (Fig. 6).

Let the unit sphere S have center $O(0, 0, 0)$ and the parallel be the intersection circle of S with the plane $Z = c$. Choose the coordinates of the points as $A(0, 0, 1)$, $B(0, 0, -1)$, $C(x, y, z)$ and $M(X, Y, Z)$. Then we have the following polynomial equations for the geometric conditions

$$\begin{aligned}
H_1 &= x^2 + y^2 + z^2 - 1 = 0, && (C \text{ lies on } S)\\
H_2 &= z - c = 0, && (C \text{ is in the plane } Z = c)\\
H_3 &= xY - yX = 0,\\
H_4 &= xZ - zX = 0,
\end{aligned}$$

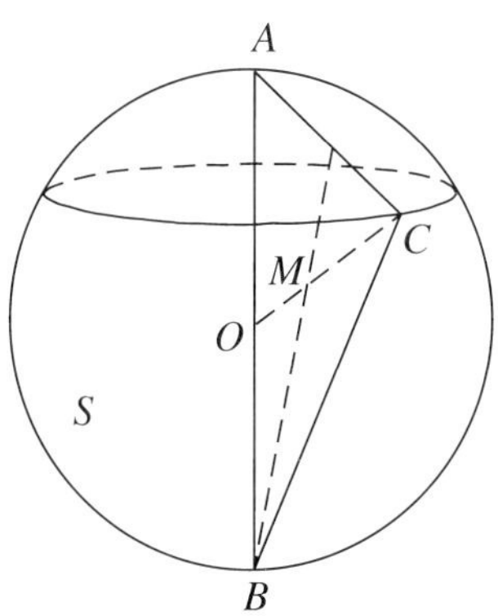

Fig. 6

10 For any set union $S = \cup_{A\in\Delta} S_A$, by *removing redundant sets* from S we mean determining a subset Δ' of Δ such that $\cup_{A\in\Delta\setminus\Delta'} S_A = S$. By *simplifying* S we mean finding another set Ω such that $\cup_{A\in\Omega} S_A = S$ and $\cup_{A\in\Omega} S_A$ as a representation of S is *simpler* than $\cup_{A\in\Delta} S_A$.

Observe that $TF_i, US_i \in \boldsymbol{K}(u)[x_1, \ldots, x_n]$, while $TF, US \in \boldsymbol{K}(u)[x_1, \ldots, x_n, y_1, \ldots, y_m]$ for any $[TF, US] \in \Psi$.

$$H_5 = yZ - zY = 0, \qquad (M \text{ is the centroid of } ABC)$$
$$H_6 = x(Z+1) - (z+3)X = 0,$$
$$H_7 = y(Z+1) - (z+3)Y = 0.$$

With respect to the ordering $X \prec Y \prec Z \prec x \prec y \prec z$, the triangular series of $\{H_1, \ldots, H_7\}$ with projection for z, y, x, computed in 2.434 s, contains 3 triangular systems as follows

$$[[9X^2 + 9Y^2 + c^2 - 1, -3Z + c, -3X + x, -3Y + y, -z + c], \{X, Y\}],$$
$$[[9X^2 + c^2 - 1, Y, -3Z + c, -3X + x, y, -z + c], \{X\}],$$
$$[[X, 9Y^2 + c^2 - 1, -3Z + c, x, y - 3Y, -z + c], \{Y\}].$$

Intersection of these triangular systems with $\boldsymbol{Q}[X, Y, Z]$ yields $[TF_1, US_1] = [[9X^2+9Y^2+c^2-1, -3Z+c], \{X, Y\}]$, $[TF_2, US_2] = [[9X^2+c^2-1, Y, -3Z+c], \{X\}]$ and $[TF_3, US_3] = [[X, 9Y^2+c^2-1, -3Z+c], \{Y\}]$. It is not difficult to see that $\bigcup_{i=1}^{3} \mathrm{Zero}(TF_i/US_i)$ can be simplified to $\mathrm{Zero}(TF_1)$. Hence the locus equations are $9X^2 + 9Y^2 + c^2 - 1 = 0$, $-3Z + c = 0$, which represent a circle with radius $\sqrt{1 - c^2}/3$ and center $(0, 0, c/3)$ in the plane $Z = c/3$.

Example B (Biarcs; Nutbourne and Martin 1988). Given two points A and C of two different circular arcs which have given tangent directions at A and C (see Fig. 7), determine the locus of an intermediate point B at which the two circular arcs join together with a common tangent.

Choose the coordinates of the points as $A(0, 0)$, $D(u_1, 0)$, $C(u_2, u_3)$, $B(X, Y)$, $O_1(0, x_1)$, $O_2(x_2, x_3)$. Then as usual we get from the geometric conditions some polynomial equations, as follows

$$H_1 = (u_2 - u_1)(x_2 - u_2) + u_3(x_3 - u_3) = 0, \qquad (CO_2 \perp DC)$$
$$H_2 = X^2 + (x_1 - Y)^2 - x_1^2 = 0, \qquad (O_1A = O_1B)$$

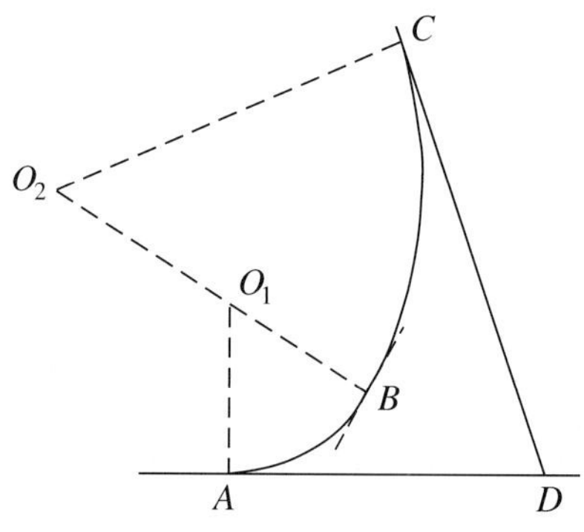

Fig. 7

$$H_3 = (x_2 - u_2)^2 + (x_3 - u_3)^2 - (x_2 - X)^2 - (x_3 - Y)^2 = 0, \qquad (O_2C = O_2B)$$
$$H_4 = X(x_3 - x_1) - x_2(Y - x_1) = 0. \qquad (B \text{ lies on } O_1O_2)$$

The triangular series of $\{H_1, \ldots, H_4\}$ (computed with projection for x_3, x_2, x_1) with respect to the ordering $X \prec Y \prec x_1 \prec x_2 \prec x_3$ contains 3 triangular systems[11] $[TF_1, US_1]$, $[TF_2, \emptyset]$, $[TF_3, \emptyset]$. The first polynomial in TF_1 (the principal one) is

$$\begin{aligned} T = {} & 2u_3X^2Y^2 - u_3u_2^2X^2 + u_3u_2^2Y^2 - 2u_1u_3X^3 + 2u_2^3YX - u_3^3X^2 - \\ & - 2u_2^2Yu_1X + u_3^3Y^2 + u_3Y^4 + u_3X^4 + 2u_3^2Yu_2X + 2u_3^2Yu_1X - \\ & - 2u_1u_3Y^2X + 2u_1u_3u_2X^2 + 2u_1Y^3u_2 - 2u_3^2Y^3 + 2u_1Yu_2X^2 - \\ & - 2u_3^2X^2Y - 2u_2^2Y^3 - 2u_2^2YX^2 - 2u_1u_3u_2Y^2, \end{aligned}$$

the remaining three have index triples $[3\ x_1\ 1]$, $[12\ x_2\ 1]$ and $[6\ x_3\ 1]$, and

$$US_1 = \{Y, -u_1Y + u_2Y - u_3X + u_1u_3\}.$$

The two other triangular forms are

$$\begin{aligned} TF_2 &= [X - u_2, -u_1Y + u_2Y - u_3X + u_1u_3, -X^2 + 2x_1Y - Y^2, \\ &\qquad [8\ x_2\ 1], [6\ x_3\ 1]], \\ TF_3 &= [X, Y, x_1, [4\ x_2\ 1], [6\ x_3\ 1]]. \end{aligned}$$

Intersection of the three triangular systems with $\boldsymbol{Q}[X, Y]$ results in

$$[[T], US_1], \qquad [[X - u_2, Y - u_3], \emptyset], \qquad [[X, Y], \emptyset].$$

It is easy to see that the last two correspond respectively to the points C and A which are actually on the curve $T = 0$, so that $\mathrm{Zero}(T/US_1) \cup \mathrm{Zero}([X - u_2, Y - u_3]) \cup \mathrm{Zero}([X, Y])$ can be simplified to $\mathrm{Zero}(T)$. Therefore, $T = 0$ is the locus equation of the point B we wanted. Its derivation as explained above took 2.116 s on our computer.

Using a method presented in Wang (1987), we can factorize T as the product of the following two polynomials

11 The factors $u_3, u_2 - u_1$ and $(u_2 - u_1)^2 + u_3^2$ etc. in the parameters u_1, u_2, u_3 only are assumed to be non-zero and removed during the computation. Actually, the vanishing of such factors corresponds to some degenerate cases such as the three points A, D, C are collinear and the line DC is isotropic.

$$T_1 = \left(X + \frac{a-u_1}{2}\right)^2 + \left(Y + \frac{-a^2+u_1^2-u_1u_2-au_2}{2u_3}\right)^2 + \\ + \frac{a(-a^2+u_1^2-2u_1u_2)}{2(u_1+a-u_2)},$$

$$T_2 = \left(X - \frac{a+u_1}{2}\right)^2 + \left(Y + \frac{-a^2+u_1^2-u_1u_2+au_2}{2u_3}\right)^2 - \\ - \frac{a(-a^2+u_1^2-2u_1u_2)}{2(u_1-a-u_2)},$$

where

$$a = (u_3^2+u_1^2-2u_1u_2+u_2^2)^{1/2} = |CD|.$$

Hence the locus of B has two components for any fixed u_1, u_2, u_3. One can see easily that $T_1 = 0$ and $T_2 = 0$ represent two circles passing through A and C. Their centers and radii may be simply determined from the above derived equations. One of these circles corresponds to the biarc of convex shape and the other to the biarc of S-shape.

6 Implicitization of parametric objects

Some geometric objects like curves and surfaces can be represented algebraically either by implicit equations or by parametric equations. The advantage of each representation depends upon the type of problems to be treated. There is a need of converting one representation to the other. The methods of resultants, Gröbner bases and characteristic sets have been used for the implicitization of parametric objects, see Arnon and Sederberg (1984), Buchberger (1987), Gao and Chou (1991), Hoffmann (1989), Kalkbrener (1991), Li (1989), Wang (1991), Wu (1990), for instance. In this section we explain how our method can also be applied to the implicitization problem.

6.1 Problem

The rational parametrization of a geometric object in an n-dimensional space is usually represented in the form

$$x_1 = \frac{P_1(y_1,\ldots,y_m)}{Q_1(y_1,\ldots,y_m)}, \ldots, x_n = \frac{P_n(y_1,\ldots,y_m)}{Q_n(y_1,\ldots,y_m)},$$

where $y_1,\ldots,y_m$ are parametric variables. The problem of implicitization is to find implicit equations in $x_1,\ldots,x_n$ which define the same geometric object as the parameterized representation does. A formulation of this problem reads as follows.

Given two sets of polynomials $P_1,\ldots,P_n$ and $Q_1,\ldots,Q_n$ in $\boldsymbol{K}[y_1,\ldots,y_m]$, where $Q_1 \ldots Q_n \neq 0$ and $m \leq n$, find a sequence of polynomial systems $[PS_1, QS_1], \ldots, [PS_e, QS_e]$ in $\boldsymbol{K}[x_1, \ldots, x_n]$ such that for any $\bar{x}_1, \ldots, \bar{x}_n$,

$$(\bar{x}_1, \ldots, \bar{x}_n) \in \bigcup_{i=1}^{e} \mathrm{Zero}(PS_i/QS_i)$$

if and only if $\bar{x}_1 = P_1(\bar{y}_1, \ldots, \bar{y}_m)/Q_1(\bar{y}_1, \ldots, \bar{y}_m), \ldots, \bar{x}_n = P_n(\bar{y}_1, \ldots, \bar{y}_m)/Q_n(\bar{y}_1, \ldots, \bar{y}_m)$ for some $\bar{y}_1, \ldots, \bar{y}_m$.

6.2 Method

The above implicitization problem can be solved by using the following method based on our elimination procedure with projection.

Method (for implicitization of parametric objects).

1. Let $PS \leftarrow \{P_1 - x_1Q_1, \ldots, P_n - x_nQ_n\}$ and $QS \leftarrow \{Q_1, \ldots, Q_n\}$. Compute a triangular series Ψ of $[PS, QS]$ with projection for $y_m, \ldots, y_1$ with respect to the variable ordering $x_1 \prec \ldots \prec x_n \prec y_1 \prec \ldots \prec y_m$.
2. Remove redundant sets from $\bigcup_{[TF,US]\in\Psi} \mathrm{Zero}(TF \cap \boldsymbol{K}[x_1, \ldots, x_n]/US \cap \boldsymbol{K}[x_1, \ldots, x_n])$, simplify it and let the obtained zero set be $\bigcup_{i=1}^{e} \mathrm{Zero}(TF_i/US_i)$. Then $[TF_1, US_1], \ldots, [TF_e, US_e]$ are the polynomial systems to be found.

Note that the above $[TF_i, US_i]$'s are all triangular systems (see the explanation following Theorem B in Sect. 2).

6.3 Examples

Example A (Buchberger 1987, Hoffmann 1989, Wu 1990). Consider the parametric surface given by the following three equations

$$x = rt, \qquad y = rt^2, \qquad z = r^2.$$

Let $PS = \{x - rt, y - rt^2, z - r^2\}$ and compute a triangular series Ψ of PS with projection for r and t with respect to the ordering $z \prec y \prec x \prec t \prec r$. One finds that Ψ contains three triangular systems

$$[[y^2z - x^4, y - xt, -x + rt], \{x, y\}], \qquad [[y, x, t, -z + r^2], \emptyset], \qquad [[z, y, x, t], \{r\}].$$

Their intersection with $\boldsymbol{Q}[z, y, x]$ yields $\mathrm{Zero}(y^2z - x^4/\{x, y\}) \cup \mathrm{Zero}([y, x]) \cup \mathrm{Zero}([z, y, x]) = \mathrm{Zero}(y^2z - x^4/\{x, y\}) \cup \mathrm{Zero}([y, x])$. From this we get the implicit equations: $y^2z - x^4 = 0, xy \neq 0$, or $x = 0, y = 0$. The determination took 0.55 CPU seconds.

Example B (communicated by P. Vermeer, Purdue University). Find the implicit form (in the variables x and y) of the curve given by the following system of equations

$$
\begin{aligned}
&(x-u)^2+(y-v)^2-1=0,\\
&v^2-u^3=0,\\
&2v(x-u)+3u^2(y-v)=0,\\
&(3wu^2-1)(2wv-1)=0.
\end{aligned}
$$

This is a formulation of an offset to the curve $y^2-x^3=0$. The computation of the triangular series of the corresponding system with projection for u, v, w with respect to $x \prec y \prec u \prec v \prec w$ took 18.534 s. The series contains 5 triangular systems, from which with some simplification we are able to determine the implicit equations

$$
\begin{aligned}
&729x^8+216x^7+729x^6y^2-2900x^6-1458x^5y^2-2376x^5-\\
&-2619x^4y^2+3870x^4+4072x^3-1458y^4x^3-4892x^3y^2-\\
&-1188x^2-297x^2y^2+729y^4x^2+5814xy^2-1656x-4158xy^4+\\
&+427y^2-1685y^4+729y^6+529=0,\\
&x\neq 0,
\end{aligned}
\tag{6.1}
$$

or

$$
729y^4-956y^2-529=0, \quad x=0, \tag{6.2}
$$

which are the same as those derived by using the characteristic set method with Wu's projection theorem (1990). However, the computing time for our method is much less than that for Ritt–Wu's.

Our method can also be applied to deal with such problems as the independency of parameters, the propriety of parametrization and the inversion of parametric representation which are related to the implicitization problem.

7 Existence conditions and detection of singularities

There are good reasons for studying the singularities of geometric objects. Buchberger (1987), Hoffmann (1989), and Wang (1989a) addressed the application of Gröbner bases and characteristic sets to detect singularities of curves, to determine the sufficient and necessary conditions for algebraic hypersurfaces with parameters to have singularities and to depict the structure of singular varieties by computing all singular points or their irreducible decomposition. In this section we illustrate how our method can be used to detect singularities and to determine the conditions for their existence.

7.1 Problem

An algebraic hypersurface $\mathfrak{H}$ in an n-dimensional projective space $\mathbf{P}^n$ or affine space $\mathbf{A}^n$ is an algebraic variety of dimension $n-1$ given by a homogeneous polynomial equation $F(x_0, x_1, \ldots, x_n) = 0$ or an "ordinary" polynomial equation $F(x_1, \ldots, x_n) = 0$ with coefficients in $\boldsymbol{K}$. It is called an algebraic curve and an algebraic surface, respectively, for $n = 2, 3$. A point $\bar{x} = (\bar{x}_0, \bar{x}_1, \ldots, \bar{x}_n)$ of the algebraic hypersurface $\mathfrak{H}$ in $\mathbf{P}^n$ is said to be of *multiplicity* p if all partial derivatives of order $< p$ of F vanish at $\bar{x}$, but some of order p do not, i.e.,

$$\frac{\partial^r F}{\partial x_0^{r_0} \partial x_1^{r_1} \ldots \partial x_n^{r_n}}(\bar{x}) = 0 \quad \text{for all } r_0 + r_1 + \ldots + r_n = r < p,$$

$$\frac{\partial^r F}{\partial x_0^{r_0} \partial x_1^{r_1} \ldots \partial x_n^{r_n}}(\bar{x}) \neq 0 \quad \text{for some } r_0 + r_1 + \ldots + r_n = r = p.$$

A point $\bar{x} = (\bar{x}_1, \ldots, \bar{x}_n)$ of $\mathfrak{H}$ in $\mathbf{A}^n$ is said to be of *multiplicity* p if

$$\frac{\partial^r F}{\partial x_1^{r_1} \ldots \partial x_n^{r_n}}(\bar{x}) = 0 \quad \text{for all } r_1 + \ldots + r_n = r < p,$$

$$\frac{\partial^r F}{\partial x_1^{r_1} \ldots \partial x_n^{r_n}}(\bar{x}) \neq 0 \quad \text{for some } r_1 + \ldots + r_n = r = p.$$

Any point of multiplicity $p \geq 2$ is said to be a *singular point*. Under these definitions we may formulate the problem of our concern as follows.

Let an algebraic hypersurface in $\mathbf{P}^n$ or $\mathbf{A}^n$ be given by a homogeneous polynomial equation $F(x_0, x_1, \ldots, x_n) = 0$ or an ordinary polynomial equation $F(x_1, \ldots, x_n) = 0$ with parameters $t_1, \ldots, t_m$ involved in its coefficients. Find the necessary and sufficient conditions in terms of $t_1, \ldots, t_m$ for the hypersurface to have singularities of multiplicity $\geq p + 1$. In case it has, describe for some specialized $t_1, \ldots, t_m$ the structure of the singular variety by computing all singular points or an irreducible decomposition.

7.2 Method

Let us consider the affine case and set

$$DS_p = \left\{ \frac{\partial^p F}{\partial 1^{r_0} \partial x_1^{r_1} \ldots \partial x_n^{r_n}} \;\middle|\; r_0 + r_1 + \ldots + r_n = p \right\},$$

where $\partial F / \partial 1$ is defined to be $F_{m-1}(x_1, \ldots, x_n) + 2F_{m-2}(x_1, \ldots, x_n) + \ldots + mF_0$ with each F_i the homogeneous part of order i of F, and accordingly the successive derivatives of higher order of F with respect to 1. The following method provides a solution to the first half of the above problem for affine hypersurfaces.

Method (for determining the necessary and sufficient conditions for affine hypersurfaces to have singularities of multiplicity $\geq p+1$).

1. Compute a triangular series Ψ of the polynomial set DS_p with projection for $x_n, \ldots, x_1$ with respect to the variable ordering $t_1 \prec \ldots \prec t_m \prec x_1 \prec \ldots \prec x_n$. If $\Psi = \emptyset$, then the hypersurface $\mathfrak{H}$ has no singularity for any $t_1, \ldots, t_m$ and the procedure terminates.

2. Remove redundant sets from $\bigcup_{[TF,US]\in\Psi} \mathrm{Zero}(TF \cap \boldsymbol{K}[t_1, \ldots, t_m]/US \cap \boldsymbol{K}[t_1, \ldots, t_m])$, simplify it and let the obtained zero set be $\bigcup_{i=1}^{e} \mathrm{Zero}(TF_i/US_i)$. Then the hypersurface $\mathfrak{H}$ has singularities of multiplicity $\geq p+1$ if and only if

$$(t_1, \ldots, t_m) \in \bigcup_{i=1}^{e} \mathrm{Zero}(TF_i/US_i).$$

Note that our method may be used to determine the conditions for projective hypersurfaces as well. In that case we need to compute the triangular series of every polynomial set obtained from the corresponding DS_p by specializing one homogeneous variable x_i to 1 ($0 \leq i \leq n$). See Example A below.

If for some specialized $t_1, \ldots, t_m$ the hypersurface has only finitely many singular points of multiplicity $\geq p+1$ (which can be easily determined from the triangular series), then the computation of all such singular points is the problem of solving systems of polynomial equations. If the singular variety of multiplicity $\geq p+1$ is of dimension > 0, then we can compute an irreducible triangular series of DS_p. From this series, the dimension of each component of the singular variety can be simply determined. Furthermore, one can compute an irreducible decomposition of the singular variety if necessary (which we shall explain in more detail in the next section).

We remark that one may easily determine the necessary and sufficient conditions for the hypersurface to have singularities of exact multiplicity $p+1$ and the structure of the corresponding singular variety for specialized $t_1, \ldots, t_m$ by taking difference of zero sets when the problem for multiplicity $\geq p+1$ is solved.

7.3 Examples

Example A. Consider the projective algebraic surface with equation

$$F(x_0, x_1, x_2, x_3) = x_0^3 + x_1^3 + x_2^3 + x_3^3 + 3ax_0x_1x_2 + 3bx_1x_2x_3 = 0.$$

The polynomial set consisting of the four first partial derivatives of F with the constant 3 removed is

$$DS = \{ax_1x_2 + x_0^2, bx_2x_3 + ax_0x_2 + x_1^2, bx_1x_3 + ax_0x_1 + x_2^2, x_3^2 + bx_1x_2\}.$$

Consider in particular the case in which x_0 is replaced by 1. Then the polynomial

F becomes

$$F(1, x_1, x_2, x_3) = 1 + x_1^3 + x_2^3 + x_3^3 + 3ax_1x_2 + 3bx_1x_2x_3.$$

Let this polynomial define an algebraic surface in 3-dimensional affine space. The set consisting of the four first partial derivatives $\partial F/\partial 1$, $\partial F/\partial x_1$, $\partial F/\partial x_2$, $\partial F/\partial x_3$ of F with the constant 3 removed is the one obtained from the above DS by replacing x_0 with 1; let us denote it by $DS^{(0)}$. With respect to the ordering $a \prec b \prec x_1 \prec x_2 \prec x_3$, the triangular series of the polynomial set $DS^{(0)}$ with projection for x_3, x_2, x_1 consists of two triangular systems

$$\begin{aligned}
[TF_1, US_1] = [[&2a^3 + b^6 - 2b^3a^3 + 2b^3 + a^6 + 1, b^3 + 2a^3x_1^3 - a^3 + 1,\\
&ax_1x_2 + 1, x_2^2 + ax_1 + bx_1x_3], \{a, b, b^3 - a^3 + 1\}],\\
[TF_2, US_2] = [[&a^3 + 1, b, x_1^3 - 1, x_1^2 + ax_2, x_3], \{a\}]
\end{aligned}$$

and was computed in 1.15 s. Intersection of these two triangular systems with $\boldsymbol{Q}[a, b]$ yields

$$\mathrm{Proj}_{[a,b]}\,\mathrm{Zero}(DS^{(0)}) = \mathrm{Zero}(\delta/US_1) \cup \mathrm{Zero}(\{a^3 + 1, b\}/a) = \mathrm{Zero}(\delta/a),$$

where $\delta = 2a^3 + b^6 - 2b^3a^3 + 2b^3 + a^6 + 1$. Therefore, the surface has singular points if and only if $\delta = 0$ but $a \neq 0$. Using the same method, one can see that the surface has no singularity of multiplicity ≥ 3.

To illustrate how to determine the necessary and sufficient conditions for projective hypersurfaces to have singularities by using our method, we compute the triangular series of $DS^{(0)}, \ldots, DS^{(3)}$ with projection, where $DS^{(i)} = DS|_{x_i=1}$ for each i. They were found to consist of 2, 3, 3 and 3 triangular systems respectively (in 5.7 s). For the intersection of these triangular systems with $\boldsymbol{Q}[a, b]$, besides the one given above we have

$$\begin{aligned}
\mathrm{Proj}_{[a,b]}\,\mathrm{Zero}(DS^{(1)}) &= \mathrm{Proj}_{[a,b]}\,\mathrm{Zero}(DS^{(2)}) = \mathrm{Zero}(\delta/\{a, b, b^3 - a^3 + 1\}) \cup\\
&\cup\ \mathrm{Zero}(\{a, b^3 + 1\}/b) \cup \mathrm{Zero}(\{a^3 + 1, b\}/a),\\
\mathrm{Proj}_{[a,b]}\,\mathrm{Zero}(DS^{(3)}) &= \mathrm{Zero}(\delta/\{a, b, a^3 + 1, b^3 - a^3 - 1\}) \cup\\
&\cup\ \mathrm{Zero}(\{a, b^3 + 1\}/b) \cup \mathrm{Zero}(\{a^3 + 1, b^3 + 4\}/\{a, b\}).
\end{aligned}$$

With some simplification we know that

$$\mathrm{Proj}_{[a,b]}\,\mathrm{Zero}(DS^{(0)}) \cup \ldots \cup \mathrm{Proj}_{[a,b]}\,\mathrm{Zero}(DS^{(3)}) = \mathrm{Zero}(\delta).$$

Therefore, the necessary and sufficient condition for the projective surface to have singularities is $\delta = 0$.

Take, for instance, $a = b = -1/\sqrt[3]{4}$, which satisfy both of the conditions obtained above. Thus the surface must have singular points in either case. All the three singular points (cf. Wang 1991) may be determined from the triangular series with ease.

Example B. In Buchberger (1987), the following planar curve (four circles) was used as illustration for detecting singularities by means of Gröbner bases

$$F = (x^2+y^2-1)[(x-1)^2+y^2-1][(x+1)^2+y^2-1][x^2+(y-1)^2-1)] = 0.$$

Now consider this curve with our elimination method. Using the same variable ordering $y \prec x$, the triangular series of the corresponding polynomial set DS_1, consisting of two triangular systems $[TF_1, US_1]$, $[TF_2, US_2]$ with

$$\begin{aligned} TF_1 &= [8y^4 - 12y^3 - 2y^2 + 9y - 3, \quad 120y^5 - 200y^4 + 120x^2y^3 - \\ &\quad - 68y^3 + 207y^2 - 200x^2y^2 - 66y + 108x^2y - 21x^2], \\ US_1 &= \{x, y, 4y - 1, 120y^3 - 200y^2 + 108y - 21, 2y + 1\}, \\ TF_2 &= [y, x], \qquad US_2 = \emptyset, \end{aligned}$$

was computed without projection in 3.1 s. From the series, all the nine singular points can be easily determined as well.

Example C (Wang 1989a). For the unary quartic equation

$$F(x) = x^4 + x_1x^3 + x_2x^2 + x_3x + x_4 = 0$$

with indeterminate coefficients x_1, x_2, x_3 and x_4, one can easily compute the discriminant of F, a polynomial of total degree 6, as follows

$$\begin{aligned} \Delta_F = {} & 256x_4^3 - 192x_1x_3x_4^2 - 128x_2^2x_4^2 + 144x_1^2x_2x_4^2 - 27x_1^4x_4^2 + 144x_2x_3^2x_4 - \\ & - 6x_1^2x_3^2x_4 - 80x_1x_2^2x_3x_4 + 18x_1^3x_2x_3x_4 + 16x_2^4x_4 - 4x_1^2x_2^3x_4 - 27x_3^4 + \\ & + 18x_1x_2x_3^3 - 4x_1^3x_3^3 - 4x_2^3x_3^2 + x_1^2x_2^2x_3^2. \end{aligned}$$

$\Delta_F = 0$ defines an algebraic hypersurface, called the discriminant surface of F, in 4-dimensional affine space. Let us investigate the singularities of this hypersurface. The existence of singular points, for example $(0, \ldots, 0)$, is obvious. Let DS be the set of the five first partial derivatives of Δ_F; then the irreducible triangular series of DS, consisting of three triangular systems[12] $[TF_1, \emptyset]$, $[TF_2, \emptyset]$,

12 Write TF_2 as $[T_1, T_2]$; then all polynomials other than T_2 in the triangular forms are the same as or similar to the corresponding polynomials in the ascending sets of the irreducible characteristic series of DS given in Wang (1991). To see the correspondence of T_2 to the one in the ascending set, we pseudo-divide T_2 by T_1 to make it reduced with respect to T_1. One finds that the remainder can be factorized as $-(8x_2 - 3x_1^2)^3(64x_4 -$

$[TF_3, \emptyset]$ with

$$TF_1 = [8x_2 - 3x_1^2, 16x_3 - x_1^3, 256x_4 - x_1^4],$$

$$\begin{aligned} TF_2 = [&8x_3 - 4x_1x_2 + x_1^3, 3168x_2^2x_1^2x_4 + 432x_3^3x_1 + 3456x_3^2x_4 - 648x_3^2x_2x_1^2 + \\ &+ 864x_3^2x_2^2 + 2160x_1^3x_4x_3 - 512x_2^3x_4 - 6912x_1x_4x_3x_2 + 18x_2^3x_1^4 - \\ &- 104x_2^4x_1^2 - 1728x_2x_1^4x_4 + 27x_3^2x_1^4 + 243x_1^6x_4 - 81x_2x_1^5x_3 + \\ &+ 504x_2^2x_1^3x_3 + 128x_2^5 - 640x_2^3x_1x_3], \end{aligned}$$

$$\begin{aligned} TF_3 = [&108x_3^2 - 108x_1x_2x_3 + 27x_1^3x_3 + 32x_2^3 - 9x_1^2x_2^2, \\ &27x_1^2x_4 - 9x_1x_3x_2 - 72x_2x_4 + 2x_2^3 + 27x_3^2], \end{aligned}$$

can be computed in 122.433 s. They are of dimensions 1, 2 and 2 respectively. By Theorem C we have

$$\text{Zero}(DS) = \text{Zero}(TF_1) \cup \text{Zero}(TF_2) \cup \text{Zero}(TF_3) = \text{Zero}(TF_2) \cup \text{Zero}(TF_3).$$

This is actually an irreducible decomposition of the singular variety of the discriminant surface. See the following section for discussions on the decomposition of algebraic varieties and Wang (1991) for some detailed geometric interpretation of the decomposition above.

It is shown in Wang (1993) that for 73 out of 80 test cases our elimination method is faster than Ritt–Wu's characteristic set method. Example C above is however among the notable ones in our list that lead to cases in which our method is slower than Ritt–Wu's.

8 Decomposition of algebraic varieties

A collection $\mathfrak{V}$ of points in an n-dimensional space is called an *algebraic variety* (cf. Hodge and Pedoe 1947) if it is exactly the set of common zeros of a set PS of n-variate polynomials, i.e., $\mathfrak{V} = \text{Zero}(PS)$. In other words, algebraic varieties (e.g., algebraic curves and algebraic surfaces) are geometric figures defined by sets of polynomial equations. It is often desirable to decompose an algebraic variety into proper subvarieties. Our method in combination with the method of Gröbner bases provides an efficient algorithm for the decomposition.

8.1 Problem

An algebraic variety is said to be *irreducible* if it cannot be expressed as the union of two proper subvarieties $\mathfrak{V}_1$ and $\mathfrak{V}_2$. The statement of the decomposition problem is rather simple as it follows.

$16x_2^2 + 8x_1^2x_2 - x_1^4$), of which the first factor has been considered already as in TF_1 and the second is just the one in the corresponding ascending set and may be used to replace T_2.

Let an algebraic variety $\mathfrak{V}$ be defined by a polynomial set $PS = \{P_1(x_1, \ldots, x_n), \ldots, P_s(x_1, \ldots, x_n)\}$ over $\boldsymbol{K}$. Find a sequence of polynomial sets $PS_1, \ldots, PS_e$ such that

$$\mathrm{Zero}(PS) = \bigcup_{i=1}^{e} \mathrm{Zero}(PS_i), \tag{8.1}$$

or equivalently

$$\mathfrak{V} = \mathfrak{V}_1 \cup \ldots \cup \mathfrak{V}_e, \tag{8.2}$$

and the algebraic variety $\mathfrak{V}_i$ given by $\mathrm{Zero}(PS_i)$ is irreducible for each i. It is desired that the decomposition is non-contractible, i.e., none of $\mathfrak{V}_1, \ldots, \mathfrak{V}_e$ is a subvariety of the others.

The decomposition (8.1) or (8.2) is called an *irreducible decomposition* of the algebraic variety $\mathfrak{V}$ defined by PS (see Hodge and Pedoe 1947; Wang 1989b, 1992b; Wu 1984a, b).

8.2 Method

The following method based on our elimination procedure and Gröbner bases permits to compute an irreducible decomposition of any algebraic variety defined by PS.

Method (for irreducible decomposition of algebraic varieties).

1. Compute an irreducible triangular series $[TF_1, US_1] \ldots, [TF_e, US_e]$ of PS. If $e = 0$ then $\mathrm{Zero}(PS) = \emptyset$. If $e = 1$ then the variety defined by PS is irreducible. In both cases the procedure terminates.
2. For each i, if the initials of the polynomials in TF_i are all constants then set $GB_i \leftarrow TF_i$. Otherwise, let $I_1, \ldots, I_r$ be all the non-constant initials and compute the Gröbner basis GB_i of the polynomial set $TF_i \cup \{I_1 \cdot z_1 - 1, \ldots, I_r \cdot z_r - 1\}$ with respect to the purely lexicographic ordering determined by $x_l \prec z_j$, where z's are newly introduced variables.
3. Let $PS_i \leftarrow GB_i \cap \boldsymbol{K}[x_1, \ldots, x_n]$ for each i and remove[13] the redundant polynomial sets from $PS_1, \ldots, PS_e$. Then the obtained sequence of polynomial sets gives the defining sets of the irreducible subvarieties in the decomposition.

8.3 Examples

Example A (Neff 1989). Let an algebraic curve in 3-dimensional space be defined by the intersection of the following algebraic surfaces

---

13 If $\mathrm{Zero}(PS_i) \subset \mathrm{Zero}(PS_j)$ for some i and j, then PS_i can be removed from the sequence of polynomial sets. The inclusion relation can be verified by computing either the normal forms of the polynomials in PS_j with respect to PS_i when PS_i is a Gröbner basis, or the pseudo-remainders of the polynomials in PS_j with respect to TF_i.

$$F_1 = 3x^2 - 4y^2 + z^2 - 8zy + 4zx - 4x + 1 = 0,$$
$$F_2 = x^2 + 2y^2 + 2zy + zx - 2x - y - 3z = 0.$$

The irreducible triangular series of the polynomial set $\{F_1, F_2\}$ with respect to the ordering $z \prec y \prec x$ can be easily computed, resulting in four triangular systems with the triangular forms shown as follows

$$\begin{aligned} TF_1 &= [50y^3 - 5y^2 + 140zy^2 - 24y - 58yz + 94yz^2 - 6z^3 - 42z - 74z^2 - 5, \\ &\quad 10y^2 - z^2 + 14yz - xz - 2x - 3y - 9z - 1], \\ TF_2 &= [z + 2, 5y - 13, 25x^2 - 100x + 163], \\ TF_3 &= [2y - 1, x + z], \\ TF_4 &= [z + 2, 2y - 1, x - 2]. \end{aligned}$$

Since the polynomials in TF_2, TF_3, TF_4 all have constant initials, $PS_2 = TF_2$, $PS_3 = TF_3$, $PS_4 = TF_4$ already define irreducible algebraic curves. To determine the curve from TF_1, we compute the Gröbner basis of $TF_1 \cup \{(z+2) \cdot u - 1\}$ with respect to $z \prec y \prec x \prec u$. It is found that all the polynomials in this Gröbner basis involving the variables z, y, x only form the following set

$$\begin{aligned} PS_1 = \{&-6z^3 + 94yz^2 - 74z^2 + 140y^2z - 58yz - 42z + 50y^3 - 5y^2 - \\ &- 24y - 5, \\ &-10y^2 - 14yz + xz + 2x + 3y + 9z + z^2 + 1, \\ &-75z - 6z^2 - 29y + 99yz - 13x + 70y^2 + 5xy - 9, \\ &-x^2 + 4x - 12y^2 - 16yz + 4y + 12z + z^2 + 1\}. \end{aligned}$$

Hence, $PS_1, \ldots, PS_4$ are the defining sets of curves in the irreducible decomposition of the given algebraic curve. It can be verified that the two points defined by PS_2 and the point defined by PS_4 are actually on the curve defined by PS_1, so that these two components are redundant and can be removed from the decomposition.

The total CPU time for the decomposition is 4.25 s, of which 1.5 s are spent for computing the irreducible triangular series and 2.116 s for the Gröbner basis.

Example B. Let us consider a more complex example. The algebraic variety $\mathfrak{V}$ is defined by the following eight polynomials in an 8-dimensional space

$$\begin{aligned} F_1 &= b_1 + b_2 + b_3 - a - b, \\ F_2 &= 2b_2c_2 + 2b_3c_3 - b - 2b^2 + 2ab - 1, \\ F_3 &= 3b_2c_2^2 + 3b_3c_3^2 - a - 3ab^2 + 4b + 3b^2 + 3b^3, \end{aligned}$$

$$F_4 = 6b_3a_{32}c_2 - a - 3ab - 6ab^2 + 4b + 6b^2 + 6b^3,$$
$$F_5 = 4b_2c_2^3 + 4b_3c_3^3 - b - 10b^2 - 6b^3 - 4b^4 + 4ab + 4ab^3 - 1,$$
$$F_6 = 8b_3c_3a_{32}c_2 - 3b - 14b^2 - 12b^3 - 8b^4 + 4ab + 4ab^2 + 8ab^3 - 1,$$
$$F_7 = 12b_3a_{32}c_2^2 - b - 14b^2 - 18b^3 - 12b^4 + 8ab + 12ab^2 + 12ab^3 - 1,$$
$$F_8 = 7b + 26b^2 + 36b^3 + 24b^4 - 8ab - 24ab^2 - 24ab^3 + 1.$$

With respect to the variable ordering $b \prec c_2 \prec c_3 \prec a \prec b_3 \prec b_2 \prec a_{32} \prec b_1$, the irreducible triangular series of the polynomial set $\{F_1, \ldots, F_8\}$ contains seven triangular systems. The five simpler triangular forms are

$$TF_1 = [b + 1, a + 1, b_3, b_2, b_1 + 2],$$
$$TF_2 = [b + 1, c_2, c_3, a + 1, b_1 + b_2 + b_3 + 2],$$
$$TF_3 = [b + 1, c_2, a + 1, b_3, b_1 + b_2 + 2],$$
$$TF_4 = [b + 1, c_3, a + 1, b_2, a_{32}, b_1 + b_3 + 2],$$
$$TF_5 = [b + 1, -c_3 + c_2, a + 1, b_2 + b_3, a_{32}, b_1 + 2]$$

(which are the same as the ascending sets in the irreducible characteristic series of *PS*) and the two more complicated ones read as follows

$$TF_6 = [12b^2 + 12b + 1, T_2, \ldots, T_8],$$
$$TF_7 = [12b^3 + 6b^2 + b - 1, T_2, \ldots, T_8],$$

where

$$T_2 = 36b^4 + 54b^3 + 12c_2b^2 + 18b^2 + 9c_2b + c_2,$$
$$T_3 = 72b^5 + 108b^4 + 42b^3 - 12c_3b^2 + 9b^2 + 3b - 9c_3b - c_3,$$
$$T_4 = -7b - 26b^2 - 36b^3 - 24b^4 + 8ab + 24ab^2 + 24ab^3 - 1,$$
$$T_5 = 2a - 6b_3c_3^2 + 6ab^2 - 8b - 6b^2 - 6b^3 + 6b_3c_3c_2 - 3c_2 - 3c_2b - 6c_2b^2 + 6c_2ab,$$
$$T_6 = 2b_2c_2 + 2b_3c_3 - b - 2b^2 + 2ab - 1,$$
$$T_7 = 6b_3a_{32}c_2 - a - 3ab - 6ab^2 + 4b + 6b^2 + 6b^3,$$
$$T_8 = b_1 + b_2 + b_3 - a - b.$$

One sees that the polynomials in $TF_1, \ldots, TF_5$ all have constant initials, so the triangular forms constitute by themselves irreducible algebraic varieties. The initials of the polynomials in TF_6 and TF_7 are not all constants. Since TF_6 and TF_7 are of dimension 0 and irreducible, by the dimension theorem in Wu (1984b) any zero of TF_i does not vanish the initial of any polynomial in TF_i for $i = 6, 7$. Hence, these two triangular forms themselves define irreducible subvarieties of $\mathfrak{V}$ as well. We have easily checked that none of these 7 varieties is a subvariety of the other. Therefore, we get an irredundant irreducible decomposition of $\mathfrak{V}$ which consists of seven irreducible components of dimensions 3, 3, 3, 2, 2, 0, 0 respectively.

The total CPU time for the decomposition is 29.35 s, of which 21.527 s are spent for computing the irreducible triangular series.

9 Inverse robot kinematics

It has been shown that both the Gröbner basis method and the characteristic set method can be applied to the problem of inverse robot kinematics (Buchberger 1987, Wang 1991, Wu 1989). As solving inverse kinematics problems may be simply reduced to solving systems of algebraic equations, our elimination method can be naturally used to deal with the problem as well. In this section we report on some preliminary experiments on solving two types of inverse kinematic equations using our method.

9.1 Problem

The problem of inverse robot kinematics amounts to finding the joint variables for positioning the end-effector of the robot arm at the desired position with desired orientation, given the position and the orientation of the end-effector of the robot with respect to a reference coordinate system and the various geometric link parameters. While parameters and variables are introduced for positions, orientations, joints and geometric links, the relations among these parameters and variables may be expressed by transformations of N 4×4-matrices (see Paul 1981). The relation which describes the physical entities of the robot arm is given as

$$T_N = A_1 A_2 \ldots A_N,$$

where

$$A_i = \begin{pmatrix} \cos\theta_i & -\sin\theta_i \cos\alpha_i & \sin\theta_i \sin\alpha_i & a_i \cos\theta_i \\ \sin\theta_i & \cos\theta_i \cos\alpha_i & -\cos\theta_i \sin\alpha_i & a_i \sin\theta_i \\ 0 & \sin\alpha_i & \cos\alpha_i & d_i \\ 0 & 0 & 0 & 1 \end{pmatrix},$$

$$T_N = \begin{pmatrix} n_x & o_x & a_x & p_x \\ n_y & o_y & a_y & p_y \\ n_z & o_z & a_z & p_z \\ 0 & 0 & 0 & 1 \end{pmatrix}.$$

Then, by multiplying the matrices and equating the corresponding elements, and by introducing new variables for the trigonometric functions and adding some basic relations among these functions, we may get a system of polynomial equations. The problem is thereby reduced to solving such a polynomial system for $\sin\theta_i, \cos\theta_i$ in terms of $n_x, n_y, n_z, o_x, o_y, o_z, a_x, a_y, a_z, p_x, p_y, p_x$ and a_i, d_i. From the obtained solutions, each θ_i can be finally determined.

9.2 Method

Dealing with the inverse kinematics problem in this context lies at computing symbolic solutions of inverse kinematic equations in closed form, that is, solving systems of algebraic equations symbolically. In this case, the application of our method is straightforward (see Theorems A–C in Sect. 2). Nevertheless, the systems of equations to be solved for non-trivial robots are usually too complicated and beyond the applicability of our method as well as other existing ones. First, the computation may either take many hours or run out of a reasonable limit of time. Second, the resulting expressions are often large polynomials which are difficult to handle and have to be simplified for practical use. Therefore, particular efforts are required to improve the methods both for the efficiency and for the simplicity of output for this class of problems.

9.3 Examples

Example A. Let us recall the example of a toy robot having two revolute joints considered in Buchberger (1987) and Wang (1991). To be convenient for comparison, we use the same notations and variables. The interrelation of the physical entities as described therein is a system of 17 equations. Let us omit copying those equations and denote the corresponding set of polynomials by *PS*.

With respect to $c_1 \prec c_2 \prec s_1 \prec s_2 \prec py \prec cf \prec ct \prec cp \prec sf \prec st \prec sp$, the triangular series of *PS* contains only one triangular system $[TF, \{c_1, cf, s_1\}]$, which is the principal one, with polynomials in *TF* having index triples

$$\begin{array}{llllll} [5\ c_1\ 2], & [2\ c_2\ 1], & [3\ s_1\ 2], & [3\ s_2\ 1], & [2\ py\ 1], & \\ [2\ cf\ 2], & [1\ ct\ 1], & [2\ cp\ 1], & [2\ sf\ 1], & [2\ st\ 1], & [2\ sp\ 1], \end{array}$$

which is similar to the characteristic set but somewhat simpler than the Gröbner basis of *PS*. In the irreducible triangular series of the polynomial set, two irreducible triangular systems $[TF_1, \emptyset]$, $[TF_2, \emptyset]$ were found, with the two triangular forms shown as follows

$$\begin{aligned} TF_1 = [&c_1^2 \cdot l_2^2 - c_1^2 \cdot l_1^2 + 2 \cdot c_1^2 \cdot l_1 \cdot pz - c_1^2 \cdot pz^2 - px^2, l_2 \cdot c_1 \cdot c_2 - px, \\ &c_1^2 \cdot l_2^2 - c_1^2 \cdot l_1^2 + 2 \cdot c_1^2 \cdot l_1 \cdot pz - c_1^2 \cdot pz^2 - c_1^2 \cdot px^2 - s_1^2 \cdot px^2, \\ &l_2 \cdot s_2 + l_1 - pz, l_2 \cdot s_1 \cdot c_2 - py, cf + s_1, ct, -s_2 + cp, -sf + c_1, \\ &st + 1, c_2 + sp], \\ TF_2 = [&c_1^2 \cdot l_2^2 - c_1^2 \cdot l_1^2 + 2 \cdot c_1^2 \cdot l_1 \cdot pz - c_1^2 \cdot pz^2 - px^2, l_2 \cdot c_1 \cdot c_2 - px, \\ &c_1^2 \cdot l_2^2 - c_1^2 \cdot l_1^2 + 2 \cdot c_1^2 \cdot l_1 \cdot pz - c_1^2 \cdot pz^2 - c_1^2 \cdot px^2 - s_1^2 \cdot px^2, \\ &l_2 \cdot s_2 + l_1 - pz, l_2 \cdot s_1 \cdot c_2 - py, cf - s_1, ct, s_2 + cp, sf + c_1, \\ &st - 1, c_2 - sp], \end{aligned}$$

which are slightly different from the ascending sets in the irreducible characteristic series of *PS*. Now the solutions for the variables $c_1, \ldots, sp$ can be successively found either from the triangular form *TF* or from the irreducible triangular forms TF_1 and TF_2 with ease. The computation of the triangular series and the irreducible triangular series took 5.567 and 9.484 CPU seconds respectively.

Example B. A sketch on solving the inverse kinematics equations of PUMA-type robots with 6 degrees of freedom using characteristic sets was given in Wu (1989). In this case, the manipulator link parameters are specified as in Table 1.

Table 1

Link	α	a	d
1	90°	0	0
2	0°	a_2	0
3	-90°	0	0
4	90°	0	d_4
5	-90°	0	0
6	0°	0	0

The corresponding set consists of 18 polynomials as listed in Wang (1991) and Wu (1989). Wu (1989) was able to determine the zero structure of this set of polynomials by computing the modified characteristic sets. We have tried to compute the "ordinary" characteristic set and the principal triangular system without success. Some of the occurring polynomials consist of many thousand terms and the program ran several hours without termination.

10 Intersection of geometric objects

10.1 Problem

One basic problem in motion planning is to test the intersection of physical bodies. For efficient computation, the physical bodies are enclosed by some regular geometric objects like polygons, discs and spheres. The problem is then reduced to detecting the intersection of these geometric objects (of which some may be in motion). For example, one may consider two simple cases of the path finding and decision (collision detection) problem:

1. Given two geometric objects A and B, determine whether they intersect one another.
2. Given a region R bounded by a collection of polyhedral or other simple walls and an object (or a collection of objects) O, determine whether object O can pass through region R.

A great amount of work on problems of this kind has been done in the area of robot motion planning (see Schwartz and Yap 1987, for instance).

10.2 Method

The algebraic form of the above problems, in general, involves both polynomial equations and polynomial inequalities; therefore, their solution requires solving systems of polynomial equations and inequalities over the reals. Due to this nature, the method of cylindrical algebraic decomposition (CAD) introduced by G. Collins (1975) is among the most appropriate ones for solving the problem. The reader may refer to Schwartz et al. (1987) for detailed description of algorithms dealing with this type of problem. In principle, our method is unable to reach a complete solution of the detection problem. However, with certain efforts such as the use of Seidenberg's trick and Lagrange's multiplier technique, our method may also help solve the problem in some cases.

10.3 Examples

Example A. Wang (1991) considered a "Piano Movers" problem proposed by Davenport (1986) using the CAD method. This problem is however beyond the applicability of our elimination method and therefore we do not discuss it here.

Example B. Buchberger (1987) presented an example for illustrating the application of Gröbner bases to test the intersection of a sphere and a superellipsoid. The problem was reduced by using Lagrange's multiplier to finding the solutions to the following polynomial equations

$$\begin{aligned}
&(bcx)^{2/\epsilon} + (acy)^{2/\epsilon} + (abz)^{2/\epsilon} - (abc)^{2/\epsilon} = 0,\\
&a^{2/\epsilon}\epsilon(x - A) + \lambda x^{2/\epsilon - 1} = 0,\\
&b^{2/\epsilon}\epsilon(y - B) + \lambda y^{2/\epsilon - 1} = 0,\\
&c^{2/\epsilon}\epsilon(z - C) + \lambda z^{2/\epsilon - 1} = 0.
\end{aligned}$$

The Gröbner bases (with respect to lexicographic ordering determined by $x \prec y \prec z \prec \lambda$) of the corresponding polynomial set for $\epsilon = 1$ and $\epsilon = -1$ were computed by Buchberger in SAC-2 on an IBM4341 in 15 min and 19 h respectively. Wang (1991) repeated the computation of Gröbner basis for $\epsilon = 1$ in Maple and applied the characteristic set method to deal with the problem. Using the same variable ordering, the triangular series of the polynomial set, containing only one triangular system (which is actually irreducible) with the triangular form having index triples

$$[66\ x\ 6], \quad [4\ y\ 1], \quad [4\ z\ 1], \quad [3\ \lambda\ 1],$$

was computed without projection in 1.133 s. The first polynomial in this triangular form is the same as that in the Gröbner basis, and the last three are similar to those in the characteristic set but much simpler than those in the Gröbner basis. From the triangular system, the solutions for x, y, z, λ can be successively determined as well.

Acknowledgements

This work was supported by the Austrian Ministry of Science and Research and the Commission of the European Communities under ESPRIT Basic Research Action 3125 (MEDLAR I) and Project 6471 (MEDLAR II). The author wishes to thank Jochen Pfalzgraf, the project leader of the RISC-Linz team, for his enthusiasm and ability to keep the project running smoothly. This chapter was written when the author was moving from RISC-Linz to LIFIA-IMAG. Special thanks to Ricardo Caferra and Thierry Boy de la Tour for their thorough arrangement.

References

Arnon, D. S. (1986): Geometric reasoning with logic and algebra. Artif. Intell. 37: 37–60.

Arnon, D. S., Sederberg, T. W. (1984): Implicit equation for a parametric surface by Gröbner bases. In: Golden, V. E. (ed.): Proceedings of the 1984 MACSYMA User's Conference. General Electric, Schenectady, NY, pp. 431–436.

Buchberger, B. (1985): Gröbner bases: an algorithmic method in polynomial ideal theory. In: Bose, N. K. (ed.): Multidimensional systems theory. Reidel, Dordrecht, pp. 184–232.

Buchberger, B. (1987): Applications of Gröbner bases in non-linear computational geometry. In: Rice, J. R. (ed.): Mathematical aspects of scientific software. Springer, Berlin Heidelberg New York Tokyo, pp. 59–87 (The IMA volumes in mathematics and its applications, vol. 14).

Buchberger, B., Collins, G. E., Kutzler, B. (1988): Algebraic methods for geometric reasoning. Annu. Rev. Comput. Sci. 3: 85–119.

Chou, S. C. (1987): A method for the mechanical derivation of formulas in elementary geometry. J. Autom. Reason. 3: 291–299.

Chou, S. C. (1988): Mechanical geometry theorem proving. Reidel, Dordrecht.

Chou, S. C., Gao, X. S. (1990): Mechanical formula derivation in elementary geometries. In: Proceedings ISSAC '90, Tokyo, August 20–24, 1990, pp. 265–270.

Collins, G. E. (1975): Quantifier elimination for real closed fields by cylindrical algebraic decomposition. In: Brakhage, H. (ed.): Automata theory and formal languages. Springer, Berlin Heidelberg New York, pp. 134–165 (Lecture notes in computer science, vol. 33).

Davenport, J. M. (1986): A "Piano movers" problem. SIGSAM Bull. 20: 15–17.

Gao, X. S., Chou, S. C. (1991): Computations with parametric equations. In: Proceedings ISSAC '91, Bonn, July 15–17, 1991, pp. 122–127.

Hodge, W. V. D., Pedoe, D. (1947/1952): Methods of algebraic geometry, vols. I, II. Cambridge University Press, Cambridge.

Hoffmann, C. (1989): Geometric and solid modeling. Morgan Kaufmann, Los Altos.

Kalkbrener, M. (1991): Three contributions to elimination theory. Ph.D. thesis, University of Linz, Linz, Austria.

Kapur, D., Mundy, J. L. (eds.) (1989): Geometric reasoning. MIT Press, Cambridge, MA.

Li, Z. M. (1989): Automatic implicitization of parametric objects. Math. Mech. Res. Preprints 4: 54–62.

Neff, C. A. (1989): Decomposing algebraic sets using Gröbner bases. Comput. Aided Geom. Des. 6: 249–263.

Nutbourne, A. W., Martin, R. R. (1988): Differential geometry applied to curve and surface design, vol. 1, foundations. Ellis Horwood, Chichester.

Paul, R. P. (1981): Robot manipulators: mathematics, programming and control. MIT Press, Cambridge, MA.

Pfalzgraf, J., Stokkermans, K., Wang, D. M. (1990): The robotics benchmark. In: Proceedings 12-Month MEDLAR Workshop (Weinberg Castle, Austria, November 4–7, 1990), Department of Computing, Imperial College, University of London.

Ritt, J. F. (1950): Differential algebra. American Mathematical Society, New York.

Schwartz, J. T., Yap, C. K. (1987): Advances in robotics, vol. 1, algorithmic and geometric aspects of robotics. Lawrence Erlbaum, Hillsdale.

Schwartz, J. T., Sharir, M., Hopcroft, J. (1987): Planning, geometry, and complexity of robot motion. Ablex, Norwood.

Sederberg, T. W., Anderson, D. C. (1984): Implicit representation of parametric curves and surfaces. Comput. Vision Graphics Image Process. 28: 72–84.

Seidenberg, A. (1956a): Some remarks on Hilbert's Nullstellensatz. Arch. Math. 7: 235–240.

Seidenberg, A. (1956b): An elimination theory for differential algebra. Univ. California Publ. Math. (N.S.) 3: 31–66.

Seidenberg, A. (1969): On k-constructable sets, k-elementary formulae, and elimination theory. J. Reine Angew. Math. 239/240: 256–267.

Tarski, A. (1951): A decision method for elementary algebra and geometry, 2nd ed. University of California Press, Berkeley.

Wang, D. M. (1987): Mechanical approach for polynomial set and its related fields. Ph.D. thesis, Academia Sinica, Beijing, People's Republic of China.

Wang, D. M. (1989a): On the singularities of algebraic hypersurfaces – the discriminant systems. Preprint, School of Mathematical Sciences, Queen Mary College, University of London.

Wang, D. M. (1989b): Characteristic sets and zero structure of polynomial sets. Lecture Notes, RISC Linz.

Wang, D. M. (1990): Some notes on algebraic methods for geometry theorem proving. Preprint, RISC Linz.

Wang, D. M. (1991): Reasoning about geometric problems using algebraic methods. In: Proceedings MEDLAR 24-Month Workshop, Grenoble, December 8–11, 1991. Department of Computing, Imperial College, University of London.

Wang, D. M. (1992a): A method for factorizing multivariate polynomials over successive algebraic extension fields. Preprint, RISC Linz.

Wang, D. M. (1992b): Irreducible decomposition of algebraic varieties via characteristic sets and Gröbner bases. Comput. Aided Geom. Des. 9: 471–484.

Wang, D. M. (1993): An elimination method for polynomial systems. J. Symb. Comput. 16: 83–114.

Wang, D. M. (1994): Algebraic factoring and geometry theorem proving. In: Proceedings CADE-12, Nancy, June 28 – July 1, 1994. Springer, Berlin Heidelberg New York Tokyo, pp. 386–400 (Lecture notes in artificial intelligence, vol. 814).

Wang, D. M. (1995): Elimination procedures for mechanical theorem proving in geometries. Ann. Math. Artif. Intell. (to appear)

Wu, W.-t. (1978): On the decision problem and the mechanization of theorem-proving in elementary geometry. Sci. Sin. 21: 159–172 [also in Bledsoe, W. W., Loveland, D. W. (eds.): Automated theorem proving: after 25 years. American Mathematical Society, Providence, pp. 213–234 (1984)].

Wu, W.-t. (1984a): Basic principles of mechanical theorem proving in elementary geometries. J. Syst. Sci. Math. Sci. 4: 207–235 [also in J. Automat. Reason. 2: 221–252 (1986)].

Wu, W.-t. (1984b): Basic principles of mechanical theorem proving in geometries (part on elementary geometries). Science Press, Beijing (in Chinese); English-language edition, Springer, Wien New York (1994).

Wu, W.-t. (1986a): On zeros of algebraic equations – an application of Ritt principle. Kexue Tongbao 31: 1–5.

Wu, W.-t. (1986b): A mechanization method of geometry and its applications – I. distances, areas and volumes. J. Syst. Sci. Math. Sci. 6: 204–216.

Wu, W.-t. (1988): A mechanization method of geometry and its applications – III. mechanical proving of polynomial inequalities and equations-solving. Syst. Sci. Math. Sci. 1: 1–17 [also in Math. Mech. Res. Preprints 2: 1–17 (1987)].

Wu, W.-t. (1989): A mechanization method of geometry and its applications – VI. solving inverse kinematic equations of PUMA-type robots. Math. Mech. Res. Preprints 4: 49–53.

Wu, W.-t. (1990): On a projection theorem of quasi-varieties in elimination theory. Chin. Ann. Math. 11B/2: 220–226.

An implementation of the characteristic set method in Maple

Dongming Wang

1 Introduction and notations

The method of characteristic sets was introduced by J. F. Ritt (1932, 1950) in the context of his work on differential algebra in the early 1930s and was revitalized and further developed by Wen-tsün Wu (1984a, b, 1986) through his recent work on mathematics-mechanization. In addition to being a powerful tool for Wu's general theory and method of mechanical theorem proving, the characteristic set method has proved efficient for solving a wide class of problems in geometry and algebra (see the series of work in "Mathematics-Mechanization Research Preprints" 1–11, 1987–1994, for example). It has been partially implemented by different research groups in China, USA and Austria (Chou 1988, Ko 1986, Kusche et al. 1989) for geometry theorem proving and solving other relevant problems. The author has learned that an implementation of this method in the Reduce system is ongoing at the University of Bath, England. However, to the best of our knowledge neither a complete implementation exists nor a partial implementation has been generally available in current symbolic and algebraic computation systems. The incompleteness of the existing implementations was mainly due to difficulties in polynomial factorization over successive algebraic extension fields (for which there was a lack of general and efficient procedures) and the determination of prime bases of ideals from their characteristic sets (for which no simple and practical method was available). We have overcome the difficulties through the discovery of a new method for polynomial factorization and the application of Gröbner bases for determining the prime bases.

In this paper we describe a complete, general-purpose implementation of the characteristic set method, considering mainly the zero structure of polynomial sets. This implementation has been included in the Maple share library as a package under the name `charsets`[1] and can be considered as a practical basis for designing and implementing other related algorithms. The method of characteristic sets as well as its underlying theory has been well developed by Ritt and

1 The Maple code can be obtained via anonymous FTP on two sites: 129.132.101.33 (neptune) ETH Zurich, Switzerland and 129.97.140.58 (daisy) University of Waterloo, Canada. The printings of the help file and source code are also included in a technical report bearing the same title as this paper, available as RISC-Linz Series no. 91-25.0.

Wu. It provides rich contents for dealing with systems of (multivariate) polynomials (as well as differential polynomials). For the present implementation we essentially follow Wu's improved version of the method but use the algorithmic form we described previously (Wang 1989b), taking most of the remarks there into account. The implemented algorithms include those for computing characteristic sets of polynomial sets, decomposing polynomial sets into ascending sets and irreducible ascending sets, decomposing algebraic varieties into irreducible components, factorizing polynomials over algebraic number fields and solving systems of polynomial equations. We have supplied several possible variants of these algorithms in order to make the package comprehensive and flexible.

The characteristic set method has an important application to mechanical theorem proving in geometries. On the basis of this package, the author has also developed a new and rather powerful geometry theorem prover GEOTHER which provides again a first complete implementation of Wu's general method. The prover has been treated as part of a geometry problem solver under development and is not included in this package. A detailed description of GEOTHER will be published elsewhere.

In the later sections we shall describe 15 user level functions available in our package, discuss the modification and generalization of some basic and utilized algorithms with our implementation strategies, and present a set of test results for all functions with variants. Before doing this, let us first explain our notations (which are similar to those used in Wang 1989b) in order to avoid confusion with notations used by other authors.

In the whole package all input polynomials are in parameters $u_1, \ldots, u_d$ and variables $x_1, \ldots, x_n$ with integer or rational coefficients. By a *constant* polynomial we mean one involving only the parameters. While the order of the variables is fixed, say

$$x_1 \prec x_2 \prec \ldots \prec x_n,$$

we call the variable with biggest index occurring in a non-constant polynomial F the *leading variable* of F, denoted as[2] $\operatorname{lvar}(F)$. The leading coefficient of a non-constant polynomial F with respect to $\operatorname{lvar}(F)$ is called the *initial* of F, denoted as $\operatorname{ini}(F)$. A polynomial G is said to be *reduced* with respect to F if the degree of G in $\operatorname{lvar}(F)$ is less than the degree of F in $\operatorname{lvar}(F)$.

A finite set $\{A_1, A_2, \ldots, A_r\}$ of polynomials is called a *quasi-ascending set* or a *triangular form* if either $r = 1$ and $A_1 \neq 0$, or $r > 1$ and $\operatorname{lvar}(A_1) \prec \operatorname{lvar}(A_2) \prec \ldots \prec \operatorname{lvar}(A_r)$. A quasi-ascending set AS is called an *ascending set* if in the case $r > 1$, A_j is reduced with respect to A_i for each pair $j > i$. A quasi-ascending set AS is called a *weak-ascending set* if in the case $r > 1$, the initial of A_j is reduced with respect to A_i for each pair $j > i$. A (weak-, quasi-) ascending set is said to be *contradictory* if $r = 1$ and A_1 is a non-zero constant.

Let G be any non-zero polynomial and $AS = \{A_1, \ldots, A_r\}$ a non-contradictory (weak-, quasi-) ascending set. One can pseudo-divide G successively by $A_r, \ldots, A_1$ – considered as polynomials in their leading variables. The final

2 When we speak about $\operatorname{lvar}(F)$, it always implies that F is not a constant.

remainder R is called the *pseudo-remainder* or simply the *remainder* of G with respect to AS.

Let PS be a finite, non-empty set of non-zero polynomials. The set of all non-zero remainders of the polynomials in PS with respect to a (weak-, quasi-) ascending set AS is called the *remainder set* of PS with respect to AS. The set of all common zeros of the polynomials in PS is denoted by Zero(PS). For any other non-zero polynomial G, we write $\mathrm{Zero}(PS/G)$ for $\mathrm{Zero}(PS) \setminus \mathrm{Zero}(G)$.

2 Description of user functions

In this section we describe the user level functions, which provide with great flexibility for using our package. There are two trivial functions `iniset` and `remset`: `iniset` computes the set of all distinct factors of initials of the polynomials in a non-contradictory (weak-, quasi-) ascending set AS, and `remset` computes the remainder set of a polynomial set PS with respect to AS. The other 13 non-trivial functions are given below.

2.1 charset and mcharset

A (weak-, quasi-) ascending set CS is called a *(weak-, quasi-) characteristic set* of a polynomial set PS if any polynomial in CS is a linear combination of the polynomials in PS with polynomial coefficients (i.e., CS is contained in the ideal generated by the polynomials in PS) and the remainder set of PS with respect to CS is empty. For a characteristic set CS of PS, we have therefore

$$\mathrm{Zero}(CS/J) \subset \mathrm{Zero}(PS) \subset \mathrm{Zero}(CS),$$

where J is the product of initials of the polynomials in CS. A (weak-, quasi-) ascending set CS is called a *modified (weak-, quasi-) characteristic set* of PS if

$$\mathrm{Zero}(CS/J) \subset \mathrm{Zero}(PS), \qquad \mathrm{Zero}(PS/F) \subset \mathrm{Zero}(CS),$$

where J is the same as before and F is a non-zero polynomial.

The functions `charset` and `mcharset` compute respectively a (weak-, quasi-) characteristic set and a modified (weak-, quasi-) characteristic set of any polynomial set. For these two functions there is an option of 8 possible choices `basset`, `wbasset`, `qbasset`, `charsetn`, `wcharsetn`, `qcharsetn`, `trisetc` and `triset` for the so-called *medial sets*. These medial sets correspond respectively to those computed by the algorithms `BasicSet`, `CharacteristicSetN`, `TriangularSetC` and `TriangularSet`, described in Wang (1989a, b). If `basset`, `charsetn` or `trisetc` is chosen, then a characteristic set or a modified characteristic set is computed; if `wbasset` or `wcharsetn` is chosen, then a weak-characteristic set or a modified weak-characteristic set is computed; if `qbasset`, `qcharsetn` or `triset` is chosen, then a quasi-characteristic set or a modified quasi-characteristic set is computed. The default is `charsetn`.

2.2 charser, mcs, ecs and mecs

If a polynomial set *PS* and a sequence of (weak-) ascending sets $CS_1, \ldots, CS_e$ are such that

$$\mathrm{Zero}(PS) = \bigcup_{i=1}^{e} \mathrm{Zero}(CS_i/J_i),$$

where each J_i is the product of initials of the polynomials in CS_i, then $\{CS_1, \ldots, CS_e\}$ is called a *(weak-) characteristic series*[3] of *PS*. If they are such that

$$\mathrm{Zero}(PS/G) = \bigcup_{i=1}^{e} \mathrm{Zero}(CS_i/F_i),$$

where G is a non-zero polynomial and each F_i a polynomial having remainder non-zero with respect to CS_i, then $\{[CS_1, F_1], \ldots, [CS_e, F_e]\}$ is called an *extended (weak-) characteristic series* of $[PS, G]$.

Both functions `charser` and `mcs` compute a (weak-) characteristic series of *PS*, while the functions `ecs` and `mecs` compute an extended (weak-) characteristic series of $[PS, G]$. The only difference between `charser` and `mcs` and between `ecs` and `mecs` is: with `mcs` and `mecs`, which in general are fast with large problems, some factors are examined and allowed to be removed during the internal computation of characteristic sets. Since we are unable to judge which function is better, both are kept in the package. For these functions there is an option of 5 medial sets `basset`, `wbasset`, `charsetn`, `wcharsetn` and `trisetc`, of which `charsetn` is again the default. A characteristic series or an extended characteristic series is computed if `basset`, `charsetn` or `trisetc` is chosen, and a weak-characteristic series or a modified weak-characteristic series is computed if any of the others is chosen.

2.3 triser and csolve

The function `triser` computes, from a polynomial set *PS*, a sequence of ascending sets, weak-ascending sets or quasi-ascending sets $CS_1, \ldots, CS_e$ such that

$$\mathrm{Zero}(PS) = \bigcup_{i=1}^{e} \mathrm{Zero}(CS_i/J_i),$$

where each J_i is the product of initials of the polynomials in CS_i. It is designed mainly to prepare a sequence of triangular forms for solving the corresponding system of polynomial equations. The function `csolve` finds all solutions of a system of polynomial equations. It basically uses the function `triser` to prepare a sequence of triangular forms and then solves each triangular form by successive substitution, where the Maple function `solve` is used for the resolution of univariate polynomial equations.

---

3 In fact, all the polynomials in *PS* have 0 remainder with respect to each CS_i in the (weak-) characteristic series. This is also true for extended, irreducible and quasi-irreducible (weak-) characteristic series discussed below.

2.4 qics, ics and eics

If all polynomials in the (weak-) ascending sets of a characteristic series of *PS* are irreducible over $\boldsymbol{Q}$ (the rational number field), then the (weak-) characteristic series is said to be *quasi-irreducible*. If all ascending sets of a characteristic series or an extended characteristic series of *PS* are irreducible, then the characteristic series or extended characteristic series is said to be *irreducible*.

The functions `qics`, `ics` and `eics` compute respectively a quasi-irreducible (weak-) characteristic series, an irreducible characteristic series, and an extended irreducible characteristic series of a polynomial set *PS* or $[PS, G]$. For `qics` there is an option of 5 medial sets `basset`, `wbasset`, `charsetn`, `wcharsetn` and `trisetc` too. A quasi-irreducible weak-characteristic series is computed if `wbasset` or `wcharsetn` is chosen, and a quasi-irreducible characteristic series is computed if one of the others is chosen. For `ics` and `eics`, an option of 3 medial sets `basset`, `charsetn` and `trisetc` is allowed. In all three functions `charsetn` is again the default.

2.5 ivd

If a polynomial set *PS* and a sequence of polynomial sets $VS_1, \ldots, VS_t$ are such that

$$\mathrm{Zero}(PS) = \bigcup_{i=1}^{t} \mathrm{Zero}(VS_i),$$

and the algebraic variety defined by VS_i is irreducible for all i, then the above zero decomposition is called an *irreducible decomposition* of the algebraic variety defined by *PS*, and $VS_1, \ldots, VS_t$ are called the defining sets of irreducible components of the decomposition.

The function `ivd` computes a sequence of irredundant defining sets of the irreducible decomposition of the algebraic variety defined by a polynomial set *PS*. For this function, there is again an option of 3 medial sets `basset`, `charsetn` and `trisetc` with `charsetn` as default.

2.6 cfactor

Let $AS = \{A_1(u, y_1), A_2(u, y_1, y_2), \ldots, A_r(u, y_1, y_2, \ldots, y_r)\}$ (where u stands for $u_1, \ldots, u_d$) be an irreducible ascending set and $F = F(u, y_1, \ldots, y_r, y)$ any polynomial in $u, y_1, \ldots, y_r, y$ with integer or rational coefficients. Consider F as a polynomial in y and suppose its leading coefficient has a non-zero remainder with respect to *AS*. The function `cfactor` computes an irreducible factorization of F over the algebraic number field $\boldsymbol{Q}(u, y_1, \ldots, y_r)$, where $u_1, \ldots, u_d$ are transcendental elements and $y_1, \ldots, y_r$ are algebraic elements with each y_i having minimal polynomial $A_i(u, y_1, \ldots, y_i)$.

3 Modifications and strategies

The theory of characteristic sets developed by Ritt and Wu provides a constructive method for dealing with systems of polynomials (as well as differential polynomials). However, from a computational aspect many details have to be carefully taken into account for the sake of efficiency. These details are not treated in Ritt's work. It was Wu who recognized the power of Ritt's method and considerably improved the method both in theory and in practice by bringing to it many new and important ideas. Through the design and implementation of our package we have made several further modifications and improvements and adopted a number of strategies. It is not possible to list all of them here but we want to mention a few as follows, of which some are given as remarks in Wang (1989b).

3.1 Modification of the pseudo-division

The basic operation underlying all characteristic-set-based algorithms is the pseudo-division of two polynomials F and G with respect to a variable x. While dividing G by F, one gets a remainder formula of the form

$$I^s \cdot G = Q \cdot F + R,$$

where I is the leading coefficient of F in x. The integer s is determined to be the smallest so that the formula holds true according to Wu. Such a choice of the smallest s is important for reducing the degree and size of the remainder R. Now let us modify the formula above by replacing I^s with $I_1^{s_1} \ldots I_e^{s_e}$, where $I_1, \ldots, I_e$ are all distinct irreducible factors of I, and choosing the smallest $s_1, \ldots, s_e$ so that the corresponding remainder formula still holds. For this modification the determination of R requires GCD (greatest common divisor) computation and thus takes more time at every individual step. However, we have observed that the modification can often avoid some redundant factors so that the subsequent computation profits, in particular, when the occurring polynomials become large. So in our package this modified pseudo-division is used.

3.2 Generalization of the characteristic set algorithm

The characteristic set algorithm has several variants. Our implementation of this algorithm is based on a generalization described previously (Wang 1989a). We use the notion of *medial sets* of a polynomial set *PS* which are (weak-, quasi-) ascending sets with rank not higher than that of the (weak-, quasi-) basic set of *PS* and in which all polynomials are linear combinations of the polynomials in *PS* with polynomial coefficients. Thus, any (weak-, quasi-) basic set itself is a special (weak-, quasi-) medial set of the polynomial set. We proved that in Ritt's original algorithm, *basic set* can be replaced by any *medial set*. Besides basic set itself we have used in our implementation other kinds of medial sets including those computed by the algorithms `CharacteristicSetN`, `TriangularSetC`, `TriangularSet` described previously (Wang 1989a, b) and by an algorithm designed for computing the so-called *normal* characteristic sets which are necessary for our factorization method to be mentioned below. With the notion of medial sets several variants of the characteristic set algorithm can be given in a uniform manner.

3.3 Removing possible factors of intermediate polynomials

During the computation of characteristic sets, there appear inevitably some redundant factors which are initials of other occurring polynomials. These factors should be removed in order to control the expansion of polynomial size. If one allows the removal of factors, then the ascending sets computed by the characteristic set algorithm are no longer characteristic sets in Ritt's sense: they are what we call modified characteristic sets. Polynomials in a modified characteristic set are not necessarily elements of the ideal generated by the polynomials in the original set. If one considers only the zero structure of polynomial sets such as the case of solving polynomial equations, the modified characteristic sets are already well suited. If the removed factors are denoted by $F_1, \ldots, F_t$, then we have a zero relation of the form

$$\mathrm{Zero}(PS) = \mathrm{Zero}(CS/J) \cup \bigcup_{i=1}^{r} \mathrm{Zero}(PS_i) \cup \bigcup_{j=1}^{t} \mathrm{Zero}(QS_j),$$

where $J = I_1 \ldots I_r \cdot F_1 \ldots F_t$ and $PS_i = PS \cup \{I_i\}$, $QS_j = PS \cup \{F_j\}$.

In the functions `mcharset`, `mcs`, `mecs`, `triser`, `qics`, `ics`, `eics` and `ivd`, we allow all to remove possible factors. If the option of medial sets is `triset` or `trisetc`, we remove initials of the previous polynomials as factors from the newly produced polynomials in the computation of remainder sequence. Otherwise, we collect all the initials which have appeared in the previous computation and remove them as factors from the subsequently produced polynomials at certain stages. In all cases, the variables themselves as polynomials are examined and removed if possible. This process is of course time-consuming and does not seem to be recommendable for small problems. However, the removal of possible factors is very crucial for large problems. During our experiments we have seen that for many problems (e.g., Problem 4 as shown in Table 1) the application of `charset` yields no result after a great amount of computing time, whereas `mcharset` gets the desired results easily. Since we are unable to predicate the computational cost for a given problem, we arrange to remove factors in most of our functions in order to avoid the trouble caused by large polynomials.

3.4 Polynomial factorization

Polynomial factorization over both the rational number field and its algebraic extension fields is required in our implementation. As for factorization over the rationals, we use the Maple built-in function `factor` (either as a strategy for reducing the size of polynomials, or for computing the quasi-irreducible characteristic series, or as a subfunction of our procedure for factorizing polynomials over algebraic number fields).

To verify the reducibility of an ascending set, and if reducible to decompose it into irreducible ones (which are needed in the functions `ics`, `eics` and `ivd`), we have to factorize polynomials over successive algebraic extensions of the rational number field which is considered as a difficult problem in general.

Except for Chou's (1988) implementation which can factorize quadratic polynomials, all other implementations of the characteristic set method do not contain procedures for algebraic factorization. The general factorization algorithms are too complicated and not available in Maple. The author has implemented the factorization method by Hu and Wang (1986), which was considered suitable for our purpose. Experiments demonstrate that the method is feasible only for factorizing quadratic and cubic polynomials while degrees of the minimal polynomials are also not high. It is still too slow for polynomials of high degree. Recently, the author has found another method which can be used to factorize polynomials of rather high degree and reduce dramatically the difficulty of our factorization problem. This method has been implemented in combination with our early method, as the function `cfactor`, and used for the irreducible decomposition of ascending sets. The full details of our new method with experimental results are described elsewhere (Wang 1992b).

Since polynomial factorization is expensive in general, we have used some strategies for carrying out the factorization at an appropriate stage. For example, to verify the reducibility of a characteristic set we do the test soon after a medial set is computed in the option of `charsetn` and `trisetc`. Other strategies like factorizing initials and the removed factors in some cases are also very helpful for speeding up the computation.

3.5 Determining the bases of ideals from their characteristic sets

In our implemented algorithm for decomposing algebraic varieties into irreducible components, we first compute an irreducible characteristic series of the defining polynomial set and then determine the prime bases of ideals from the ascending sets in the series. For the latter an algorithm based on the Gröbner primbasissatz and Gröbner bases as described in Wang (1992a) is implemented, where the Maple function `gbasis` in the `grobner` package is used for the computation of Gröbner bases.

3.6 Removing redundant branches of the decomposition tree

As argued previously (Wang 1992a), the characteristic-set-based decomposition algorithms can be viewed as computations for a multi-branch decomposition tree. The number of branches of the tree can be hundred and thousand due to the recursive generation of initials. Some of the branches are completely redundant. Strategies must be used to avoid redundant computation in order to speed up the decomposition. In our implementation we have adopted various strategies for obtaining an equivalent but simpler tree with an aim at reducing the computing time and space. As most branches of the tree are produced from the recursive generation of initials, we observed that it is often profitable to decrease the depth and width of the decomposition tree by adjoining not the initials and the removed factors but the distinct irreducible factors of them. Even though this requires extensive polynomial factorization, the computation is not very expensive, mainly because the initials and remove factors are relatively simple.

We cut off some redundant branches during the computation of various characteristic series according to a fact as follows: Let QS and QS' be two polynomial sets associated with two nodes of the decomposition tree of PS and $QS \subset QS'$. If the decomposition tree of QS is already computed, then the decomposition tree of QS' as a subtree of PS can be cut away. After the characteristic series has been produced, we remove some redundant ascending sets by another fact: For two ascending sets AS_1 and AS_2 of which the former is irreducible, if with respect to AS_1 the remainder set of AS_2 is empty and the remainder of J_2 is non-zero, then $\mathrm{Zero}(AS_1/J_1) \subset \mathrm{Zero}(AS_2/J_2)$, where J_i is the product of initials of the polynomials in AS_i for $i = 1, 2$, and thus AS_1 can be removed. For the function `ivd`, we also cut off some redundant branches by the affine dimension theorem in algebraic geometry: The dimension of an irredundant component of a variety is not less than $n - s$, where n is the number of variables and s the number of defining polynomials. Finally, all the redundant components are removed by using a lemma of Wu (1984b).

3.7 Optimization of variable ordering

The time for computing characteristic sets and thus all relevant decompositions depends heavily upon the choice of variable ordering. For example, if we order the variables in Problem 4 as $r \prec z \prec y \prec x$, then the characteristic set can be computed within one second. Therefore, the optimization of variable ordering must be considered for some applications, such as the decomposition of algebraic varieties. In our implementation, if the variables are given as a set, a *heuristically* optimal variable ordering in the following sense is used.

Let X be a set of variables and PS a set of polynomials in X. For any variable $x \in X$ we define

$$\Omega(x, PS) = \max_{p \in PS} \deg(p, x), \qquad \omega(x, PS) = \max\{1, \min_{p \in PS} \deg(p, x)\},$$

$$\Lambda(x, PS) = \text{number of elements in } \{p \in PS \mid \deg(p, x) = \Omega(x, PS)\},$$

$$\lambda(x, PS) = \text{number of elements in } \{p \in PS \mid \deg(p, x) = \omega(x, PS)\},$$

$$\Delta(x, PS) = \min_{p \in PS, \deg(p,x) = \omega(x,PS)} \mathrm{Tdeg}(\mathrm{lc}(p, x)),$$

$$\delta(x, PS) = \min_{p \in PS, \deg_x(p) = \omega(x,PS)} \mathrm{Term}(\mathrm{lc}(p, x)),$$

where $\deg(p, x)$ denotes the degree of p in x, $\mathrm{lc}(p, x)$ the leading coefficient of p with respect to x, $\mathrm{Tdeg}(q)$ the total degree of q and $\mathrm{Term}(q)$ the number of actual terms in q.

Then, a partial order of the variables with respect to PS is introduced as follows:

1. If a variable $x \in X$ occurs in one and only one polynomial $p \in PS$, then x has order higher than all the others.
2. A variable x has order higher than the variable y if one of the following holds:

(a) $\Omega(x, PS) < \Omega(y, PS)$;
(b) $\Omega(x, PS) = \Omega(y, PS)$ but $\Lambda(x, PS) < \Lambda(y, PS)$;
(c) $\Omega(x, PS) = \Omega(y, PS)$, $\Lambda(x, PS) = \Lambda(y, PS)$ but $\omega(x, PS) < \omega(y, PS)$;
(d) $\Omega(x, PS) = \Omega(y, PS)$, $\Lambda(x, PS) = \Lambda(y, PS)$, $\omega(x, PS) = \omega(y, PS)$ but $\lambda(x, PS) > \lambda(y, PS)$;
(e) $\Omega(x, PS) = \Omega(y, PS)$, $\Lambda(x, PS) = \Lambda(y, PS)$, $\omega(x, PS) = \omega(y, PS)$, $\lambda(x, PS) = \lambda(y, PS)$ but $\Delta(x, PS) < \Delta(y, PS)$;
(f) $\Omega(x, PS) = \Omega(y, PS)$, $\Lambda(x, PS) = \Lambda(y, PS)$, $\omega(x, PS) = \omega(y, PS)$, $\lambda(x, PS) = \lambda(y, PS)$, $\Delta(x, PS) = \Delta(y, PS)$ but $\delta(x, PS) < \delta(y, PS)$.

Under this partial order, the variables in Problem 4 can be optimally reordered as $z \prec x \prec y \prec r$.

4 Test results and remarks

Since all the functions plus their options in our package lead to many variants, we are unable to give a long list of test problems here due to the page restriction. We present some test results by taking only 3 problems with given variable ordering for each function. These problems were selected in a quite random way but so that they are representative and proper for testing most of the functions. For instance, the problems 1, 2 and 3 are all chosen so that polynomial factorization over algebraic number fields is involved. The experiments were made in Maple 4.3 running on an Apollo DN10000 under a UNIX operating system. All timings are given in CPU seconds without excluding the time for garbage collection. The timing statistics here aim at showing a rough magnitude of the computational cost of each function and do not necessarily reflect its overall behaviour. The computation of very similar problems may lead to much different computing times, while 3 test problems cannot say too much at all. In view of this, we add below a few remarks on each function based on our extensive experiments with other problems.

Table 1. Timings for `charset` and `mcharset` (CPU seconds)

	Problem 2		Problem 3		Problem 4	
Option	`charset`	`mcharset`	`charset`	`mcharset`	`charset`	`mcharset`
`basset`	>1800	161.633	14.100	15.650	>1800	540.400
`charsetn`	27.116	22.733	14.100	15.650	>1800	540.400
`trisetc`	21.933	34.850	4.350	6.717	>1800	>1800
`wbasset`	714.200	30.266	6.750	6.133	>1800	>1800
`wcharsetn`	23.084	7.600	3.466	3.766	>1800	1606.883
`qbasset`	1.684	2.250	2.967	2.984	>1800	105.600
`qcharsetn`	1.600	2.100	1.967	2.100	>1800	21.184
`triset`	1.383	2.350	2.150	4.333	>1800	29.817

Table 2. Timings for `charser` and `mcs` (CPU seconds)

Option	Problem 1		Problem 2		Problem 3	
	`charser`	`mcs`	`charser`	`mcs`	`charser`	`mcs`
`basset`	1.383	1.550	>1800	1751.050	48.516	64.588
`charsetn`	1.017	1.283	59.616	70.966	18.850	35.734
`trisetc`	0.917	1.467	49.983	77.316	24.450	97.050
`wbasset`	3.067	1.617	1277.667	415.517	18.050	25.950
`wcharsetn`	3.766	1.467	46.967	45.250	33.133	21.517

Table 3. Timings for `ecs` and `mecs` (CPU seconds)

Option	Problem 1		Problem 2		Problem 3	
	`ecs`	`mecs`	`ecs`	`mecs`	`ecs`	`mecs`
`basset`	1.716	1.883	>1800	816.567	48.900	53.750
`charsetn`	1.367	1.500	60.750	59.784	20.217	21.133
`trisetc`	0.900	1.067	48.283	65.484	27.217	26.800
`wbasset`	3.350	4.083	821.250	230.400	17.616	18.616
`wcharsetn`	3.834	3.416	44.500	33.317	32.017	14.067

Table 4. Timings for `qics` and `eics` (CPU seconds)

Option	Problem 1		Problem 2		Problem 3	
	`qics`	`eics`	`qics`	`eics`	`qics`	`eics`
`basset`	3.583	11.367	359.867	384.783	188.233	239.150
`charsetn`	2.950	10.100	65.417	80.666	109.733	107.284
`trisetc`	4.417	12.717	61.850	99.583	173.800	158.000
`wbasset`	3.616		111.100		79.916	
`wcharsetn`	3.300		36.500		84.250	

Table 5. Timings for `ics` and `ivd` (CPU seconds)

Option	Problem 1		Problem 2		Problem 3	
	`ics`	`ivd`	`ics`	`ivd`	`ics`	`ivd`
`basset`	10.533	12.616	369.100	381.683	279.733	352.000
`charsetn`	12.084	12.833	92.150	95.384	162.716	228.433
`trisetc`	12.950	14.983	61.334	75.650	274.150	398.583

Table 6. Timings for `triser`, `csolve` and `cfactor` (CPU seconds)

Problem	`triser`	`csolve`	Problem	`cfactor`
1	1.667	3.434	5	4.884
2	54.117	>1800	6	7.883
3	23.700	28.567	7	12.850

Remark 1. For (modified) characteristic sets, the computation in the quasi-sense usually is faster than that in the other senses, whereas the computation in the weak sense only sometimes is faster than that in the standard sense. However, the quasi-sense is theoretically weak. For example, in this sense we are unable to compute characteristic series since the decomposition algorithm can no longer be guaranteed to terminate. Also, the irreducibility of a quasi-ascending set cannot be well-defined. In the same sense, the computation is fast in general if the medial set `qcharsetn`, `wcharsetn`, `charsetn`, `triset` or `trisetc` is chosen. It is rather slow when the medial set `qbasset`, `wbasset` or `basset` is used. Here, the choice of `basset` results in Ritt's original version, the choice of (`w-`, `q-`) `charsetn` results in Wu's improved version of the algorithm, and the choice of `triset` and `trisetc` results in a version suggested by us.

Remark 2. `charset` sometimes is faster than `mcharset` for small problems, but it is slower for large ones. Consequently, `mcs` and `mecs` are respectively faster than `charser` and `ecs` for large problems. In general, the output of `mcs` and `mecs` is also more succinct than that of `charser` and `ecs`. The computing times for `charser` and `ecs`, for `mcs` and `mecs`, and for `ics` and `eics` may vary from each other as different strategies are used, but neither of them in a pair seems superior to the other. In `eics` an extended zero decomposition algorithm proposed by Wu (1986) is implemented. It somewhat speeds up the computation in most cases but produces additional polynomials whose manipulation may cost time at other stages. Note that the implemented algorithms for the functions `mcs`, `qics` and `ics` have a similar structure and all the three examine and remove possible factors, while `qics` factorizes every polynomial in all ascending sets and `ics` decomposes all ascending sets into irreducible ones. The function `ics` is used as the main subfunction of `ivd`.

Remark 3. The function `triser` is designed for computing a hybrid sequence of ascending sets, weak-ascending sets and quasi-ascending sets from a given polynomial set. The first few characteristic sets are computed in the quasi-sense for ease and the others are computed in the weak and standard senses in order to ensure the termination. This function is faster than the others for computing the characteristic series in some cases and may be used to prepare a sequence of triangular forms for polynomial equations-solving. Actually, the function `csolve` is mainly based on `triser`.

Remark 4. During the implementation of our package, we always try to attack large problems – *large* being defined in terms of the computational cost. Several strategies are used for this purpose and can reduce both the computing space and time for a number of large problems, but they may in turn increase the cost for small ones. Concerning the adoption of these strategies, we have difficulties in judging, before the computation, which kinds of problems are large. For this issue the author guesses that a careful analysis of the practical complexity of the applied algorithms must be given first. Also, one variant of an algorithm may be fast for some problems but very slow for others. We have tried to choose between different algorithms and their variants by examining the sort of input according to our own experience. However, this works well only in some cases.

The characteristic sets and thus various related zero decompositions in general are not unique. To avoid redundant or unpleasant output expressions, we have also arranged to tidy up the output in case the postprocess is not expensive.

Appendix: Test problems

The source of the following test problems: Problems 1–5 are taken from the papers by D. M. Wang (1989b), C. J. Butcher (BIT Comput. Sci. Numer. Math. 24: 425–440), W.-t. Wu (Math. Mech. Res. Preprints 2: 1–17), M. Bronstein (Proc. SYMSAC '86, pp. 247–249) and P. S. Wang (Math. Comput. 30: 324–336) respectively. The polynomial F in Problem 6 is one that has to be factorized for computing the irreducible zero decompositions of PS in Problem 2. Problem 7 is a test example used by the author.

Problem 1. $PS = \{x_4^2+x_1x_4^2-x_2x_4-x_1x_2x_4+x_1x_2+3x_2, x_1x_4+x_3-x_1x_2, x_3x_4-2x_2^2-x_1x_2-1\}$ with variable ordering $x_1 \prec \ldots \prec x_4$.

Problem 2. $PS = \{p_1, \ldots, p_8\}$ with variable ordering $b \prec c_2 \prec c_3 \prec a \prec b_3 \prec b_2 \prec a_{32} \prec b_1$, where

$p_1 = b_1 + b_2 + b_3 - a - b,$
$p_2 = 2b_2c_2 + 2b_3c_3 - 1 - b - 2b^2 + 2ab,$
$p_3 = 3b_2c_2^2 + 3b_3c_3^2 - a - 3ab^2 + 4b + 3b^2 + 3b^3,$
$p_4 = 6b_3a_{32}c_2 - a - 3ab - 6ab^2 + 4b + 6b^2 + 6b^3,$
$p_5 = 4b_2c_2^3 + 4b_3c_3^3 - 1 - b - 10b^2 - 6b^3 - 4b^4 + 4ab + 4ab^3,$
$p_6 = 8b_3c_3a_{32}c_2 - 1 - 3b - 14b^2 - 12b^3 - 8b^4 + 4ab + 4ab^2 + 8ab^3,$
$p_7 = 12b_3a_{32}c_2^2 - 1 - b - 14b^2 - 18b^3 - 12b^4 + 8ab + 12ab^2 + 12ab^3,$
$p_8 = 1 + 7b + 26b^2 + 36b^3 + 24b^4 - 8ab - 24ab^2 - 24ab^3.$

Problem 3. $PS = \left\{y^2 - p_1, \frac{\partial p_2}{\partial x_1}, \ldots, \frac{\partial p_2}{\partial x_6}, \frac{\partial p_2}{\partial \lambda_1}, \frac{\partial p_2}{\partial \lambda_2}, \frac{\partial p_2}{\partial \lambda_3}\right\}$ with variable ordering $x_1 \prec \ldots \prec x_6 \prec \lambda_1 \prec \lambda_2 \prec \lambda_3 \prec y$, where $p_1 = (x_4+x_5)(x_5+x_6)(x_6+x_4)x_2^2x_1^2x_3^2$, $p_2 = p_1 + \lambda_1(x_2^2x_6 - 1) + \lambda_2(x_1^2x_4 - 1) + \lambda_3(x_3^2x_5 - 1)$.

Problem 4. $PS = \{x^2 + y^2 + z^2 - r^2, xy + z^2 - 1, xyz - x^2 - y^2 - z + 1\}$ with variable ordering $r \prec x \prec y \prec z$.

Problem 5. $AS = \{a^4 + a^3 + a^2 + a + 1\}$ and $F = 16x^4 + 8x^3 + 4x^2 + 2x + 1$.

Problem 6. $AS = \{-1 + b + 6b^2 + 12b^3\}$ and $F = 745092b - 252156 + 540900c + 21032664c^2b^2 + 2010720b^2 + 7117713c^2b - 132367c^2 + 3076830c^3 - 7843500c^3b^2 + 2792322c^3b - 3779244bc - 10724400b^2c + 21225240bc^5 + 26306208b^2c^5 + 8257464c^5 - 436536c^4 + 6094008b^2c^4 + 594432bc^4$.

Problem 7. $AS = \{r^2 - 2 + z^2, -rz + y + 4y^2\}$ and $F = -370x^2y - 10x^3 + 60x^2z + 4xy - 24zy + 74rzy + 2rzx + 37rz - 37y + 12r^3 - 24r$ with variable ordering $z \prec y \prec x$.

Note. This paper was written in Winter 1990 when the first version of `charsets` was completed. It was accepted for publication in the Proceedings of DISCO '92 (Bath, April 13–15, 1992). However, the paper is not contained in the proceedings (Springer, Lecture notes in computer science, vol. 721) because the editor did not receive its final camera-ready copy which the author sent in April 1992. After `charsets`'s version 1.0 was included in the Maple share library for distribution, several improvements were incorporated into the package. The up-to-date version of `charsets` is available via anonymous FTP on site 193.170.33.112 (ftp.risc.uni-linz.ac.at).

Acknowledgement

This work is supported in part by the Austrian Ministry of Science and Research under ESPRIT Basic Research Action 3125 (MEDLAR).

References

Chou, S. C. (1988): Mechanical geometry theorem proving. Reidel, Dordrecht.

Hu, S., Wang, D. M. (1986): Fast factorization of polynomials over rational number field or its extension fields. Kexue Tongbao 31: 150–156.

Ko, H. P. (1986): ALGE-Prover II – a new edition of ALGE-Prover. Corporate Research and Development Tech. Rep. 86CRD081. General Electric, Schenectady, NY.

Kusche, K., Kutzler, B., Mayr, H. (1989): Implementation of a geometry theorem proving package in Scratchpad II. In: Davenport, J. H. (ed.): EUROCAL '87. Springer, Berlin Heidelberg New York Tokyo, pp. 246–257 (Lecture notes in computer science, vol. 378).

Ritt, J. F. (1932): Differential equations from the algebraic standpoint. American Mathematical Society, New York.

Ritt, J. F. (1950): Differential algebra. American Mathematical Society, New York.

Wang, D. M. (1989a): A generalization of characteristic sets algorithm. Tech. Rep. RISC Linz 89-51.0.

Wang, D. M. (1989b): Characteristic sets and zero structure of polynomial sets. Lecture Notes, RISC Linz.

Wang, D. M. (1992a): Irreducible decomposition of algebraic varieties via characteristic sets and Gröbner bases. Comput. Aided Geom. Des. 9: 471–484.

Wang, D. M. (1992b): A method for factorizing multivariate polynomials over successive algebraic extension fields. Preprint, RISC Linz.

Wu, W.-t. (1984a): Basic principles of mechanical theorem proving in elementary geometries. J. Syst. Sci. Math. Sci. 4: 207–235 [also in J. Automat. Reason. 2: 221–252 (1986)].

Wu, W.-t. (1984b): Basic principles of mechanical theorem proving in geometries (part on elementary geometries). Science Press, Beijing (in Chinese); English-language edition, Springer, Wien New York (1994).

Wu, W.-t. (1986): On zeros of algebraic equations – an application of Ritt principle. Kexue Tongbao 31: 1–5.

Math. Mech. Res. Preprints (1987–1994) 1–11. MM Research Center, Academia Sinica.

A nonmonotonic extension to Horn-clause logic

Thomas J. Weigert

1 Introduction

Standard first-order logic, and therefore, any description of the world that relies on it, ordinarily requires the absence of contradiction. It has been repeatedly pointed out that in describing the real world it is often very difficult to avoid making contradictory statements (e.g., when realizing that an assumption had proven wrong, we might have to assert the denial of what we had assumed to hold true). The example that has become a classic in the AI literature is the problem that *Birds fly*, *Penguins are birds*, but *Penguins don't fly*.

Nonmonotonic logic is intended to apply specifically to situations where the initial information is incomplete. Using nonmonotonic reasoning procedures we can jump to conclusions, but withdraw them later, when we gain additional information. As McDermott and Doyle (1980) point out, this phenomenon is ubiquitous in AI applications and commonsense reasoning.

Typically, nonmonotonic logics formulate claims allowing for exceptions, such as *Birds fly*, by adding special conjuncts which permit derivation of the consequent of a conditional only if no contradiction can arise. For example, if the intuitive understanding of the expression $\P Fly(opus)$ is *It is consistent with everything else in the theory that Opus flies* (McDermott and Doyle 1980; McDermott 1982), above claim is formulated as

$$\forall x(Bird(x) \wedge \P Fly(x) \rightarrow Fly(x)).$$

Similarly, if $ab(x)$ holds for birds abnormal with respect to flying (McCarthy 1982), then we could write

$$\forall x(Bird(x) \wedge \neg ab(x) \rightarrow Fly(x)).$$

A number of nonmonotonic logics have been introduced and have been widely discussed; for surveys of the field consult the collections by Ginsberg (1987) and Reinfrank et al. (1989).

Most nonmonotonic logics presented require prohibitively expensive computational mechanisms. Thus, some effort has recently shifted to identifying subsets of nonmonotonic theories which can be efficiently computed. Particularly, the relation between nonmonotonic theories and logic programming has been investigated. Gelfond and Lifschitz (1989) present a mechanism to translate certain circumscriptive theories into logic programs. In earlier papers (Weigert 1989, Tsai et al. 1992, Weigert and Tsai 1994), we described a nonmonotonic logic for the Horn-clause subset of first-order predicate logic. Theories formulated in this nonmonotonic logic are executable as logic programs (in a computationally tractable manner). We showed completeness and soundness of nonmonotonic Horn-clause logic.

The number of schemes proposed for nonmonotonic reasoning is rapidly increasing while the differences between them often are quite subtle and technical. It becomes almost obligatory to place presented approaches against the background of more conventional semantics. In the logic programming community, it is customary to identify the *intended* meaning of nonmonotonic theories with augmentations which minimize positive information. There are three prevalent approaches: the closed world assumption (Reiter 1978), predicate completion (Clark 1978), and point-wise circumscription (Lifschitz 1987). In this paper, we study the relationship between the fix-point semantics of the nonmonotonic Horn-clause logic presented earlier and model-theoretic semantics applied to the completion of a theory. We show that these semantics differ in the general case, but that they coincide under certain assumptions on the theory.

2 Semantics of nonmonotonic Horn-clause theories

We use a first order language with a finite number of object, function and predicate constants. The logical operators have their standard meaning; in addition there is the operator "¶". The intuitive reading of ¶A is *It is consistent with everything else that* A, as alluded above. Although the proper treatment of negation is an interesting and vexing problem for logic programming (see Sheperdson 1988, 1989, for a survey), in this paper we are not concerned with logic programs that include negation. We express negative information through the notion of predicate negation: If A is a predicate symbol, then $\widehat{A}$ denotes the complement of the extension of A. $\widehat{A}$ is also a predicate symbol.

A literal is an atomic formula, or a formula of the form ¶A, where A is an atomic formula. A *nonmonotonic Horn-clause* ("clause" for short) is a formula of the form $\forall x_1 \ldots x_m(B \leftarrow B_1 \wedge \ldots \wedge B_n), n \geq 0$, where B is an atomic formula, each B_i, $1 \leq i \leq n$, is a literal, $x_1, \ldots, x_m$ are the variables occurring in $B \leftarrow B_1 \wedge \ldots \wedge B_n$. B is called the *head*, $B_1 \wedge \ldots \wedge B_n$ is called the *body* of the clause.

In the following we adopt the usual convention that clauses are understood to be implicitly universally quantified and the quantifiers are dropped in case no confusion can arise. Note also that a clause with empty body, $B \leftarrow$, is written as simply B. Such clauses are called facts. A clause with empty head and body is called the empty clause and is denoted by "□".

In the language just presented the non-logical part of the classical birds theory is formulated as:

$$\Theta_1 = \left\{ \begin{array}{l} Fly(x) \leftarrow Bird(x) \wedge \P Fly(x) \\ \widehat{Fly}(x) \leftarrow Penguin(x) \\ Bird(x) \leftarrow Penguin(x) \\ Penguin(opus) \\ Bird(tweety) \end{array} \right\}.$$

The absence of negation opens us to difficulties stemming from recursion through both the ¶ operator and predicate negation, as, for example, in the clause $A \leftarrow \P\widehat{A}$. We restrict ourselves to stratified sets of formulae (Apt et al. 1988), with the notion of stratification adapted to nonmonotonic Horn-clauses. In the following, we understand *theory* to mean a set of clauses for which we can give a stratification.

The notion of an *Herbrand universe* is standardly defined. The *Herbrand base*, Π_Θ of a theory Θ is the set of all ground facts which can be formed in the language of Θ by taking terms from its Herbrand universe. Lastly, the *complement* $\overline{P}$ of the atomic formula P is $\widehat{R}(t_1, \ldots, t_n)$, if P is $R(t_1, \ldots, t_n)$, or $R(t_1, \ldots, t_n)$, if P is $\widehat{R}(t_1, \ldots, t_n)$.

Let the notion of an *interpretation* be understood as usual, i.e., an interpretation is a non-empty set of objects, called the domain, and an assignment of meaning to the constant symbols, function symbols, and predicate symbols. Given an interpretation, the meaning of a ground (variable-free) formula is standardly defined through a set of functions that allows one to calculate the semantic value of that formula. Due to the semi-decidability of the predicate calculus, a mechanical decision as to the truth of a formula hinges on the possibility of reducing that formula to one or more formulae of the propositional calculus. One cannot generally reduce formulae of the predicate calculus to a single formula of the propositional calculus. However, a fundamental fact is that a clause can be reduced in a systematic way to a countable set of formulae of the propositional calculus. Through Herbrand's theorem, e.g., Chang and Lee (1973: p. 61), we know that a clause is satisfiable iff the countable set of formula e of the propositional calculus, to which it can be reduced, is satisfiable. By an argument similar to Herbrand's, the same property holds in our extended language. Therefore, to test whether a clause is satisfiable, it suffices to consider assignments to variables of the clause with elements drawn from the Herbrand universe. Moreover, it is unnecessary to consider arbitrary interpretations for the symbols in that clause. It suffices to interpret function symbols syntactically, i.e., consider a function symbol to denote functions from the Herbrand universe to itself. We call such interpretations *Herbrand interpretations*.

No restriction on the assignment of predicate symbols is made, so that different Herbrand interpretations arise by taking different assignments. However, for Herbrand interpretations the assignment of constants and function symbols is fixed. Since Herbrand interpretations differ at most on what they assign to predicate symbols, we identify Herbrand interpretations for a theory Θ with subsets of the Herbrand base. For any Herbrand interpretation, the corresponding subset of the Herbrand base is the set of all ground atoms true with respect to this particular interpretation.

We explicate the notion of logical consequence in terms of fix-points of the theory operator $\mathcal{T}_{\Theta,\pi}$. For motivation of the use of fix-points, see Lloyd (1987: pp. 29–32). If Θ is a theory, then the set of all Herbrand interpretations of Θ, i.e., the powerset 2^{Π_Θ} of the Herbrand base Π_Θ, is a complete lattice under the partial order of set inclusion. (The top element of the lattice is the Herbrand base Π_Θ, the bottom element is $\emptyset$. The least upper bound and greatest lower bound are the union of Herbrand interpretations and their intersection, respectively.) We define the theory operator associated with Θ as a map from the set of all Herbrand interpretations to itself.

Definition 1. Let Θ be a theory, π a set of literals, and $\mathcal{I}$ a Herbrand interpretation. Then the theory operator $\mathcal{T}_{\Theta,\pi}$ is a mapping from 2^{Π_Θ} to 2^{Π_Θ}, defined by

$$\mathcal{T}_{\Theta,\pi}(\mathcal{I}) = \left\{ A \in \Pi_\Theta \,\middle|\, \begin{array}{l} B \leftarrow B_1 \wedge \ldots \wedge B_n \in \Theta, \exists\theta, \text{ such that } A = B\theta \\ \text{and either } B_i\theta \in \mathcal{I} \text{ or } B_i\theta \in \pi, 1 \le i \le n \end{array} \right\}.$$

Theorem 2. The theory operator $\mathcal{T}_{\Theta,\pi}$ is continuous.

This claim is established by showing that, for all directed subsets Γ of Π_Θ, $\mathcal{T}_{\Theta,\pi}(\bigcup \Gamma) = \bigcup \mathcal{T}_{\Theta,\pi}(\Gamma)$.

The k-th ordinal power of the theory operator

$$\mathcal{T}^k_{\Theta,\pi}(\Gamma) = \mathcal{T}_{\Theta,\pi}(\mathcal{T}^{k-1}_{\Theta,\pi}(\Gamma))$$

for some set Γ, if $k > 0$; $\mathcal{T}^0_{\Theta,\pi}(\Gamma) = \Gamma$. Since the theory operator $\mathcal{T}_{\Theta,\pi}$ is continuous (and therefore, monotonic), by the Knaster–Tarski theorem (Tarski 1955) we know that $\mathcal{T}_{\Theta,\pi}$ has a greatest fix-point as well as a least fix-point.

We define the *approximation* to the fix-points of the theory operator in terms of its ordinal powers.

Definition 3. Let Θ be a theory, $\mathcal{T}_{\Theta,\pi}$ be the theory operator, and ω be the limit ordinal; then

$$\mathcal{T}_{\Theta,\pi}\downarrow_\omega = \bigcap_{k \ge 0} \mathcal{T}^k_{\Theta,\pi}(\Pi_\Theta)$$

and

$$\mathcal{T}_{\Theta,\pi}\uparrow_\omega = \bigcup_{k \ge 0} \mathcal{T}^k_{\Theta,\pi}(\emptyset).$$

$\mathcal{T}_{\Theta,\pi}\downarrow_\omega$ is the approximation from above to the greatest fix-point of the theory operator associated with theory Θ and the set π. $\mathcal{T}_{\Theta,\pi}\uparrow_\omega$ is the approximation from below to the least fix-point of the theory operator associated with Θ and π. We know that the approximation from below reaches the least fix-point of the theory operator $\mathcal{T}_{\Theta,\pi}$ at ω, i.e., $\mathcal{T}_{\Theta,\pi}\uparrow_\omega$ is the least fix-point of the theory operator

$\mathcal{T}_{\Theta,\pi}$. The corresponding claim does not hold for $\mathcal{T}_{\Theta,\pi}\downarrow_{\omega}$ in general, as can be demonstrated by simple counter-examples (Lloyd 1987).

The approximations to the fix-points of the theory operator play a central role in explicating the semantics of nonmonotonic logic programs.

Definition 4. The *failure set* for theory Θ, $\mathcal{F}ail_{\Theta}$, is defined by

$$\mathcal{F}ail_{\Theta} = \Pi_{\Theta} - \mathcal{T}_{\Theta,\emptyset}\downarrow_{\omega} .$$

Definition 5. The *nonmonotonic extension* of a theory Θ is the set of literals $\mathcal{N}m(\Theta)$, where

$$\mathcal{N}m(\Theta) = \{\P A\theta \mid \P A \text{ is mentioned in } \Theta,\ A\theta \in \Pi_{\Theta}, \text{ and } \overline{A} \in \mathcal{F}ail_{\Theta}\}.$$

As illustration, consider the calculation of the nonmonotonic extension of theory Θ_1. Starting from the Herbrand base of Θ_1 we obtain

$$\mathcal{F}ail_{\Theta_1} = \left\{ \begin{array}{l} Fly(opus) \\ Fly(tweety) \\ \widehat{Fly}(tweety) \\ Penguin(tweety) \end{array} \right\}.$$

The literals in Π_{Θ_1} of the shape $\P A$ to consider are $\P Fly(opus)$ and $\P Fly(tweety)$. $\widehat{Fly}(opus) \notin \mathcal{F}ail_{\Theta_1}$, but $\widehat{Fly}(tweety) \in \mathcal{F}ail_{\Theta_1}$, and so

$$\mathcal{N}m(\Theta_1) = \{\P\, Fly(tweety)\}.$$

The approximation from above to the greatest fix-point of the theory operator $\mathcal{T}_{\Theta,\pi}$ at ω defines the set of ground formulae not logical consequences of a theory. If a literal $\P A$ is mentioned in Θ, and if $\overline{A}\theta$ is not a logical consequence of the theory, then the ground literal $\P A\theta$ is added to the nonmonotonic extension of the theory. The consideration of the nonmonotonically extended theory instead of the theory itself is what makes the logic presented here nonmonotonic.

We now define the notion of logical consequence in the nonmonotonic logic presented.

Definition 6. A set of clauses Θ and a goal G is unsatisfiable iff either

(i) G contains the ground literal $\leftarrow B$ and $B \in \mathcal{T}_{\Theta,\mathcal{N}m(\Theta)}\uparrow_{\omega}$,
(ii) G contains the ground clause $\leftarrow B_1 \wedge \ldots \wedge B_n$ and $\Theta \cup \{\leftarrow B_i\}$ is unsatisfiable, $1 \le i \le n$,
(iii) G contains the clause $\leftarrow B_1 \wedge \ldots \wedge B_n$ and $\exists\theta$, such that $B_1\theta, \ldots, B_n\theta$ are ground, and $\Theta \cup \{\leftarrow B_1\theta \wedge \ldots \wedge B_n\theta\}$ is unsatisfiable.

Definition 7. Let C be a clause. A is a logical consequence of a set of clauses Θ,

$$\Theta \models^{\mathrm{nm}} A \text{ iff} \begin{cases} A \neq \P C \text{ and } \Theta \cup \{\leftarrow A\} & \text{is unsatisfiable, or} \\ A \in \mathcal{N}m(\Theta). \end{cases}$$

For the example theory, we have

$$\mathcal{T}_{\Theta_1,\mathcal{N}m(\Theta)}\uparrow_{\omega} = \left\{ \begin{array}{l} \mathit{Penguin}(\mathit{opus}) \\ \mathit{Bird}(\mathit{opus}) \\ \widehat{\mathit{Fly}}(\mathit{opus}) \\ \mathit{Bird}(\mathit{tweety}) \\ \mathit{Fly}(\mathit{tweety}) \end{array} \right\}.$$

We want to know whether *Fly*(*opus*) is a logical consequence of Θ_1, i.e., whether $\Theta_1 \models^{\mathrm{nm}} \mathit{Fly}(\mathit{opus})$. Since *Fly*(*opus*) is ground, this is true just in case $\mathit{Fly}(\mathit{opus}) \in \mathcal{T}_{\Theta_1,\mathcal{N}m(\Theta)}\uparrow_{\omega}$, which it is not. Since $\mathit{Fly}(\mathit{tweety}) \in \mathcal{T}_{\Theta_1,\mathcal{N}m(\Theta)}\uparrow_{\omega}$, $\Theta_1 \models^{\mathrm{nm}} \mathit{Fly}(\mathit{tweety})$.

Note again the difference between predicate negation and the negation symbol of standard first-order logic. From Definitions 6 and 7 one can see that $\Theta \models^{\mathrm{nm}} \widehat{A}$ if (for a ground literal A), $\widehat{A} \in \mathcal{T}_{\Theta,\mathcal{N}m(\Theta)}\uparrow_{\omega}$, which is obviously different from the claim $\Theta \models^{\mathrm{nm}} \widehat{A}$ iff $\Theta \not\models^{\mathrm{nm}} A$ made by standard first-order logic. As far as negation is concerned, our language functions just as unaugmented Horn-clause logic does.

The semantic notion that is central to logic programming and reasoning in the Herbrand universe is the notion of correct answer substitution. A nonmonotonic correct answer substitution is defined in terms of nonmonotonic logical consequence.

Definition 8. θ is a *nonmonotonic correct answer substitution* for theory Θ and goal $G = \{\leftarrow B_1 \wedge \ldots \wedge B_n\}$ iff θ is a substitution for variables in G (not necessarily ground), and for any substitution θ_1 of elements of the domain to the remaining variables in G, $\Theta \models^{\mathrm{nm}} (B_1 \wedge \ldots \wedge B_{n'})\theta\theta_1$. Let this situation be denoted by $\Theta \models^{\mathrm{nm}} \forall((B_1 \wedge \ldots \wedge B_n)\theta)$.

Note that if $\Theta \cup \{\leftarrow B_1 \wedge \ldots \wedge B_n\} \models^{\mathrm{nm}} \Box$, then there exists a substitution θ, such that $\Theta \models^{\mathrm{nm}} (B_1 \wedge \ldots \wedge B_n)\theta$. Thus, the claim that Θ is a correct answer substitution for the goal G is stronger than the claim that $\Theta \cup G\theta \models^{\mathrm{nm}} \Box$. The intuitive idea is that a correct answer substitution replaces those variables of the goal G over which one cannot universally generalize.

3 Soundness and completeness of nonmonotonic Horn-clause theories

The syntactic notion of interest is whether a formula can be derived from a theory.

Definition 9. Let Θ be a theory, $G = \{\leftarrow A_1 \wedge \ldots \wedge A_n\}$ a goal; then G' is derived from G and Θ if A_m is a literal in G selected as subgoal, and either

(i) $A_m \neq \P C$, there is a clause $D' = B \leftarrow B_1 \wedge \ldots \wedge B_k$, where D' is an alphabetic variant of a clause $D \in \Theta$ with all new variables, there is a substitution θ such that $A_m\theta = B\theta$, and $G' = \{(\leftarrow A_1 \wedge \ldots \wedge A_{m-1} \wedge B_1 \wedge \ldots \wedge B_k \wedge A_{m+1} \wedge \ldots \wedge A_n)\theta\}$, or
(ii) A_m is a ground literal $\P C$, the attempt to construct a derivation of $\Theta \cup \{\leftarrow \overline{C}\}$ fails after finitely many steps, and $G' = \{(\leftarrow A_1 \wedge \ldots \wedge A_{m-1} \wedge A_{m+1} \wedge \ldots \wedge A_n)\theta\}$.

It is important that the literal $\P C$ is only selected in case it is ground. Consider, for example, the theory $\{A(a) \leftarrow \P B(x), \widehat{B}(a)\}$. If we could select unground goals, an attempted refutation for this theory would fail.

A derivation is a sequence of goals, such that each goal is derived from an earlier goal in the sequence. A derivation is either an infinite sequence, or it stops after a finite number of steps. If the last element in the sequence when the derivation stops is the empty clause $\square$, we say the derivation succeeded. Such a derivation is called a *refutation*. Otherwise, we say the derivation failed finitely, either because the derivation could not continue as defined in Definition 9 (ii), or because no head of a clause D' unifies with a literal in the last goal. If a formula G together with a theory Θ has a refutation, then we say that the clause forming G can be derived from Θ.

The syntactic counterpart to the correct answer substitution for a theory Θ and a goal G is the computed answer substitution.

Definition 10. θ is a nonmonotonic computed answer substitution for theory Θ and goal $G = \{\leftarrow B_1 \wedge \ldots \wedge B_n\}$ iff θ is the sequence of most general unifiers $\theta_1 \ldots \theta_n$ used in the refutation of $\Theta \cup G$, restricted to the variables in G.

Soundness establishes that if a substitution is a computed answer substitution, it is also a correct answer substitution:

Theorem 11. Let Θ be a theory, $G = \{\leftarrow A_1 \wedge \ldots \wedge A_m\}$ a goal. Then if θ is a nonmonotonic computed answer substitution for $\Theta \cup G$, then θ is correct.

This result relies on several well-known lemmas due to Apt and van Emden (1982), where they are established for standard Horn-clause logic. In addition, we need to show that if a derivation of a formula fails in finitely many steps, then that formula is in the nonmonotonic failure set.

Lemma 12. If $\Theta \cup \{\leftarrow A\}$ fails finitely, then $A \in \mathcal{F}ail_{\Theta}$.

The proof shows by induction on the length of the attempted refutation n, that if the derivation of $\Theta \cup \{\leftarrow A\}$ fails with length $\leq n$, then $A \not\in \mathcal{T}_{\Theta,\emptyset}\downarrow_n$. But then $A \in \mathcal{F}ail_{\Theta}$.

The completeness result of interest states that if a substitution is a correct answer substitution, it is also a computed answer substitution. It is not possible to prove the exact converse to the soundness result Theorem 11 because computed answer substitutions are always most general. However, we can prove that every correct answer substitution is an instance of a computed answer substitution.

Theorem 13. If θ is a correct answer substitution for $\Theta \cup G$, then $\exists\theta_1, \theta_2$, such that θ_1 is the computed answer substitution for $\Theta \cup G$, and $\theta = \theta_1\theta_2$.

The proof proceeds by demonstrating that $\Theta \cup \{\leftarrow A_i\theta\}$ has a refutation, for $1 \leq i \leq n$, and combines (at the ground level) these individual refutations into a refutation of $\Theta \cup G\theta$. By the "lifting lemma" (Genesereth and Nilsson 1988: p. 88) we thus also have a refutation of $\Theta \cup G$, although θ may not be a most general unifier.

Again the cases of nonmonotonicity are treated special, with the help of the following lemmas.

Lemma 14. Let Θ be a theory, let A be a ground atom; then if $A \in \mathcal{T}_{\Theta,\mathcal{N}m(\Theta)}\uparrow_\omega$, $\Theta \cup \{\leftarrow A\}$ has a refutation.

Lemma 15. If $\Theta \cup \{\leftarrow A\}$ has a refutation, then $A \in \mathcal{T}_{\Theta,\emptyset}\downarrow_\omega$.

Lemma 16. If the derivation of $\Theta \cup \{\leftarrow A_1 \wedge \ldots \wedge A_m\}$ is infinite, then the set of all ground instances of A_i is in $\mathcal{T}_{\Theta,\emptyset}\downarrow_\omega$, for $i = 1, 2, \ldots, m$.

We show these results by induction on the length of the attempted derivation. The latter two lemmas establish the following claim:

Lemma 17. Let Θ be a theory, let A be a ground atom. If $A \notin \mathcal{T}_{\Theta,\emptyset}\downarrow_\omega$, then the derivation of $\Theta \cup \{\leftarrow A\}$ fails finitely.

Proofs of these lemmas as well as a discussion relating this approach to circumscription can be found in Weigert (1989) and Tsai and Weigert (1993). Note that Lemma 16 relies on the fact that theories are stratified. A stratified set of clauses can be partitioned such that some relations are defined without (direct or indirect) recursion through ¶ and predicate negation. From a semantic viewpoint, we only apply ¶ to relations whose meaning is fixed beforehand. We can, therefore, be sure that a derivation of literals of the form ¶A either succeeds or fails finitely.

4 Relationship to model-theoretic semantics

The logic programming community generally identifies the intended meaning of nonmonotonic theories with augmentations which minimize positive information. There are three prevalent approaches: the closed world assumption (Reiter 1978), predicate completion (Clark 1978), and point-wise circumscription (Lifschitz 1987). Although originally these were intended to explicate the nonmonotonic behavior of the "negation as failure" rule, we can easily adapt them to more general cases of nonmonotonicity. Under the closed world assumption, ¶A can be assumed true if A cannot be derived from a theory. Predicate completion assumes the given sufficient conditions on a predicate are also necessary. Point-wise circumscription expresses the impossibility of changing the value of a predicate from true to false at only one point. These schemes effectively augment a theory, and a model-theoretic semantics can be given for the augmented theory. The relationship between these schemes has been studied extensively (Reiter 1980, Lifschitz 1985, Sheperdson 1984); for general theories they are not equivalent.

In this section, we describe the meaning of a formula model-theoretically, and show the relationship between model-theoretic semantics and fix-point semantics. We present a version of Clark's predicate completion adapted to nonmonotonic logic. We then study under what conditions a formula that is a logical consequence of the completed theory (under the model-theoretic semantics) is also a logical consequence of the theory (under the fix-point semantics).

The semantic valuation of a formula is as usual, with the exception of the interpretation of the "¶" symbol. We hold that

$$\models^{\mathrm{nm}} \P A \text{ iff } \models^{\mathrm{nm}} \neg \overline{A}, \tag{1}$$

if A is an atomic formula. As stated earlier, we do not discuss logic programs with negation, and so the standard negation symbol of first-order logic, "$\neg$", may not appear in a clause. However, we may want to state negative information, as when we claim that *Penguins do not fly*. The meaning of this claim is evaluated through the interpretation directly, rather than derived from the falsity of the claim that *Penguins fly*. The use of predicate negation to express such claims may appear unintuitively (for example, there is no connection given between the meaning of A and the meaning of $\widehat{A}$).

Similarly to the notion of the nonmonotonic extension $\mathcal{N}m(\Theta)$ of a theory Θ we introduce the notion of the nonmonotonic completion of Θ. The concept of the completion of a theory was first presented by Clark (1978) to provide Horn-clause logic with some form of negation. Clark uses the completion of a theory to explicate his "negation as failure" inference rule. "Negation as failure" allows one to conclude (for some predicate A) that all things not known to be A are $\neg A$. Using similar intuitions we want to be able to conclude that all those things known not to be $\widehat{A}$ are ¶A. Following the discussion in Clark (1978) we define the nonmonotonic completion $\mathcal{C}omp(\Theta)$ of a theory Θ as follows: Let Θ be a theory such that none of the clauses of Θ have an occurrence of the two-place predicate symbol "=". Let $A(t_1, \ldots, t_n) \leftarrow B_1 \wedge \ldots \wedge B_m$ be a clause in Θ. For each such clause in Θ, replace it by

$$A(x_1, \ldots, x_n) \leftarrow \exists y_1 \ldots y_p(x_1 = t_1 \wedge \ldots \wedge x_n = t_n \wedge B_1 \wedge \ldots \wedge B_m)$$

where "=" is interpreted as the identity relation, $y_1 \ldots y_p$ are the variables occurring in the original clause, and $x_1, \ldots, x_n$ are variables not appearing in this clause. This way of writing the clause is called the *normal form* of the clause. After this replacement Θ contains, for each head of a clause with matching predicate symbol A, a set of clauses of the form

$$A(x_1, \ldots, x_n) \leftarrow E_1, \ldots, A(x_1, \ldots, x_n) \leftarrow E_k$$

where each clause $A(x_1, \ldots, x_n) \leftarrow E_i$ is in normal form. If we group these clauses together into a single formula, we obtain

$$A(x_1, \ldots, x_n) \leftarrow E_1 \vee \ldots \vee E_k.$$

Now consider only those E_i that do not contain a literal of the form $\P C$, and form the formula

$$E_j \vee \ldots \vee E_l \leftarrow A(x_1, \ldots, x_n)$$

(call this formula the completion of A). Add these formulae to the set of clauses obtained so far. For any predicate symbol A occurring in the body of a clause in Θ within a literal of the form $\P A$, but not in the head of a clause in Θ, we add the formula

$$\neg A(x_1, \ldots, x_n).$$

The resultant set of clauses is referred to as the *nonmonotonic completion* $\mathcal{C}omp(\Theta)$ of the theory Θ. We also make use of the subset of $\mathcal{C}omp(\Theta)$ in which no literals of the form $\P C$ appear. We denote this subset by $\Theta^\dagger$.

The described procedure begins by noticing that any atom $A(t_1, \ldots, t_n)$ is equivalent to the formula

$$\forall x_1 \ldots x_n (A(x_1, \ldots, x_n) \leftarrow \exists y_1 \ldots y_p (x_1 = t_1 \wedge \ldots \wedge x_n = t_n)).$$

Such a formula could be taken as the "if" half of a definition for A. The intuitions of McCarthy (1980) and Moore (1985) lead to the assumption that there are no other objects satisfying A, which is made by writing the "only if" half as

$$\forall x_1 \ldots x_n (\exists y_1 \ldots y_p (x_1 = t_1 \wedge \ldots \wedge x_n = t_n) \leftarrow A(x_1, \ldots, x_n)).$$

By adding the "only if" halves to all clauses in Θ (which do not contain literals of the form $\P C$) we then obtain the nonmonotonic completion of Θ. The nonmonotonic completion expresses the assumption that Θ is "all we know." To be precise, reasoning with the completion of a theory Θ relies on a suitable identity theory being added to the theory. In addition, we need to make the "unique names assumption," i.e., the claim that every constant symbol denotes a unique object of the domain. From now on, we assume Θ also includes the interpretation of the "="-sign as equality relation, and the unique names assumption.

For example, the nonmonotonic completion of the example theory Θ_1 becomes

$$Fly(y) \leftarrow \exists x(y = x \wedge Bird(x) \wedge \P\, Fly(x)) \tag{2}$$

$$\widehat{Fly}(y) \leftarrow \exists x(y = x \wedge Penguin(x)) \tag{3}$$

$$Penguin(y) \leftarrow \exists x(y = x \wedge \widehat{Fly}(x)) \tag{4}$$

$$Bird(y) \leftarrow \exists x(y = x \wedge Penguin(x)) \vee y = tweety \tag{5}$$

$$Penguin(y) \vee y = tweety \leftarrow \exists x(x = y \wedge Bird(x)) \tag{6}$$

$$Penguin(y) \leftarrow y = opus \tag{7}$$

$$y = opus \leftarrow \exists x(y = x \wedge Penguin(x)). \tag{8}$$

Using standard first-order inference and an inference rule capturing the definition of valuation in (1), we can easily deduce that *Tweety flies*: From (5) we can obtain *Bird(tweety)*. Equations (7) and (3) let us conclude that $\neg\widehat{Fly}(tweety)$ by using the contrapositive of (4). Now we conclude that *Fly(tweety)* by (2). When considering the substitution $\{^{x}/_{opus}\}$ we can conclude *Penguin(opus)*, by (7), *Bird(opus)*, by (5), and $\widehat{Fly}(opus)$, by (3). We cannot, however, use (2) to derive *Fly(opus)*, since this inference is blocked by the presence of $\widehat{Fly}(opus)$. An inference rule capturing (1) permits us to conclude $\P Fly(x)$ only when we know that $\neg\widehat{Fly}(x)$.

Call a Herbrand interpretation $\mathcal{I}$ that is a model for a theory Θ a Herbrand model for Θ. We introduce the notion of a least Herbrand model for Θ. We then show that the least Herbrand model is the set of ground atoms logical consequences of the theory Θ. The least Herbrand model provides the connection between the model-theoretic semantics of nonmonotonic logic programs and their fix-point theoretic semantics.

We continue by showing that a model of the nonmonotonic completion $\mathcal{C}omp(\Theta)$ of a theory Θ is also a model of Θ.

Theorem 18. Let Θ be a theory. If an interpretation $\mathcal{I}$ is a model of $\mathcal{C}omp(\Theta)$, then $\mathcal{I}$ is a model of Θ.

Proof. Let $A(t_1, \ldots, t_n) \leftarrow B_1 \wedge \ldots \wedge B_m$ be a clause of the theory Θ, and let $B_1 \wedge \ldots \wedge B_m$ be true in $\mathcal{I}$, for some assignment to the variables $y_1 \ldots y_p$ of this clause. Let the grouped normal forms of clauses whose head contains the predicate A be $A(x_1, \ldots, x_n) \leftarrow E_1 \vee \ldots \vee E_k$, where each E_i has the form $\exists y_1 \ldots y_p(x_1 = t_1 \wedge \ldots \wedge x_n = t_n \wedge B_1 \wedge \ldots \wedge B_m)$. Let the assignment of x_i be t_i, for $1 \leq i \leq n$, for the same assignment of the variables $y_1 \ldots y_p$ as above; then E_i is true in $\mathcal{I}$, $1 \leq i \leq k$, and thus $\mathcal{I}$ is a model of $A(t_1, \ldots, t_n)$. Therefore, $\mathcal{I}$ is a model of every clause in Θ, and thus $\mathcal{I}$ is a model of Θ. $\square$

Now, consider only those models of $\mathcal{C}omp(\Theta)$ that are Herbrand models. The intersection of the set of all Herbrand models is itself a Herbrand model. If Θ is a set of formulae, $\mathcal{H}m(\Theta)$ denotes the set of all Herbrand models of Θ.

Lemma 19. Let Θ be a theory, $\mathcal{I}$ a Herbrand interpretation of $\Theta^\dagger$; then

$$\mathcal{I} \text{ is a model for } \Theta^\dagger \text{ iff } \mathcal{I} = \mathcal{T}_{\Theta,\emptyset}(\mathcal{I}).$$

Proof. Only if. Let $\Theta^\dagger$, let the completed definition of the predicate A be $(A(x_1, \ldots, x_n) \leftarrow E_j \vee \ldots \vee E_l) \wedge (E_j \vee \ldots \vee E_l \leftarrow A(x_1, \ldots, x_n))$ (remember that none of the E_i contains a literal of the form $\P C)$. Show that $\mathcal{I} = \mathcal{T}_{\Theta,\emptyset}(\mathcal{I})$.

(i) Let $A(t_1, \ldots, t_n) \in \mathcal{I}$, for some substitution θ. Since $\mathcal{I}$ is a model of $\Theta^\dagger$, $\mathcal{I}$ is a model of $(E_j \vee \ldots \vee E_l)\theta$. But then $A(t_1, \ldots, t_n) \in \mathcal{T}_{\Theta,\emptyset}(\mathcal{I})$, and $\mathcal{I} \subseteq \mathcal{T}_{\Theta,\emptyset}(\mathcal{I})$.
(ii) Let $A(t_1, \ldots, t_n) \in \mathcal{T}_{\Theta,\emptyset}(\mathcal{I})$, for some substitution θ. Then $\mathcal{I}$ is a model of $(E_j \vee \ldots \vee E_l)\theta$, and since $\mathcal{I}$ is a model of $\Theta^\dagger$, $A(t_1, \ldots, t_n) \in \mathcal{I}$. But then $\mathcal{I} \supseteq \mathcal{T}_{\Theta,\emptyset}(\mathcal{I})$.

If. Let $\mathcal{I} = \mathcal{T}_{\Theta,\emptyset}(\mathcal{I})$.

(i) Consider completed definitions of the form $\neg A(x_1, \ldots, x_n)$. Since $\mathcal{I}$ is a fix-point, $\mathcal{I}$ is a model of $\neg A(x_1, \ldots, x_n)$.
(ii) Let the completed definition of the predicate A be $(A(x_1, \ldots, x_n) \leftarrow E_j \vee \ldots \vee E_l) \wedge (E_j \vee \ldots \vee E_l \leftarrow A(x_1, \ldots, x_n))$. Since $\mathcal{I} \supseteq \mathcal{T}_{\Theta,\pi}(\mathcal{I})$, $\mathcal{I}$ is a model of $A(x_1, \ldots, x_n) \leftarrow E_j \vee \ldots \vee E_l$; since $\mathcal{I} \subseteq \mathcal{T}_{\Theta,\emptyset}(\mathcal{I})$, $\mathcal{I}$ is a model of $E_j \vee \ldots \vee E_l \leftarrow A(x_1, \ldots, x_n)$.

Therefore, $\mathcal{I}$ is a model for all formulae in $\Theta^\dagger$. (This lemma is due to Apt and van Emden 1982.) □

We are now able to establish a relationship between the fact that an atom is in the failure set of a theory and the fact that a Herbrand interpretation of the completion of the theory is not a model for this atom:

Lemma 20. Let A be a ground atom in the Herbrand base of a theory Θ, let $\mathcal{I}$ be a Herbrand interpretation of $\mathcal{C}omp(\Theta)$.

$$\text{If } A \notin \mathcal{T}_{\Theta,\emptyset}\downarrow_\omega, \text{ then, if } \mathcal{I} \subseteq \mathcal{T}_{\Theta,\emptyset}(\mathcal{I}), \mathcal{I} \text{ is a model of } \neg A.$$

Proof. Let $A \notin \mathcal{T}_{\Theta,\emptyset}\downarrow_\omega$. Since $\mathcal{T}_{\Theta,\emptyset}\downarrow_\omega \supseteq \text{gfp}(\mathcal{T}_{\Theta,\emptyset})$, $A \notin \text{gfp}(\mathcal{T}_{\Theta,\emptyset})$, i.e., $A \notin \text{lub}\{\mathcal{I} \mid \mathcal{I} \subseteq \mathcal{T}_{\Theta,\emptyset}(\mathcal{I})\}$, by the Knaster–Tarski fix-point theorem. But then $A \notin \mathcal{I}$, for any Herbrand interpretation $\mathcal{I}$, such that $\mathcal{I} \subseteq \mathcal{T}_{\Theta,\emptyset}(\mathcal{I})$. Therefore, $\mathcal{I}$ is a model of $\neg A$, if $\mathcal{I} \subseteq \mathcal{T}_{\Theta,\emptyset}(\mathcal{I})$. □

The converse direction cannot be established for the general case. However, for theories where the approximation from above to the theory operator is the greatest fix-point, we can show that the converse also holds:

Lemma 21. Let Θ be a theory, such that $\mathcal{T}_{\Theta,\emptyset}\downarrow_{\omega} = \mathrm{gfp}(\mathcal{T}_{\Theta,\emptyset})$. Let A be a ground atom in the Herbrand base of Θ, let $\mathcal{I}$ be a Herbrand interpretation of $\mathit{Comp}(\Theta)$. Let $\mathcal{I} \subseteq \mathcal{T}_{\Theta,\emptyset}(\mathcal{I})$; then,

$$\text{if } \mathcal{I} \text{ is a model of } \neg A,\ A \notin \mathcal{T}_{\Theta,\emptyset}\downarrow_{\omega} .$$

Proof. Let any model $\mathcal{I}$, such that $\mathcal{I} \subseteq \mathcal{T}_{\Theta,\emptyset}(\mathcal{I})$ be a model of $\neg A$; then $A \notin \mathcal{I}$, if $\mathcal{I} \subseteq \mathcal{T}_{\Theta,\emptyset}(\mathcal{I})$. Using the Knaster–Tarski fix-point theorem, we conclude that $A \notin \mathrm{gfp}(\mathcal{T}_{\Theta,\emptyset})$, and by the assumption that $\mathcal{T}_{\Theta,\emptyset}\downarrow_{\omega} = \mathrm{gfp}(\mathcal{T}_{\Theta,\emptyset})$ we know that $A \notin \mathcal{T}_{\Theta,\emptyset}\downarrow_{\omega}$. □

By utilizing Lemmas 12 and 17 we obtain as a corollary:

Lemma 22. Let Θ be a theory, such that $\mathcal{T}_{\Theta,\emptyset}\downarrow_{\omega} = \mathrm{gfp}(\mathcal{T}_{\Theta,\emptyset})$. Let A be a ground atom in the Herbrand base of Θ, let $\mathcal{I}$ be a Herbrand interpretation of $\mathit{Comp}(\Theta)$. Let $\mathcal{I} \subseteq \mathcal{T}_{\Theta,\emptyset}(\mathcal{I})$; then, if $\mathcal{I}$ is a model of $\neg A$, the derivation of $\Theta \cup \{\leftarrow A\}$ fails finitely.

Lemma 23. Let Θ be a theory, let $\mathcal{I}$ be a Herbrand interpretation of $\mathit{Comp}(\Theta)$; then, if $\mathcal{I} \supseteq \mathcal{T}_{\Theta,\mathcal{N}m(\Theta)}(\mathcal{I})$, $\mathcal{I}$ is a model for $\Theta^{\dagger}$.

Proof. Let $\mathcal{I} \supseteq \mathcal{T}_{\Theta,\mathcal{N}m(\Theta)}(\mathcal{I})$, and suppose for reduction that $\mathcal{I}$ is not a model of $\Theta^{\dagger}$. Then there is a clause $B \leftarrow B_1 \wedge \ldots \wedge B_m \in \Theta$, such that under some substitution θ, $B_j\theta \in \mathcal{I}$, $1 \leq j \leq m$, but $B \notin \mathcal{I}$. Then by the definition of the theory operator, $B \in \mathcal{T}_{\Theta,\mathcal{N}m(\Theta)}(\mathcal{I})$, and since $\mathcal{I} \supseteq \mathcal{T}_{\Theta,\mathcal{N}m(\Theta)}(\mathcal{I})$, $B \in \mathcal{I}$. But that contradicts the claim that $B \notin \mathcal{I}$. Therefore, $\mathcal{I}$ is a model of any clause without a literal of the form ¶C in its body, and so $\mathcal{I}$ is a model of $\Theta^{\dagger}$. □

We can obtain a result weaker than Lemma 19 for the completion of a theory Θ:

Theorem 24. Let Θ be a theory such that $\mathcal{T}_{\Theta,\emptyset}\downarrow_{\omega} = \mathrm{gfp}(\mathcal{T}_{\Theta,\emptyset})$, $\mathcal{I}$ a Herbrand interpretation of $\mathit{Comp}(\Theta)$; then $\mathcal{I}$ is a model for $\mathit{Comp}(\Theta)$ iff $\mathcal{I} \supseteq \mathcal{T}_{\Theta,\mathcal{N}m(\Theta)}(\mathcal{I})$.

Proof. Only if. Let $\mathcal{I}$ be a model for $\mathit{Comp}(\Theta)$; then $\mathcal{I}$ is also a model for $\Theta^{\dagger}$, and by Lemma 19 $\mathcal{I} \subseteq \mathcal{T}_{\Theta,\emptyset}(\mathcal{I})$. Show that, for any atom A in the Herbrand base of Θ, if $\mathcal{T}_{\Theta,\mathcal{N}m(\Theta)}(\mathcal{I})$ is a model for A, then $\mathcal{I}$ is also a model for A. Let $\mathcal{T}_{\Theta,\mathcal{N}m(\Theta)}(\mathcal{I})$ be a model for A. In light of Lemma 19, the only case we need to consider is when A is obtained from a clause $B \leftarrow B_1 \wedge \ldots \wedge B_m \in \Theta$, such that $B\theta = A$, for some substitution θ, and there is a literal B_i in the body of the clause, such that $B_i =$ ¶C, where C is ground. (Note that for $\Theta^{\dagger}$, $\mathcal{T}_{\Theta,\mathcal{N}m(\Theta)}(\mathcal{I}) = \mathcal{T}_{\Theta,\emptyset}(\mathcal{I})$.) $\mathcal{I}$ is a model of this clause. Since $A \in \mathcal{T}_{\Theta,\emptyset}(\mathcal{I})$, $B_j\theta \in \mathcal{I}$, $1 \leq j \leq m$, $i \neq j$, and ¶$C \in \mathcal{N}m(\Theta)$, by the definition of the theory operator. Therefore, $\overline{C} \notin \mathcal{T}_{\Theta,\emptyset}\downarrow_{\omega}$, and by Lemma 20, $\mathcal{I}$ is a model of $\neg\overline{C}$. But then $\mathcal{I}$ is a model of ¶C, and therefore, $\mathcal{I}$ is a model of A.

If. Again it suffices to consider the clauses that contain literals of the form

$\P C$ in their body. Show that $\mathcal{I}$ is a model for any clause of the form $B \leftarrow B_1 \wedge \ldots \wedge B_m$, such that there is a literal $B_i = \P C$. Let $\mathcal{I}$ be a model of $B \leftarrow B_1 \wedge \ldots \wedge B_m$; therefore, $B_j\theta \in \mathcal{I}$, $1 \leq j \leq m$, $i \neq j$, for some substitution θ, and $\mathcal{I}$ is a model of $\P C$. From the latter we know that $\mathcal{I}$ is a model for $\neg\overline{C}$, and therefore, by Lemmas 23 and 21, $\overline{C} \notin \mathcal{T}_{\Theta,\emptyset}\downarrow_\omega$, and $\P C \in \mathcal{N}m(\Theta)$. Then by the definition of the theory operator, $B \in \mathcal{T}_{\Theta,\mathcal{N}m(\Theta)}(\mathcal{I})$, and by hypothesis $B \in \mathcal{I}$. □

A corollary of the above lemma is the following claim:

Theorem 25. Let Θ be a theory, such that $\mathcal{T}_{\Theta,\emptyset}\downarrow_\omega = \mathrm{gfp}(\mathcal{T}_{\Theta,\emptyset})$; then the intersection of all Herbrand models of $\mathcal{C}omp(\Theta)$, $\bigcap \mathcal{H}m(\mathcal{C}omp(\Theta))$, is a Herbrand model for Θ.

Proof. Since the theory operator is monotonic, $\bigcap\{\mathcal{I} \mid \mathcal{I} \supseteq \mathcal{T}_{\Theta,\mathcal{N}m(\Theta)}(\mathcal{I})\} \in \{\mathcal{I} \mid \mathcal{I} \supseteq \mathcal{T}_{\Theta,\mathcal{N}m(\Theta)}(\mathcal{I})\}$. By Theorem 24 this translates to $\bigcap\{\mathcal{H}m(\mathcal{C}omp(\Theta))\} \in \mathcal{H}m(\mathcal{C}omp(\Theta))$, i.e., $\bigcap\{\mathcal{H}m(\mathcal{C}omp(\Theta))\}$ is a Herbrand model for Θ. □

Theorem 26. Let Θ be a theory, such that $\mathcal{T}_{\Theta,\emptyset}\downarrow_\omega = \mathrm{gfp}(\mathcal{T}_{\Theta,\emptyset})$; then $\bigcap \mathcal{H}m(\mathcal{C}omp(\Theta)) = \mathcal{T}_{\Theta,\mathcal{N}m(\Theta)}\uparrow_\omega$.

As pointed out above, the set of all Herbrand models is a complete lattice under the partial order of set inclusion. The greatest lowest bound of the lattice of Herbrand models is set intersection, therefore

$$\bigcap \mathcal{H}m(\mathcal{C}omp(\Theta)) = \mathrm{glb}\{\mathcal{I} \mid \mathcal{I} \text{ is a model for } \mathcal{C}omp(\Theta).$$

By Lemma 19

$$\bigcap \mathcal{H}m(\mathcal{C}omp(\Theta)) = \mathrm{glb}\{\mathcal{I} \mid \mathcal{I} \supseteq \mathcal{T}_{\Theta,\mathcal{N}m(\Theta)}(\mathcal{I})\}.$$

By applying the Knaster–Tarski fix-point theorem (Tarski 1955) we know that $\bigcap \mathcal{H}m(\mathcal{C}omp(\Theta))$ is the least fix-point of $\mathcal{T}_{\Theta,\mathcal{N}m(\Theta)}$. Since $\mathcal{T}_{\Theta,\mathcal{N}m(\Theta)}$ is continuous and monotonic we conclude that

$$\bigcap \mathcal{H}m(\mathcal{C}omp(\Theta)) = \mathcal{T}_{\Theta,\mathcal{N}m(\Theta)}\uparrow_\omega .$$

This theorem shows the coincidence of a description of the semantics of our language through purely set theoretic terms and a description of the semantics of nonmonotonic logic programs through fix-point theory, under the assumption that $\mathcal{T}_{\Theta,\emptyset}\downarrow_\omega = \mathrm{gfp}(\mathcal{T}_{\Theta,\emptyset})$. Using a model-theoretic semantics, we can define the notion of logical consequence as follows:

Definition 27. Let Θ be a theory, and let A be a literal. A is a logical consequence of Θ iff for every interpretation $\mathcal{I}$ of Θ, if $\mathcal{I}$ is a model of Θ, then $\mathcal{I}$ is a model of A.

Theorem 28. Let Θ be a theory and A a ground atom; then $\bigcap \mathcal{H}m(\mathit{Comp}(\Theta)) = \{A \mid A \text{ is a logical consequence of } \mathit{Comp}(\Theta)\}$.

Proof. A is a logical consequence of $\mathit{Comp}(\Theta)$ iff $\mathcal{H}m(\{A\}) \supseteq \mathcal{H}m(\mathit{Comp}(\Theta))$. For an arbitrary set of sentences Γ, if $\mathcal{H}m(\Gamma) \supseteq \mathcal{H}m(\mathit{Comp}(\Theta))$ then $\bigcap \mathcal{H}m(\Gamma) \subseteq \bigcap \mathcal{H}m(\mathit{Comp}(\Theta))$. Substituting $\{A\}$, and realizing that $\bigcap \mathcal{H}m(\{A\}) = \{A\}$, we obtain $A \in \bigcap \mathcal{H}m(\mathit{Comp}(\Theta))$. Thus A is a logical consequence of $\mathit{Comp}(\Theta)$ iff $A \in \bigcap \mathcal{H}m(\mathit{Comp}(\Theta))$. □

According to Definitions 6 and 7, $\mathcal{T}_{\Theta,\mathcal{N}m(\Theta)}\uparrow_\omega$ is the set of all ground literals that are logical consequences of the theory Θ. Assuming $\mathcal{T}_{\Theta,\emptyset}\downarrow_\omega = \mathrm{gfp}(\mathcal{T}_{\Theta,\emptyset})$, Theorem 28 tells us that $\bigcap \mathcal{H}m(\mathit{Comp}(\Theta))$, the least Herbrand model of the completion of Θ, is the set of all ground literals such that every model of Θ is a model of every literal in $\bigcap \mathcal{H}m(\mathit{Comp}(\Theta))$. From Theorem 26 we know that these two sets are identical. In other words, by Theorem 28 the set of literals in Π_Θ that are logical consequences (as defined model-theoretically) of the theory Θ is precisely the least Herbrand model. Theorem 26 tells us that the least Herbrand model is identical to $\mathcal{T}_{\Theta,\mathcal{N}m(\Theta)}\uparrow_\omega$. But, as stated in Definition 7, $\mathcal{T}_{\Theta,\mathcal{N}m(\Theta)}\uparrow_\omega$ is the set of of literals in Π_Θ that are logical consequences (as defined through fix-point semantics) of the theory Θ. In the general case, this result cannot be demonstrated, since we then cannot establish that the intersection of all Herbrand models of the theory Θ is itself a Herbrand model.

One may wonder here whether one can find a general characterization of theories such that $\mathcal{T}_{\Theta,\emptyset}\downarrow_\omega = \mathrm{gfp}(\mathcal{T}_{\Theta,\emptyset})$. Jaffar and Stuckey (1986) suggest that any "decent" theory should satisfy this condition. They call such theories canonical, and show that negation-free Horn-clause theories are equivalent to canonical Horn-clause theories. Blair (1986) shows that all recursive relations are computable by such theories. However, deciding whether a theory has the property $\mathcal{T}_{\Theta,\emptyset}\downarrow_\omega = \mathrm{gfp}(\mathcal{T}_{\Theta,\emptyset})$ is highly non-recursive.

5 Conclusion

Standard first-order logic, and therefore, any description of the world that relies on it, ordinarily requires the absence of contradiction. It has been repeatedly pointed out that in describing the real world it is often very difficult to avoid making contradictory statements. (For example, when realizing that an assumption had proven wrong, we might have to assert the denial of what we had assumed to hold true.) Nonmonotonic logics have been developed to deal with this type of "tentative" inference.

In earlier papers (Weigert 1989, Tsai et al. 1992, Weigert and Tsai 1994), we presented an extension to the Horn-clause subset of first-order logic that permits nonmonotonic inference. We developed the semantics of this logic in terms of fix-points of a theory operator, and demonstrated this logic to be both sound and complete. Since we are dealing with the Horn-clause subset of first-order logic, we also have a decidable inference mechanism.

In this essay, we investigated the relationship between the fix-point semantics of nonmonotonic Horn-clause logic and a more standard model-theoretic semantics of completed nonmonotonic Horn-clause theories. The two semantic characterizations coincide for "decent" theories (Jaffar and Stuckley 1986).

Przymusinski (1989) independently presented a fix-point semantics for nonmonotonic theories very similar to ours, but based on three-valued logic, and studied the relationship to a semantics based on well-founded models. In Przymusinski (1991), he shows that this approach can be used also for two-valued logic. His arguments can also be applied to our nonmonotonic logic.

Investigations into nonmonotonic logic are tightly coupled with logic programming and reasoning in Horn-clause theories. For one, the widely accepted "negation as failure" rule in data base theory and logic programs is clearly nonmonotonic. Recent approaches attempt to explicate the semantics of "negation as failure" by interpreting the notion of logical consequence as being true in models of a certain kind (rather than as being true in all models). A semantics based on supported models requires that the formula is the head of a clause in the theory (Apt et al. 1988). Perfect model semantics (Przymusinski 1988) allows predicates to be minimized depending on a priority ranking imposed by the syntactic structure of the theory. Well-founded model semantics (van Gelder et al. 1988) and stable-model semantics (Gelfond and Lifschitz 1988) relies on an even stronger notion of support for a model in requiring that the positive literals in the clauses of the theory are not in an unfounded set with respect to the interpretation. Note that these models are all models of the completion of the theory.

Then, logic programming provides the hope of a tractable inference mechanism for nonmonotonic reasoning. Gelfond and Lifschitz (1989) presented a mechanism to translate certain circumscriptive theories into logic programs. In earlier papers (Weigert 1989, Tsai et al. 1992, Weigert and Tsai 1994), we described a nonmonotonic logic whose theories can be executed as logic programs by a suitable interpreter.

The nonmonotonic logic presented in this essay serves as the logical foundation of a software system requirements specification environment under development at the University of Illinois (Tsai et al. 1988, 1990, 1991, 1992; Tsai and Weigert 1989, 1990).

Acknowledgement

This research was conducted while on leave to Electrotechnical Laboratory, Umezono 1-chome 1-4, Tsukuba-shi, Ibaraki-ken 305, Japan.

References

Apt, K. R., Blair, H. A., Walker, A. (1988): Towards a theory of declarative knowledge. In: Minker, J. (ed.): Foundations of deductive databases and logic programming. Morgan Kaufmann, Los Altos, pp. 89–148.

Apt, K. R., van Emden, M. H. (1982): Contributions to the theory of logic programming. J. ACM 29: 841–862.

Blair, H. A. (1986): Decidability in the Herbrand base. In: Minker, J. (ed.): Proceedings Foundations of Deductive Databases and Logic Programming, Washington, 1986.

Chang, C., Lee, R. (1973): Symbolic logic and mechanical theorem proving. Academic Press, New York.

Clark, K. L. (1978): Negation as failure. In: Gallaire, H., Minker, J. (eds.): Logic and databases. Plenum, New York, pp. 293–322.

Gallaire, H., Minker, J. (eds.) (1978): Logic and databases. Plenum, New York.

Gelfond, M., Lifschitz, V. (1988): The stable model semantics for logic programming. In: Proceedings of the 5th International Conference on Logic Programming, Seattle, 1988, pp. 1070–1081.

Gelfond, M., Lifschitz, V. (1989): Compiling circumscriptive theories into logic programs. In: Reinfrank, M., de Kleer, J., Ginsberg, M. L., Sandewall, E. (eds.): Nonmonotonic reasoning. Springer, Berlin Heidelberg New York Tokyo, pp. 74–99 (Lecture notes in computer science, vol. 346).

Genesereth, M., Nilsson, N. (1988): Logical foundations of artificial intelligence. Morgan Kaufmann, Los Altos.

Ginsberg, M. L. (ed.) (1987): Readings in nonmonotonic reasoning. Morgan Kaufmann, Los Altos.

Jaffar, J., Stuckley, P. J. (1986): Canonical logic programs. J. Logic Program. 3: 143–157.

Lifschitz, V. (1985): Closed world databases and circumscription. Artif. Intell. 27: 229–235.

Lifschitz, V. (1987): Pointwise circumscription. In: Ginsberg, M. L. (ed.): Readings in nonmonotonic reasoning. Morgan Kaufmann, Los Altos, pp. 179–194.

Lloyd, J. W. (1987): Foundations of logic programming. Springer, Berlin Heidelberg New York Tokyo.

McCarthy, J. (1980): Circumscription – a form of nonmonotonic reasoning. Artif. Intell. 13: 27–39.

McDermott, D. (1982): Nonmonotonic logic II. J. ACM 29: 33–57.

McDermott, D., Doyle, J. (1980): Nonmonotonic logic I. Artif. Intell. 13: 27–39.

Minker, J. (ed.) (1988): Foundations of deductive databases and logic programming. Morgan Kaufmann, Los Altos.

Moore, R. (1985): Semantical considerations on nonmonotonic logic. Artif. Intell. 25: 75–94.

Przymusinski, T. (1988): On the semantics of stratified deductive databases. In: Minker, J. (ed.): Foundations of deductive databases and logic programming. Morgan Kaufmann, Los Altos, pp. 193–216.

Przymusinski, T. (1989): Nonmonotonic formalisms and logic programming. In: Proceedings of the 6th International Conference on Logic Programming, Pisa, 1989, pp. 655–674.

Przymusinski, T. (1991): Well-founded completions of logic programs. In: Proceedings of the 8th International Conference on Logic Programming, Paris, 1991, pp. 726–741.

Reinfrank, M., de Kleer, J., Ginsberg, M. L., Sandewall, E. (eds.) (1989): Non-monotonic reasoning. Springer, Berlin Heidelberg New York Tokyo (Lecture notes in computer science, vol. 346).

Reiter, R. (1978): On closed world data bases. In: Gallaire, H., Minker, J. (eds.): Logic and databases. Plenum, New York, pp. 55–76.

Reiter, R. (1980): A logic for default reasoning. Artif. Intell. 13: 81–132.

Sheperdson, J. C. (1984): Negation as failure: a comparison of Clark's completed database and Reiter's closed world assumption. J. Logic Program. 1: 51–79.

Sheperdson, J. C. (1988): Negation in logic programming. In: Minker, J. (ed.): Foundations of deductive databases and logic programming. Morgan Kaufmann, Los Altos, pp. 19–89.

Sheperdson, J. C. (1989): Logics for negation as failure. In: Moschovakis, Y. N. (ed.): Logic from computer science. Springer, Berlin Heidelberg New York Tokyo, pp. 521–585 (Mathematical Sciences Research Institute publications, vol. 21).

Tarski, A. (1955): A lattice-theoretical fixpoint theorem and its applications. Pacific J. Math. 5: 285–309.

Tsai, J. P., Weigert, T. (1989): Exploratory prototyping through the use of frame and production systems. In: Proceedings IEEE Computer Software and Applications Conference, Orlando, 1989, pp. 445–462.

Tsai, J. P., Weigert, T. (1990): A knowledge-based approach for checking software information using a non-monotonic reasoning system. Knowl. Based Syst. 3: 131–138.

Tsai, J. P., Weigert, T. (1991): HCLIE: a logic-based requirements language for new software engineering paradigms. IEE Software Eng. J. 6: 137–151.

Tsai, J. P., Weigert, T. (1992): An explication of reasoning in multiple inheritance system through non-monotonic Horn clause logic. J. Inf. Sci. 63: 261–283.

Tsai, J. P., Weigert, T. (1993): Knowledge-based software development for real-time distributed systems. World Scientific Publishing, Singapore.

Tsai, J. P., Weigert, T., Aoyama, M. (1988): A declarative approach to software requirements specification language. In: Proceedings IEEE Computer Languages Conference, Miami Beach, 1988, pp. 414–421.

Tsai, J. P., Weigert, T., Jang, H. C. (1990): A hybrid knowledge representation as a basis of requirement specification and reasoning. In: Proceedings IEEE Computer Software and Applications Conference, Chicago, 1990, pp. 70–76.

Tsai, J. P., Weigert, T., Jang, H. C. (1991): Non-monotonic logic as a basis for requirements specification and analysis. In: Proceedings of the International Symposium on Artificial Intelligence, Tokyo, 1991, pp. 13–15.

Tsai, J. P., Weigert, T., Jang, H. C. (1992): A hybrid knowledge representation as a basis of requirement specification and specification analysis. IEEE Trans. Software Eng. 18: 1076–1100.

van Gelder, A., Ross, K., Schlipf (1988): Unfounded sets and well-founded semantics for general logic programs. In: Proceedings of the Symposium on Principles of Database Systems. ACM SIGACT-SIGMOD.

Weigert, T. (1989): Nonmonotonic logic as the basis for a requirement specification language. In: Lowry, M. (ed.): Proceedings of the Workshop on Automating Software Design, St. Paul, 1989, pp. 191–206.

Weigert, T., Tsai, J. P. (1994): A computationally tractable nonmonotonic logic. IEEE Trans. Knowl. Data Eng. 6: 57–64.

Subject index

Bernd Sturmfels

Algorithms in Invariant Theory

1993. 5 figures. VII, 197 pages.
Soft cover DM 59,–, öS 415,–
ISBN 3-211-82445-6

(Texts and Monographs in Symbolic Computation)

Prices are subject to change without notice

J. Kung and G.-C. Rota, in their 1984 paper, write: "Like the Arabian phoenix rising out of its ashes, the theory of invariants, pronounced dead at the turn of the century, is once again at the forefront of mathematics."

The book of Sturmfels is both an easy-to-read textbook for invariant theory and a challenging research monograph that introduces a new approach to the algorithmic side of invariant theory. The Groebner bases method is the main tool by which the central problems in invariant theory become amenable to algorithmic solutions. Students will find the book an easy introduction to this "classical and new" area of mathematics. Researchers in mathematics, symbolic computation, and computer science will get access to a wealth of research ideas, hints for applications, outlines and details of algorithms, worked out examples, and research problems.

Surveys on Mathematics for Industry

The main goal of this journal is to bridge the gap between university and industry by the presentation of mathematical methods relevant for industry and the exposition of industrial problems which are of interest to mathematicians.

To achieve this goal, the journal publishes (exclusively in English): surveys on new mathematical techniques, surveys on established mathematical techniques with a new range of applications, surveys on industrial problems for which appropriate mathematical models or methods are not yet available, articles comparing mathematical models or methods for particular industrial problems, articles describing mathematical modelling techniques, broad historical surveys, articles of general interest about the use of mathematics in industry, occasional book reviews and reports about conferences in the field of Industrial Mathematics.

Papers may be submitted to Managing Editor or will be solicited by member of the Editorial Board. The Managing Editor also welcomes suggestions for possible topics by prospective authors with a short outline of the intended paper for a first evaluation of the suitability of the topic for the journal. All papers will be refereed.

Subscription Information:

1995. Vol. 5 (4 issues):
for institutional subscribers: DM 268,–, öS 1876,–, plus carriage charges
for individual subscribers: DM 144,–, öS 1008,–, plus carriage charges
Special rates for individual members of DMV, ECMI, GAMM, JSIAM, ÖMG, and SIMAI: DM 80,–, öS 560,–, plus carriage charges. Orders must be placed directly with the respective society or Springer-Verlag Wien.

ISSN 0938-1953, Title No. 724

Springer-Verlag Wien New York

Sachsenplatz 4–6, P.O.Box 89, A-1201 Wien · 175 Fifth Avenue, New York, NY 10010, USA
Heidelberger Platz 3, D-14197 Berlin · 3-13, Hongo 3-chome, Bunkyo-ku, Tokyo 113, Japan

Springer-Verlag and the Environment

WE AT SPRINGER-VERLAG FIRMLY BELIEVE THAT AN international science publisher has a special obligation to the environment, and our corporate policies consistently reflect this conviction.

WE ALSO EXPECT OUR BUSINESS PARTNERS – PRINTERS, paper mills, packaging manufacturers, etc. – to commit themselves to using environmentally friendly materials and production processes.

THE PAPER IN THIS BOOK IS MADE FROM NO-CHLORINE pulp and is acid free, in conformance with international standards for paper permanency.